5. Conditional probability. $P(A|B) = P(A \cap B$

CHAIN RULES. $P(A \cap B) = P(A)P(B|A) = P(B)P(A|B)$, $P(A \cap B \cap C) = P(A)P(B|A)P(C|A \cap B)$, and so on.

INDEPENDENCE. If A and B are independent, $P(A \cap B) = P(A)P(B)$.

6. Bayes' Theorem. If subsets H_i form a partition of S,

$$P(H_i|E) = P(H_i \cap E)/P(E) = P(H_i \cap E)/\Sigma P(H_i \cap E)$$
$$= P(H_i)P(E|H_i)/\Sigma P(H_i)P(E|H_i).$$

7. Odds. If $P(A) = m/n$, the odds in favor of A are $m/(n - m)$. If the odds in favor of A are a/b, then $P(A) = a/(a + b)$.

D. POPULATIONS: MEANS, VARIANCES

[*Notation:* X and Y are random variables with values x_i, y_j; $X_1, X_2, \ldots, X_n$ are random variables; a and b are constants; $P(X = x_i) = f(x_i)$; $E(X)$ is the expected value of X; σ_i^2 is the variance of X_i.]

1. Mean. $\mu_X = E(X) = \Sigma x_i f(x_i)$; $\mu_{aX+b} = a\mu_X + b$.

2. Variance. $\sigma_X^2 = E(X - \mu_X)^2 = E(X^2) - \mu_X^2 = \text{Var}(X)$; $\sigma_{aX+b}^2 = a^2\sigma_X^2$.

STANDARD DEVIATION. $\sigma_X = \sqrt{\text{Var}(X)}$; $\sigma_{aX+b} = |a|\sigma_X$.

3. Standardized random variable Z. If $Z = (X - \mu_X)/\sigma_X$, then $\mu_Z = 0$, $\sigma_Z = 1$.

4. Chebyshev's Theorem. $P(|X - \mu| > h\sigma) \leq 1/h^2$; $P(|X - \mu| \leq h\sigma) \geq 1 - 1/h^2$.

5. Sums. $E(X + Y) = E(X) + E(Y)$; $E(\Sigma X_i) = \Sigma E(X_i)$.

If X and Y are independent:

$$\sigma_{X+Y}^2 = \sigma_X^2 + \sigma_Y^2, \qquad \sigma_{aX+bY}^2 = a^2\sigma_X^2 + b^2\sigma_Y^2,$$
$$\sigma_{X-Y}^2 = \sigma_X^2 + \sigma_Y^2, \qquad E(XY) = E(X)E(Y) = \mu_X\mu_Y.$$

E. SAMPLING THEORY

[*Notation:* $X_1, X_2, \ldots, X_n$ are random variables and the mean and variance of X_i are μ_i and σ_i^2, respectively.]

1. Mean and variance of a sum. If $X_1, X_2, \ , X_n$ are independent, then

$$E(\Sigma X_i) = \Sigma\mu_i, \qquad \text{Var}(\Sigma X_i) = \Sigma\sigma_i^2.$$

(*continued on inside back cover*)

PROBABILITY:

A FIRST COURSE

This book is in the

ADDISON-WESLEY SCIENCE AND MATHEMATICS
EDUCATION SERIES

Consulting Editors

RICHARD S. PIETERS   PAUL ROSENBLOOM

GEORGE B. THOMAS, JR.   JOHN WAGNER

PROBABILITY:

A FIRST COURSE

FREDERICK MOSTELLER
Harvard University

ROBERT E. K. ROURKE
Kent School

GEORGE B. THOMAS, JR.
Massachusetts Institute of Technology

 ADDISON-WESLEY PUBLISHING COMPANY, INC.
READING, MASSACHUSETTS, U.S.A.—LONDON, ENGLAND

To

A. W. Tucker

and

S. S. Wilks

PREFACE

The reader may expect to gain three things from this book: first, an understanding of the kinds of regularity that occur amid random fluctuations; second, experience in associating probabilistic mathematical models with physical phenomena; and third, the ability to use these mathematical models to interpret the physical phenomena and to predict, with appropriate measures of uncertainty, the outcomes of related experiments. Chapter 1 explains current interpretations of probability, and illustrates how probability and statistical theory are applied to important practical and scientific problems.

As distinctive features, we think our treatment has the following:

1. The level of mathematics required for an understanding of the material is that of a second course in high-school algebra. No knowledge of calculus is assumed.

2. The first four chapters give, in a readily accessible form, a brief course in elementary probability theory for finite sample spaces.

3. Chapter 5 offers one of the few available elementary introductions to random variables, their distributions, and properties of their distributions.

4. The binomial theorem, long a topic of study in school mathematics, is put to work in Chapter 6, where the properties of binomial probability distributions are studied in detail. The binomial tables at the back of the book include values of p less than, equal to, and greater than $\frac{1}{2}$. The consequent doubling of the size of the tables is justified, we believe, by the added convenience.

5. Chapter 7 deals with acceptance sampling, hypothesis testing, and estimation. In addition to applications of classical statistical inference, we include some simple examples of modern Bayesian inference.

The authors have tried to introduce each new concept through examples, and additional examples are given after each important theorem or definition. Readers who desire a faster pace may scan some of these examples rapidly and concentrate their attention on the numbered definitions, theorems, and corollaries. However, mastery of the theory will usually be increased by studying the illustrative examples, and by working exercises in the lists appearing at the ends of most sections.

By a suitable selection of topics, the text can be used for courses of various lengths. The taste and experience of the instructor are the best guides for such selections. For example, a minimum goal might be the completion of the first four chapters on probability. A more ambitious objective is to complete through Section 6–4; and, if pressed for time, one

ix

may omit Sections 3–8 through 3–12, 4–4 through 4–6, and 5–5 through
5–7. Instructors interested in offering statistical applications (acceptance
sampling, hypothesis testing, estimation) will need to include Sections 5–5
through 5–7, and Section 6–5. Sections 7–4 and 7–6 may be omitted.

Theorems, corollaries, and important definitions are numbered se-
quentially, by chapters. For example, 5–1 Definition, 5–2 Definition,
5–3 Definition, 5–4 Definition, 5–5 Theorem, and 5–6 Corollary are the
first four definitions and the first theorem and the first corollary in Chapter 5. This numbering system, with the number on the left, set in boldface
type, is intended to make it easier to look up a reference. In the body of
the text, however, we refer to Definition 5–3, to Corollary 5–6, and so on.

The end-pages at the very front and back of the book contain a glossary
of symbols and a summary of most of the key formulas. A few formulas
are included that have not been proved in the text, but almost all are
derivable from text results and their inclusion should increase the usefulness of this handy reference.

F. M.

R. E. K. R.

G. B. T., Jr.

ACKNOWLEDGMENTS

The authors are indebted to many for help, criticism, and encouragement in connection with the writing of this book. Their experiences as members of the Commission on Mathematics of the College Entrance Examination Board have been especially valuable. In particular, they have used the evaluations and experiences associated with the experimental text *Introductory Probability and Statistical Inference*, also known as "the gray book." The authors assisted in the writing of that text, and they recall with pleasure the collaboration of Edwin C. Douglas, Richard S. Pieters, Donald E. Richmond, and Samuel S. Wilks. Parts of the present work have been based on, or quoted from, material copyrighted by the College Entrance Examination Board, and this has been done by permission. This permission does not imply any responsibility for, or endorsement of, this work by the College Entrance Examination Board or the Commission on Mathematics.

Much of the material in this text was used as the basis of the nationally televised NBC Continental Classroom course in Probability and Statistics, first presented early in 1961.

We gratefully express our appreciation to:

W. G. Cochran, A. P. Dempster, G. E. Noether, and John W. Pratt for critically reading and discussing parts of the manuscript, and for many helpful suggestions and conversations.

Rita Chartrand, Mary McQuillin, and Jane Thomas for much patient and skillful work on the production of the manuscript.

Cleo Youtz for typing, computations, tables and graphs, and for efficient organization and management.

Linda Alger, Keewhan Choi, Robert M. Elashoff, Miles Davis, and Joseph I. Naus for their assistance with problem solutions.

Laurence Herbst for his work on the binomial tables.

William and Gale Mosteller for the card-shuffling data of the first-ace example in Chapter 1.

Biometrika Trustees for permission to publish Chart I—Confidence Limits.

The Free Press, Glencoe, Illinois, and The RAND Corporation for permission to publish a page of random digits from the book *A Million Random Digits with 100,000 Normal Deviates*, copyright 1955, by The RAND Corporation.

The Macmillan Company of Canada, for permission to use some problems from *An Advanced Course in Algebra* by Norman Miller and Robert E. K. Rourke.

The staff of Addison-Wesley, whose cheerful cooperation, editorial competence, and typesetting skill lightened the labors and thereby lengthened the lives of the authors.

CONTENTS

CHAPTER

1

PROBABILITY AND STATISTICS. THE STUDY OF VARIABILITY

This chapter provides initial answers to questions such as: What is probability? What is statistics? How are they used today? The aim is to introduce some background ideas in probability and statistics, and to transmit a feeling for the questions posed and the answers given in these subjects. Algebraic skills are not involved here. Consequently:

(1) We discuss the nature and role of mathematical models, and the relation of these models to the real world.

(2) We exhibit and discuss probability models, which are special kinds of mathematical models.

(3) We offer opportunities for personal experience with the fluctuations and regularities of experiments involving chance.

At a first reading, one should not expect full understanding of all the ideas in this chapter. Something less will set the stage for the mathematical work to come.

1-1. PROBABILITY AND STATISTICS

The wealth and variety of applications of the theory of probability attract many students. Some find beauty in the extensive mathematical structure that emerges from a few assumptions and definitions; others, both the practical and the philosophical, enjoy discussing the meanings that may be attached to probabilistic statements. Still others admire the order that emerges from seeming chaos—toss a penny once, and no one knows whether it will fall heads or tails; toss two tons of pennies, and we all know that one ton will fall heads, the other tails.

1

We are used to the notion that the idealized triangles of plane geometry can be used as mathematical representations, or *mathematical models,* of physical triangles in the real world. In a similar way, we build mathematical models for probabilistic problems and develop consequences of them. For example, a tossed coin has probability $\frac{1}{2}$ of coming up "heads"; and we shall develop for coin tosses a probability model that gives the probability that when n coins are tossed, exactly x fall heads and $n - x$ fall tails. In particular, the probability that all land heads is $(\frac{1}{2})^n$. The theory and its consequences apply to idealized coins, and we hope it applies to real coins when they are tossed. In Section 1–3, we give brief descriptions of a variety of problems in the real world that are studied by probabilistic models.

The field of statistical inference leans heavily upon the theory of probability, but supplements it. When data are gathered, we may use statistical theory to help choose among alternative mathematical models. For a given town, consider drawing a sample of families to estimate the fraction of homes with color television sets. The theory of probability tells us, for a given fraction owning sets in the community, what the ownership fraction in the sample is likely to be. But statistical inference uses the sample result to estimate the fraction in the town who own sets. In this example, probability theory deduces from the known content of the population the probable content of the sample, while statistical inference infers the content of the population from the observed content of the sample. More generally, the theory of probability deduces from a mathematical model the properties of a physical process, while statistical inference infers the properties of the model from observed data.

The field of statistics includes more than statistical inference. In general, statistics is the *art and science of gathering, analyzing, and making inferences from data.* Some parts of statistics are not mathematical, while other parts are. Although we have tried to separate probability from statistics, statisticians must work on problems in probability as well as in statistics.

1–2. INTERPRETATIONS OF PROBABILITY

At the mathematical level, there is hardly any disagreement about the foundations of probability or about its mathematical consequences. The foundation in set theory was laid in 1933 by the great Russian probabilist, A. Kolmogorov, still an active research worker in 1960. At the level of interpretation and use, there are two extreme positions that are often adopted and, of course, many positions in between.

The *objective* position is, at present, the most popular. This position holds that probability is applicable only to events that can be repeated over and over under much the same conditions. Thus the objectivist is happy to talk about probabilities in connection with the tossing of a coin or the manufacture of a mass-produced item. He can readily think of many light bulbs being produced, and of the probability of a good light bulb as the long-run ratio of number of good bulbs to the total number produced. But he draws the line at unique events. For example, he would not care to talk about the probability that Romulus founded Rome, or that Chile and Argentina would unite to become a single country in the next ten years. Thus a large class of problems is set aside by the objectivist as not appropriate for the application of probability, because there is no long-run ratio in view. Furthermore, the objectivist likes to make interpretations only from repeated events, and prefers not to bring other kinds of evidence into his inferences.

The other school of thought is sometimes called *personalistic*. The personalist regards probability as a measure of personal belief in a particular proposition, such as the proposition that it will rain tomorrow. This school of thought believes that different "reasonable" individuals may differ in their degrees of belief, even when offered the same evidence; and so their personal probabilities for the same event may differ. The personalist will apply probability to all the problems an objectivist studies, and to many more. For example, at least in principle, the personalist would take the Romulus question in his stride. The personalist also has available some additional techniques; in particular, he may have more use for Bayes' Theorem, treated in Chapter 5, than the objectivist. On the other hand, when the amount of data is large, the objectivist and the personalist usually get similar answers.

A beginner would be unwise to try to decide at once where he fits in with respect to these two views. Furthermore, the last word is never said on such matters because new schools of thought arise. But the distinction between probability as a long-run relative frequency and probability as a measure of degree of belief is one that he may wish to reconsider from time to time as he understands the issues better.

1–3. ILLUSTRATIONS OF PROBABILISTIC MODELS

Games of chance loom large in the early history of probability, and even today they provide instructive problems for both the beginner and the expert. About 1654, the Chevalier de Méré, an amateur mathematician, consulted Blaise Pascal (mathematician, scientist, and theologian) about the solution of generalizations of the following problem.*

---

* You may enjoy reading Oystein Ore, "Pascal and the invention of probability theory," *American Mathematical Monthly*, Vol. 67, No. 5, May, 1960, pp. 409–419.

Problem of points. On each play of a game, one of two players scores a point, and the two players have equal chances of making the point. Three points are required to win. If the players must end the game when one has 2 points and the other 1, how should the stakes be divided? Pascal said the stakes should be split 3 to 1, in favor of the man who was ahead. What do you think?

Pascal engaged in a profitable correspondence with Fermat, another great mathematician, on this and other problems in probability, and between them they developed many results, some of which are presented in Chapters 2, 3, and 4.

Another early gambling problem is that of duration of play. We mention it because it has evolved and developed through the years, and in this evolution has become of value to both scientists and industrialists.

Duration of play. Two players in a fair game have as fortunes m and n units, and the stake on each play is one unit each. Each player has an equal chance of winning a play. If they play until one player is ruined, how long will they play, and what is the chance that the player starting with m units wins? The probability that the game lasts t trials is difficult to compute; the probability that the player with fortune m wins is $m/(m + n)$.

This problem is a forerunner of that of the random motion of a physical particle which is absorbed when it strikes a barrier—one of the many kinds of "random-walk" problems studied by physicists. To show the relation between the problems, suppose that a particle starts at the origin, O, and in each unit of time moves one unit to the right or one unit to the left, the direction being randomly determined. Erect barriers m units to the right and n units to the left of the origin, and suppose the particle stops when it strikes a barrier. The position of the particle after t units of time corresponds exactly to the amount of money won after t plays.

For each of the foregoing problems, the probability model consists, essentially, of a fair coin, a rule for assigning points for plays, and a rule for deciding the winner of the game. A few examples of problems requiring probability models for their solution may help give the flavor of applications that are made today. The answers to the questions raised are either beyond the scope of this book, or require an extensive specialized development. Such models are developed by applied mathematicians, statisticians, physicists, biologists, or other scientists.

Queueing theory. People arrive at random times at a counter to be served by an attendant, lining up in a queue if others are waiting. Given information about the rate of arrival and the length of time an attendant requires to serve each customer, how much of the time is the attendant idle? How much of the time is the queue more than 10 persons long? What would be the effect of adding another attendant? If people are not allowed to wait in line but must go elsewhere, what percentage of arrivals go unserved? Variations of this problem are of interest in the maintenance of a battery of machines, in deciding how many toll booths to provide at the entrance to a throughway, in considering equipment needed for telephone lines and for high-speed computers, and even in the construction and control of dams.

Inheritance in biology. The Mendelian theory of heredity in its simplest form requires little more probability than that presented in this text; but, of course, the theory has gone far beyond Mendel. Suppose parents are classified on the basis of one pair of genes, and that d represents a dominant gene, and r represents a recessive gene. Then a parent with genes dd is pure dominant, dr is hybrid, and rr is pure recessive. The pure dominant and the hybrid are alike in appearance. Offspring receive one gene from each parent, and are classified the same way, dd, dr, or rr. The following table gives, for a simple case, the proportions of offspring of each type, for a given type of parents. Typical problems are: Knowing the proportions of the types of parents, what can we say of the composition of the population of offspring after $1, 2, \ldots, n$ generations? If the model is modified so that dominant characteristics are favored in some way, do recessives die out?

Parents		Offspring		
		dd	dr	rr
dd	dd	1		
dd	dr	$\frac{1}{2}$	$\frac{1}{2}$	
dd	rr		1	
dr	dr	$\frac{1}{4}$	$\frac{1}{2}$	$\frac{1}{4}$
dr	rr		$\frac{1}{2}$	$\frac{1}{2}$
rr	rr			1

Theory of epidemics. Suppose an infectious disease is spread by contact, that a susceptible person has a chance of catching it with each contact with an infected person, but that one becomes immune after having had the disease and can no longer transmit it. Then the mathematical theories of epidemics describe the progress of an epidemic in terms of the numbers susceptible, infected, and immune through time. Typical questions are: How many susceptibles will be left when the number of infected is zero (epidemic over)? How long will the epidemic last? For a city of given size, what is the probability that the disease will die out?

Naturally, in this book we cannot expect to study such difficult problems in full generality, but we can lay a foundation for their study.

1–4. APPLICATIONS OF STATISTICS

We have already indicated that statistics deals, in part, with the analysis of data stemming from probability models, and that statisticians may also develop probability models like those in Section 1–3. A few examples of applications of statistics in other fields may interest the student.

Screening of drugs. A pharmaceutical house tests hundreds of new medications, trying to find one that will be safe, and superior to the standard treatment of a disease. People vary in their responses to a medication, and so do the animals on which medications are initially tested. This variation introduces a probabilistic aspect to the problem. Usually, testing is done in stages: most medications are eliminated at an initial stage based on a small number of subjects. If a medication looks promising it is carried on to a later stage where a more elaborate and severe test is made. One problem is to choose the sizes and the severities of the experiments at the successive stages so that good new medications are unlikely to be discarded, but so that poorer medications do not receive expensive investigations.

Field tests. The addition of fertilizer increases crop yield. The farmer's profit depends on yield, costs, and sale price. Agricultural experiment stations help the farmer by carrying out field trials designed to measure the additional yield, say of corn, for given amounts of nitrogen fertilizer. These trials produce curves that relate yield to amount of fertilizer, and farmers use these curves together with cost information and anticipated sales price to decide on the amount of fertilizer to use. The efficient design of the field trials is part of the work of the agricultural statistician.

Sample surveys. The use of sample surveys is not restricted to opinion polls. Surveys are also used by large companies to assess their inventories or their book value. Surveys are taken to determine what and how much mathematics is available in colleges. You may have seen figures in newspapers estimating the number of unemployed; these come from a periodic governmental sample survey. To find and correct errors in the U.S. Census, the Census Bureau uses special sample surveys. That surveys are widely used instead of a complete census is partly a matter of cost in time and money, but partly a matter of quality. A more thorough and careful job can be done on a sample than on a large population.

Many problems can be treated only by sampling methods: breaking strength of steel rods, life testing of vacuum tubes, and, in general, destructive test situations. Other problems have infinite populations; there is no end to the number of measurements the Bureau of Standards can take on its platinum-iridium standard meter bars.

Genetics and radiation. The development and testing of atomic bombs has led to extensive experiments on the genetic effects of radiation in insects and mammals. Mutation, a suddenly produced variation in the character of offspring, is sometimes produced by radiation. For example, fruit flies are exposed to radiation of different kinds and in different doses, and mutations in offspring are observed. Several sites on the fly are possible places for mutations. Here are typical questions: Are the different sites equally likely to mutate? Is the frequency of mutation proportional to dose? Do kinds of radiation differ in their effect? Statistical studies of the effects of radiation on humans are still carried on at Hiroshima and Nagasaki.

Geology. Large boulders are left scattered by a glacier. From the distribution of the angles that the long axes of the boulders make with the North, it is desired to estimate the direction of the path of the glacier.

Other examples of statistical applications will be found throughout the text.

1–5. THE EMPIRICAL STUDY OF VARIABILITY

As we have seen, probability and statistics deal with the fluctuations and the regularities in processes that have random or chance elements. Although we all experience such variability every day in traffic flow, in time taken to brush our teeth, in our own changing weight, in our expenditures for necessities, in our time used for study, and in our games and races, we rarely study variability systematically. Thus we have impressions about variability, but usually no data.

Better personal experience of probability processes can be acquired by doing a few experiments of a simple sort, keeping records of the results, and analyzing them. Some of the results will be much as expected, others a bit surprising. In the rest of this chapter, we study the results of some simple experiments that you can do, and we suggest additional ones so that you can gain experience with probability models and variability. You are asked to *write down* your initial thoughtful guess about the outcome in each example without peeking ahead, so that you will gain experience in such estimates, and so that you will honestly know whether the result is as you expected or not. When you are seriously wrong, you should ask yourself what features of the problem you did not take into account. You should understand that even professional mathematicians cannot solve all the mathematical examples without hard work, and that some cannot be solved without empirical data.

First-ace problem. An ordinary deck of 52 playing cards containing four aces is shuffled thoroughly, and we count from the top the number of cards down to and including the first ace, and record the count. The process is repeated.

(a) What is the average count? (Without reading further write down your thoughtful guess.)

TABLE 1–1

COUNT (NUMBER OF CARDS TO AND INCLUDING THE FIRST ACE)
FOR EACH OF 100 SHUFFLES.

Shuffle number	First 20 counts	Second 20 counts	Third 20 counts	Fourth 20 counts	Fifth 20 counts
1	5	17	5	7	27
2	4	8	5	15	18
3	29	19	8	17	11
4	3	18	4	16	2
5	24	20	1	9	1
6	3	13	5	11	28
7	3	2	24	10	17
8	22	2	1	1	9
9	5	19	15	21	3
10	16	9	2	1	4
11	1	7	3	4	17
12	1	1	18	15	7
13	5	3	22	4	2
14	23	6	25	26	5
15	16	2	13	8	9
16	6	15	11	13	6
17	26	3	2	13	3
18	10	4	5	11	22
19	1	12	3	1	13
20	32	5	22	29	1
Total	235	185	194	232	205
Average	11.75	9.25	9.70	11.60	10.25

(b) What is the probability that the first ace is on card 1? 2? . . . 52? (A series of three dots, as used here, stands for all the whole numbers between the numbers immediately preceding and following the dots.)

(c) Within what number of cards will we find the first ace half the time? (Write down your thoughtful guess.)

Discussion. Parts (b) and (c) of this problem are treated theoretically in Chapter 3, but here we study the matter empirically.

In Table 1–1, we list in order in columns of 20 the results of 100 shuffles for this experiment. We observe that the counts vary considerably, from 1 to 32. They might have varied more—from 1 to 49—because all four aces could be clustered on the bottom of the deck. Furthermore, as you look down a column the numbers change without much rhyme or reason. We call such changes *sampling fluctuations* or *sampling variation.* If the

TABLE 1–2

OBSERVED FREQUENCY DISTRIBUTION OF COUNTS AND
THEORETICAL FREQUENCIES OF COUNTS FOR FIRST-ACE PROBLEM.

Count	Number of times observed	Theoretical frequencies	Count	Number of times observed	Theoretical frequencies
1	11	7.7	21	1	1.7
2	7	7.2	22	4	1.5
3	9	6.8	23	1	1.3
4	6	6.4	24	2	1.2
5	9	6.0	25	1	1.1
6	3	5.6	26	2	1.0
7	3	5.2	27	1	.8
8	3	4.9	28	1	.7
9	4	4.6	29	2	.7
10	2	4.2	30	0	.6
11	4	3.9	31	0	.5
12	1	3.6	32	1	.4
13	5	3.4	33	0	.4
14	0	3.1	34	0	.3
15	4	2.9	35	0	.3
16	3	2.6	36	0	.2
17	4	2.4	37	0	.2
18	3	2.2	38	0	.1
19	2	2.0	39	0	.1
20	1	1.8	40–49	0	.3
				100	99.9

shuffling is thoroughly done, knowledge of one count is no help in predicting what the next will yield.

That there is order in this chaos is suggested by the stability of the column totals and column averages. The averages vary only from 9.25 to 11.75. The changes in the average are much less than the changes from one count to the next.

We summarize these data in a *frequency distribution* in Table 1–2, by obtaining the number of times each count occurred in our 100 shuffles. For example, the count 1 occurs 11 times in Table 1–1. We also give the theoretical frequency, computed from a probability model for this problem. We defer the calculation of such theoretical frequencies to Chapter 3, but here we can compute the probability that the count is 1. There are 4 aces out of 52 cards that can be on top of the deck, and any one of these yields a count of 1. So it is natural to say that the probability that an ace is on top is $\frac{4}{52}$ or $\frac{1}{13}$. Since we had 100 shuffles, the theoretical frequency is $\frac{100}{13} \approx 7.7$. (The symbol $\approx$ means "is approximately equal to.") Of course we cannot have 7.7 counts of 1; that is the long-run rate per 100 counts if thousands of trials are made. We call it the theoretical or *expected* frequency, and discuss it in Chapter 5. The theoretical frequencies of counts from 40 to 49 are each less than 0.05, so their sum, 0.3, is reported.

We observe that the frequencies for theoretical counts do not match those of the observed counts exactly, but that they have the same general trend, i.e., they decrease as the size of the count increases. The discrepancies you see between the observed and theoretical frequencies are part of the experience this chapter can give. There are two sources for such discrepancies—sampling variation and failure of the theoretical probability model to fit the facts of real-life shuffling and counting. The counting was carefully checked, but it is harder to check the shuffling.

The authors have made a statistical study of these counts, and they find no evidence of disagreement between the theoretical model and the actual data. The study is not presented here.

Let us return to our first question:

(a) What is the average count?

Our total for the five sets is

$$235 + 185 + 194 + 232 + 205 = 1051,$$

so the average for 100 counts is 10.51. This is close to the theoretical value, as we now show, using considerations of symmetry. But the reader needs to take the argument partly on faith.

The 4 aces break the rest of the pack into 5 parts, as shown in Table 1–3. Any part may have from 0 to 48 cards in it. It seems reasonable (and it can be proved) that all 5 parts have the same long-run average count. In Table 1–3, we show opposite each part its average count for 20 new shufflings.

TABLE 1–3. AVERAGE COUNT.

	Observed average for 20 shufflings
Part 1: cards before the first ace	9.75
Part 2: cards between the first ace and the second	12.55
Part 3: cards between the second ace and the third	6.65
Part 4: cards between the third ace and the fourth	9.40
Part 5: cards after the fourth ace	9.10

If it is true that the 5 parts have the same long-run average, then $\frac{48}{5} = 9.6$ is the theoretical count for a part. When we counted to the first ace we included the ace, so the expected count including the first ace is $9.6 + 1 = 10.6$. This theoretical number is very near our average, 10.51, for 100 hands. However, agreement this close is unexpected. Application of large-sample theory shows that one-third of the repetitions of the 100-hand experiment would produce averages that deviate more than 0.85 from 10.6, and that 5% of the repetitions would be more than 1.7 from it.

The theoretical numbers of Table 1–2, when divided by 100, answer question (b):

(b) What is the probability that the first ace is on card 1? 2? ... 52?

Our final question was

(c) Within what number of cards will we find the first ace half the time?

Table 1–2 shows that 51 times in 100 trials we observed the first ace at a count of 8 or less. So we could use the number 8 as an estimate of the answer to (c). Since we are also given the expected frequencies, we can add them starting from a count of 1 and continuing until the sum of the frequencies is 50% or more. Doing so, we find the theoretical answer to be 9; the total theoretical frequency for counts of 9 or less is 54.4%. We call this count 9 the *median* count, to distinguish it from the *mean* count of 10.6.

We next consider an example of an entirely different nature.

Distribution of word-length. What is the average length of words, measured in letters, used in sports reporting? (Write down a thoughtful guess.)

Solution. We show in Table 1–4 the results for a sample of 50 words from one newspaper article on baseball. Naturally, a more extensive sample would be needed for firm conclusions.

TABLE 1–4. DISTRIBUTION OF WORD-LENGTH IN SPORTS ARTICLE.

Length in letters	Frequency	Length in letters	Frequency
1	1	7	5
2	6	8	2
3	12	9	3
4	7	10	0
5	7	11	1
6	5	12	1
		Total	50

TABLE 1–5. FREQUENCY DISTRIBUTION OF LAST
DIGITS FROM 100 TELEPHONE NUMBERS.

Digit	Frequency
0	11
1	13
2	11
3	11
4	10
5	5
6	7
7	14
8	8
9	10
	100

The sum of the lengths for the 50 words can be obtained by multiplying each length by its frequency and adding these products to obtain a sum of 243. The average length is 243/50 ≈ 4.9. We observe that three-letter words are most frequent, and that about half the words are 1, 2, 3, or 4 letters long.

Last digits of phone numbers. From a telephone book, find the frequency distribution of the last digits for 100 phone numbers. (Write down your guess for the frequency distribution.)

Solution. Many people expect the digits 0, 1, . . . , 9 to be about equally frequent. Table 1–5 gives the results for one sample of 100. We observe that the digits are about equally frequent, as people expect. Of course, this is only one sample of 100.

Distribution of first digits. Find the frequency distribution of first (left-most) digits in counts of votes for a given candidate by some unit of population, such as state, county, or precinct (or in physical measurements such as areas of states, heights of mountains, or the first significant digits in physical constants). In the number 345, 3 is the first significant digit, as it is also in 0.00345.

Solution. Most people guess that the digits 1, 2, . . . , 9 are about equally frequent. Write down your guess. Table 1–6 gives the first digits of counts of votes for Eisenhower in counties in Illinois in the 1956 presidential

TABLE 1–6. FREQUENCY DISTRIBUTION OF FIRST
DIGITS FOR VOTING STATISTICS.

1	24
2	14
3	11
4	16
5	11
6	12
7	5
8	4
9	5
	102

election. We observe that 1's are quite frequent, and that the low numbers are much more frequent than the high ones. Note that the digits 7, 8, and 9 together, instead of representing $\frac{1}{3}$ of the total or 34, show only 14. A number of scientific papers have set up probability models to explain this phenomenon—unexpected for most of us. The high frequency for the low numbers is said to have been first pointed out by a man who observed that the early pages of a well-used table of logarithms were much dirtier than the late pages. He decided on this evidence that first digits were most frequently small, and counts on a large variety of measures have borne him out.

Random walk. Suppose a man stands facing north and tosses a coin to decide whether to take one step north or one step south. Suppose he continues tossing and stepping in this manner for 25 steps.

(a) On the average how far is he from his starting point? (Write down a thoughtful guess.)

(b) On how many steps is he on the north side of his starting point; on how many is he on the south side?

(c) How often does he return to the starting point during the walk? (Write down your guess.)

Discussion. These are difficult mathematical problems, but we can simulate the experiment by tossing a coin 25 times and counting steps north and south. (Alternatively, we could use last digits from telephone numbers, using odd numbers to represent a step north and even numbers for south. Or we could use the random digits given in Table I at the back

TABLE 1–7

RESULTS FOR 10 RANDOM WALKS OF 25 STEPS.
N AND S INDICATE NORTH AND SOUTH.

Walk	Final position	Times on north side	Times on south side	Times at origin
1	1S	16	5	4
2	7N	19	3	3
3	5N	20	2	3
4	9N	24	0	1
5	1N	4	15	6
6	5S	6	11	8
7	5S	7	12	6
8	3S	2	19	4
9	11N	25	0	0
10	3N	9	15	1
Sum of distances 50		Totals 132	82	36

of the book in the same manner.) Table 1–7 shows the results for 10 walks of 25 steps.

The column totals show that the average distance from the origin is $50/10 = 5$. A theoretical answer from advanced work is about 4. (For n steps, the theoretical mean distance is about $0.8\sqrt{n}$, for large n.)

We note that there is considerable imbalance between time spent on the north and on the south. But the symmetry of north and south and of heads and tails shows us that in the long run, over many walks, half the time will be spent on each side of the starting point. The imbalance of an average of 13.2 stops on the north versus 8.2 on the south must therefore be due to large sampling fluctuations. Note that on walk 9 all 25 stops were on the north; on walk 4, 24 out of 25 were on the north, and on walk 8, 19 were on the south. We seem to have discovered that instead of each walk being split about equally—about half on the north, and half on the south—a very substantial fraction of the time is likely to be spent on one side in any one walk. This surprising result is *not* a feature of the smallness of the total number of steps taken nor of an unusual sample. It is a general feature of this kind of random-walk problem.

Finally, the average number of returns to the origin was observed to be $36/10 = 3.6$. Advanced theory gives about 3.0 as the theoretical mean.

Random digits. You may like to see the magnitudes of departures from expected frequencies observed in a table of random numbers, entitled

TABLE 1–8. FREQUENCIES OF RANDOM DIGITS.

Digit	Frequencies in first block of 50,000	Frequencies in a million digits
0	4923	99,802
1	5013	100,050
2	4916	100,641
3	4951	100,311
4	5109	100,094
5	4993	100,214
6	5055	99,942
7	5080	99,559
8	4986	100,107
9	4974	99,280

A Million Random Digits, made by The Rand Corporation and published by The Free Press, Glencoe, Illinois. The second column in Table 1–8 gives the frequencies of the digits 0, 1, . . . , 9 in the first block of 50,000 random digits in the table; the expected frequency for each digit is, of course, $50,000/10 = 5000$. The third column gives the frequencies for the million digits, the expected frequencies being each 100,000.

Large-sample theory suggests that about $\frac{2}{3}$ of the observed frequencies for the 50,000 blocks should be within 67 of the expected frequency, and that about $\frac{2}{3}$ of the observed frequencies for the million digits should be within 300 of the expected frequencies. In both instances, 6 digits have frequencies within the interval where $\frac{2}{3}$ (or 6.7 digits) are expected, so the agreement is close.

EXERCISES FOR SECTION 1–5

1. Obtain a deck of ordinary playing cards and, after thorough shuffling, count the number of cards down to and including the first ace; record the count for five shuffles. Get the average count for the five shuffles and compare it with the theoretical value of 10.6.

2. For each of five shuffles of an ordinary deck of playing cards, record the counts of the cards before the first ace, between the first ace and the second, and so on, as in Table 1–3. Then get the averages for each part as in the final column of Table 1–3, and compare the results with 9.6.

3. Obtain a frequency distribution for the lengths of the first 50 words in a sports article in a newspaper, and compare the mean word-length with that obtained from Table 1–4.

4. Open a residential telephone book to any page, and obtain the frequency distribution of the last digit for 25 telephone numbers. Find the average value of the last digit and compare it with 4.5, the theoretical value if all digits are equally likely.

5. From an almanac, or other source, obtain the distribution of leftmost digits of areas of states of the United States of America (or populations) and compare the distribution of digits with that of Table 1–6.

6. From a chemical or physical handbook, obtain the frequency distribution of the first significant digits of 50 physical constants.

7. Use the random digits of Table I at the back of the book to carry out 4 random walks of size 25, like those described in the text. Use your data to answer the three questions in the text.

8. Use the random numbers of Table I at the back of the book to make 10 random walks of length 10 steps each, and use these results to answer the three random-walk questions in the text (for walks of length 10).

9. Obtain the frequency distribution of the digits 0, 1, . . . , 9 of the 50 random numbers in the first 5 columns and first 10 rows of the random digit Table I at the back of the book.

10. Split an ordinary pack of playing cards into two packs, the reds and the blacks. Lay out the reds in a row (in order A, 2, 3, . . . , 10, J, Q, K of diamonds, then A, 2, 3, . . . , K of hearts). Shuffle the blacks and lay them out beneath the reds. Then count the number of times the value of a black card matches that of the red. Repeat 5 times, and obtain the average number of matches for the 5 shuffles. Make a thoughtful guess at the theoretical average number of matches.

11. Open a novel to a page near the middle, and choose the first 10 full lines of text. Record the number of e's in each line, and get the average number of e's per line. Use the letter count from one line as a base, and estimate the percent of letters that are e's.

12. Consider the duration-of-play problem, Section 1–3, with $m = 3$, $n = 2$. By flipping a coin (or using random numbers, Table I) and scoring a point for the player starting with m units when a head appears, and one for the other player when a tail appears, play 10 games, recording the total tosses required for each game, and the winner. (a) Find the average number of tosses per game. (b) Compute the fraction of games won by the player starting with m units, and compare it with 0.6.

13. Refer to the problem of points, Section 1–3. Use a coin toss (or random numbers, Table I) to simulate the finish of the game 20 times. Compare the number of times the player with 2 points won to the remaining number. Are the numbers approximately in the ratio 3 to 1 as Pascal thought?

14. Record the number of rolls of a die before a 6 appears. Repeat the experiment 10 times, and obtain the average number of rolls required.

15. Record the total number of rolls of a die required before every face has appeared. Repeat the experiment 5 times, and obtain the average number of rolls.

16. *Simplified epidemic.* An infectious disease has a one-day infectious period, and after that day the patient is immune. Six hermits (numbered 1, 2, 3, 4, 5, 6) live on an island, and if one has the disease he randomly visits another hermit for help during his infectious period. If the visited hermit has not had the disease, he catches it and is infectious the next day. Assume hermit 1 has the disease today, and the rest have not had it. Throw a die to choose which hermit he

visits (ignore face 1). That hermit is infectious tomorrow. Then throw again to see whom he visits, and so on. Continue the process until a sick hermit visits an immune one and the disease dies out. Repeat the experiment 5 times and find the average number who get the disease.

17. *Server problem.* In a unit of time there is a 50:50 chance that a customer appears at a counter to be served. If others are ahead of him at the counter he lines up in the queue, otherwise the server serves him and takes 2 units of time to complete the service. In the 10th unit, what is the average number in the queue if the process starts with no customers at the counter? Use a coin to carry out the experiment 5 times and get the average number. Also get the average number served at the close of the 10th unit of time. Example (a_i stands for a customer who arrived in the ith time interval):

Time unit	1	2	3	4	5	6	7	8	9	10
Arrivals	a_1	a_2	—	—	—	a_6	a_7	a_8	a_9	a_{10}
Being served	a_1	a_1	a_2	a_2	—	a_6	a_6	a_7	a_7	a_8
In line	a_1	a_1, a_2	a_2	a_2	—	a_6	a_6, a_7	a_7, a_8	a_7, a_8, a_9	a_8, a_9, a_{10}

Total served: 4; number in queue in 10th unit: 3.

1-6. DO PROBABILITIES GROW?

Most people correctly believe that when a *fair* coin is tossed many times, the fraction of heads will be close to $\frac{1}{2}$. Some feel that a logical consequence is that, after 10 heads have appeared in a row, the probability of a tail is larger than before. This view stems from a misapprehension about the way the "law of averages" works for coins. Since the coin has neither memory, conscience, nor force of its own, it can scarcely change its probability. The great probabilist Feller puts the explanation succinctly. He says that the law of averages works by *swamping* rather than by compensation. Thus, if a set of tosses started with 10 heads, the 10 will be largely swamped after 1000 tosses, and negligible after a million.

One reason for believing that probabilities grow is that in some problems they do. Can you think of such a problem? In the first-ace problem, if we have dealt 30 cards without an ace, the probability of an ace on the next card is large, $\frac{4}{22}$; and after 48 cards without an ace, the probability of an ace is 1. This growth happens because we draw *without* replacement from the pack, and the composition of the population has changed. But when a coin is tossed, there is no sense in which we have used up a head from a finite pool of heads. The model of drawing without replacement is the wrong one for coins.

In some problems, superficially like the fair-coin problem, probabilities change from time to time. At the start of the season, a pitcher may not be in good physical condition, and his probability of throwing a strike may be low. But later he may improve. Still later a small injury may plague him. For this pitcher, one may well believe that the probability of throwing a strike will wax and wane with time. But simple forms of the law of averages are not readily applicable to such a complicated process.

2

PERMUTATIONS, COMBINATIONS, AND THE BINOMIAL THEOREM

2–1. PERMUTATIONS: THE MULTIPLICATION PRINCIPLE

For generations, people have been intrigued by problems requiring them to find the number of ways of arranging a set of objects. In how many ways can 12 people line up at a theater box office? How many automobile license plates can be made using 2 letters followed by 3 digits? In how many ways can a person take a walk of 9 blocks, if he always walks 5 blocks west and 4 blocks north? Although such questions are fascinating and challenging in their own right, we shall consider them for an additional reason: we often need answers to such questions in the study of probability.

We wish to discover a general principle that will enable us to find the number of possible arrangements of sets of objects. To this end, let us consider an example.

EXAMPLE 1. In how many ways can 3 books, denoted by A, B, and C, be arranged in order on a shelf?

Solution 1. One way to solve this problem is to list the possible arrangements and count them. A tree graph (Fig. 2–1) provides an organized way of listing the arrangements so that none is missed.

The initial point, or origin, is denoted by O. If we follow all possible branches from O to the right-hand edge of the tree, we get the 6 possible arrangements listed in the column on the extreme right. Note that the tree diagram takes *order* into account. Thus ABC and ACB count as different arrangements of the 3 books because they are in different orders. *Order is the essence of such arrangements; a change in order yields a different arrangement.*

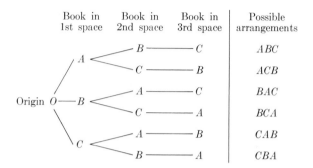

Fɪɢ. 2–1.   Tree for arrangements of 3 books.

Solution 2. A more convenient solution to this example is suggested by a further study of the tree diagram. The reasoning is as follows:

The problem requires us to fill 3 spaces, which can be represented as

In the first space, we can put *A* or *B* or *C*. Hence the first space can be filled in three ways:

| 3 | | |

(This is indicated on the tree graph by the 3 branches from *O* that end at the column headed *Book in 1st space.*) For each of the 3 ways of filling the first space, we have 2 ways of filling the second space, because either of the 2 remaining books can be used:

| 3 | 2 | |

Thus, we can fill the first 2 spaces in 3 × 2, or 6, ways. (Note that 6 branches of the tree end at the column headed *Book in 2nd space.*) For each of the 6 ways of filling the first 2 spaces, we have one way of filling the third space, because only one book remains. Therefore, we can fill the 3 spaces in 6 × 1, or 6, ways. (Note that 6 branches of the tree end at the column headed *Book in 3rd space.*) We can indicate the number of ways of filling each of the 3 spaces thus:

| 3 | 2 | 1 |

And, as indicated by the tree, we can obtain the total number of arrangements by *multiplication:*

$$3 \times 2 \times 1 = 6.$$

To this point, we have used the word "arrangements" to describe orderings of objects that result from operations such as that of placing books in a line. "Arrangement" is a common word that is informally descriptive. But we are dealing with special kinds of arrangements: we are concerned with arrangements, or orderings, of objects *in a line*, not with other kinds of arrangements, such as those of flowers in a vase. Since we refer to a special kind of arrangement, we need, for more precise description, a special word. This special word is *permutation.*

Each of the six arrangements in the foregoing example is called a permutation of the three books. We say that there are six permutations of the three books, taken three at a time, or all together.

2–1 Definition. *Permutation.* A permutation of a number of objects is any arrangement of these objects in a definite order.

To "permute" a set of objects means to arrange them in a definite order.

EXAMPLE 2. If at least 3 copies each of book A, book B, and book C are available, in how many distinguishable ways can we arrange 3 of the books on a shelf? (Regard the copies as indistinguishable.)

Solution. With at least 3 copies of each book available, we can now have arrangements like AAA or ABA. Because the copies are indistinguishable in appearance, even though they are composed of different molecules, one arrangement of 3 copies of book A is indistinguishable from any other arrangement of those copies, or of any other 3 copies of book A. However, the arrangements ABA and AAB are distinguishable. By reasoning similar to that used in Example 1, we can show that each of the 3 spaces can now be filled in 3 ways. The choices are indicated thus:

3	3	3

As before, the total number of permutations is found by multiplication:

$$3 \times 3 \times 3 = 27.$$

A short cut in counting. When the number of objects in a set is large, the number of permutations of the objects cannot, without great labor, be found by listing and counting. Fortunately, the method of reasoning suggested by the tree graph and used in Examples 1 and 2 can be extended, and used to provide a convenient general method for dealing with problems in permutations.

2–2 The multiplication principle. If an operation can be performed in n_1 ways and, after it is performed in any one of these ways, a second operation can be performed in n_2 ways and, after it is performed in any one of these ways, a third operation can be performed in n_3 ways, and so on for k operations, then the k operations can be performed together in

$$n_1 \times n_2 \times n_3 \times \cdots \times n_k \qquad \text{ways.} \qquad (1)$$

A note on notation. We have used subscripts on the letter n, along with three dots, to indicate a set of variables of arbitrary length. This device may seem complicated, but some such method is necessary. All the letters in the English alphabet would denote only 26 variables, but the subscripts and the three dots enable us to denote any finite number.

Observe the special function of the three dots. They indicate that we are to begin with the factor n_1 and write additional factors until we reach the kth factor, n_k. The dots do *not* imply that k is greater than 3. If, for example, $k = 2$, then expression (1) becomes

$$n_1 \times n_2,$$

and if $k = 1$, the expression means simply n_1.

The need for subscripts becomes apparent if we try to get along without them when the number of variables is large, or indefinite. If we denote a set of variables of arbitrary number by

$$a, b, c, \ldots, h,$$

a little thought shows that this notation implies eight variables, not an arbitrary number. When we become familiar with the use of subscripts, we appreciate their convenience and usefulness. (See Appendix II.)

A tree diagram to illustrate the multiplication principle. The tree in Fig. 2–2 illustrates the multiplication principle for $n_1 = 2$, $n_2 = 3$, and $n_3 = 2$. The total number of paths along branches of the tree, from the origin O to the right-hand edge of the diagram, is

$$n_1 \times n_2 \times n_3 = 2 \times 3 \times 2.$$

Examples such as the foregoing make the multiplication principle intuitively evident. We shall in future accept its truth, and use it freely as a short cut in counting the number of permutations of sets of objects. Note that the multiplication principle takes *order* into account.

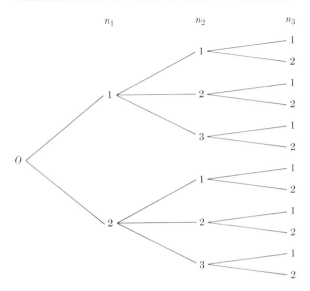

FIG. 2–2.   Tree illustrating multiplication principle.

EXAMPLE 3.   How many license plates can be made using 2 letters followed by a 3-digit number?

Solution. There are 5 spaces to fill. The first space can be filled with any one of 26 letters, and so in 26 ways. After the first space has been filled in any one of these ways, the second space can be filled in 26 ways (repetitions of a letter allowed). Similarly, the third space can be filled in 9 ways (zero not allowed), the fourth space in 10 ways, and the fifth space in 10 ways (zero and repetitions of a digit allowed). By the multiplication principle, the answer is

$$26 \cdot 26 \cdot 9 \cdot 10 \cdot 10 = 608{,}400.$$

EXAMPLE 4.   In planning a round trip from Chicago to Southampton by way of New York, a traveler decides to travel between Chicago and New York by air and between New York and Southampton by steamship. If there are 6 airlines operating between Chicago and New York, and 4 steamship lines operating between New York and Southampton, in how many ways can the round trip be made without traveling over any line twice?

Solution. The trip from Chicago to New York can be made in 6 ways; after it has been made in any one of these ways, the trip from New York to Southampton can be made in 4 ways. Then the trip from Southampton to New York can be made in 3 ways, after which the trip from New York to Chicago can be made in 5 ways. By the multiplication principle, the number of possible ways of making the round trip is

$$6 \times 4 \times 3 \times 5 = 360.$$

EXAMPLE 5. Given the digits 1, 2, 3, 4, and 5, find how many 4-digit numbers can be formed from them (a) if no digit may be repeated, (b) if repetitions of a digit are allowed, and (c) if the number must be odd, without any repeated digit.

Solution. (a) *No repetitions.* There are 4 places to fill. The first place can be filled with any one of the 5 digits, and so in 5 ways. Then, since no digit may be used more than once, the second place can be filled with any one of the remaining digits, and so in 4 ways. Similarly, the third place can be filled in 3 ways, and the fourth place in 2 ways. From the multiplication principle, it follows that the number of 4-digit numbers is

$$5 \times 4 \times 3 \times 2 = 120.$$

(b) *Repetitions allowed.* If repetitions of a digit are allowed, each of the 4 places can be filled with any one of the given 5 digits, and so in 5 ways. The number of 4-digit numbers, with repetitions allowed, is therefore

$$5 \times 5 \times 5 \times 5 = 625.$$

(c) *Odd, without repetitions.* If the number must be odd, the final digit has to be 1 or 3 or 5. Therefore the fourth place can be filled in 3 ways. After this has been done in any one of these ways, the remaining places can be filled in 4 ways, 3 ways, and 2 ways, respectively, since no digit may be used more than once. The number of odd, 4-digit numbers, without repeated digits, is

$$4 \times 3 \times 2 \times 3 = 72.$$

NOTE. We filled the fourth place first. *If some operation must be performed in a special way, it is usually advisable to do it first.* However, for nonspecial operations, the order in time of the space filling is often arbitrary. Thus in part (c) of the foregoing example, once the fourth space is filled, it doesn't matter which of the three remaining spaces is filled next.

Similarly, in Example 1, it doesn't matter which space on the shelf is filled first. We can put a book in the middle space, then put a book to its left, and then one to its right. The multiplication principle still applies and gives the same answer as before. We think of the first operation as that of placing a book in the middle space; the second, as that of placing a book in the leftmost space; and the third, as that of placing a book in the rightmost space. It helps us in analyzing the problem if we think of performing a definite sequence of operations one after another, even though we might do things in a different order. In fact, the three books can all be put on the shelf at the same time, rather than one after another; but such a way of looking at the problem provides no insight into its solution, whereas the one-book-after-another approach does.

EXAMPLE 6. Bill's Pizza Palace offers pepper, onion, sausage, mushrooms, and anchovies as toppings for the plain cheese base of the pizzas. How many different pizzas can be made?

Solution. There are 5 ingredients. In adding a topping to the base, we deal with the available ingredients one at a time. The pepper can be dealt with in 2 ways—take it or leave it. After the pepper has been dealt with, we can dispose of the onion in 2 ways—take it or leave it. Similarly, each of the 5 toppings can be dealt with in 2 ways. Therefore, there are 2^5, or 32, possible pizzas, including the plain pizza and the one with everything.

The addition principle. Consider two operations, one of which can be performed in m ways and the other in n ways. Then the *multiplication principle* says: If, after the first operation is performed in any one of the m ways, the second operation can be performed in n ways, the two operations can be performed together in mn ways. In short, the multiplication principle is concerned with situations where we can perform the first operation *and then* perform the second.

A different situation is faced if we wish to perform the first operation *or* the second operation, not both. Consider the following example.

EXAMPLE 7. Three different flags are available. In how many ways can a signal with at least 2 flags be arranged on a flagpole, if the order of the flags on the flagpole counts?

Solution. As our first operation, let us arrange 2 flags on the flagpole (Fig. 2–3). By the multiplication principle, this can be done in 3 × 2, or

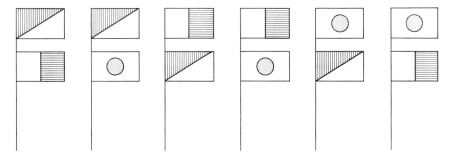

FIG. 2–3. Signals using 2 flags out of 3.

6, ways. As our second operation, let us arrange 3 flags on the flagpole. This can be done in $3 \times 2 \times 1$, or 6, ways.

Now we have only one signal to arrange, and this signal may be a two-flag signal or a three-flag signal, but not both together. It is a question of performing the first operation *or* the second, not the first operation *and then* the second. The operations are mutually exclusive: they cannot both occur together. The total number of signals is therefore

$$6 + 6 = 12.$$

2–3 The addition principle. If two operations are mutually exclusive, and the first can be done in m ways and the second in n ways, then one operation or the other can be done in $m + n$ ways.

This principle is readily generalized to include any finite number of operations. The statement is left as an exercise.

EXERCISES FOR SECTION 2–1

Use the multiplication principle to solve the following exercises.

1. In how many ways can eight people line up at a theater box office?

2. How many 5-digit numbers can be formed from the integers 1, 2, 4, 6, 7, 8, if no integer can be used more than once? How many of these numbers will be even? How many odd?

3. If the call letters of a broadcasting station must begin with the letter W, how many different stations could be designated by using only 3 letters, with repetitions of a letter allowed? How many by using 4 letters, without repetitions?

4. In how many ways can 3 letters be mailed in 6 mail boxes, if each letter must be mailed in a different box? If the letters are not necessarily mailed in different boxes, how many ways are there of posting them?

5. There are 7 seats available in a sedan. In how many ways can 7 persons be seated for a journey if only 3 are able to drive? [*Hint.* See note following Example 5(c).]

6. A passenger train has 9 coaches. In how many ways can 4 people be assigned to coaches if they must ride in different coaches?

7. In how many ways can 6 students be seated in a classroom with 30 desks?

8. Twelve boys try out for the basketball team. Two can play only at center, four only as right or left guard, and the rest can play only as right or left forward. In how many ways could the coach assign a team?

9. How many numbers, each with at least 3 digits, can be formed from the 5 digits 1, 2, 3, 4, 5, if no digit may be used more than once?

10. In how many ways can 5 boys and 5 girls be seated alternately in a row of 10 chairs, numbered from 1 to 10, if a boy always occupies chair number one?

11. In how many ways can 3 different presents, A, B, and C, be given to any 3 of 15 persons? If a specified person must receive A, and if no person is to receive more than one present, in how many ways can the presents be distributed?

12. In how many ways can a selection of at least one book be made from 8 different books? (*Hint:* See Example 6 of the text.)

13. Given 4 flags of different colors, how many different signals can be made by arranging them on a vertical mast, if at least 2 flags must be used for each signal?

14. An encyclopedia consists of nine volumes numbered 1 to 9. In how many ways can the nine volumes be arranged together on a shelf so that some or all of the volumes are out of order?

15. How many 5-digit numbers can be formed? How many of these begin with 2 and end with 4? How many do not contain the digit 5? How many are divisible by 5?

16. How many different parties of 2 or more can be formed from 9 people?

17. Five boys compete in a race. In how many ways can the first two places be taken?

18. (a) How many subsets, including the empty and universal sets, can be formed from a set of 10 different objects? (b) From a set of n different objects?

19. How many ordered pairs of symbols (x, y) can be formed if x can be replaced by a or b or c, and y can be replaced by 1 or 2 or 3 or 4? Draw a tree diagram exhibiting the set of possible ordered pairs (x, y).

20. How many permutations are there of n different objects, taken r at a time, with repetitions allowed? (It is assumed that there are at least r copies of each of the n objects available.)

21. On stepping off a train, a man finds that he has a nickel, a dime, a quarter, and a half-dollar in his pocket. In how many ways can he give the porter a tip?

2–2. FORMULAS FOR PERMUTATIONS

The multiplication principle provides a general method for finding the number of permutations of sets of objects. For some important types of problems, this method can be shortened by means of some convenient symbols and formulas that we now introduce.

The factorial symbol. As we have seen in Section 2–1, the multiplication principle enables us to establish facts such as the following:

(1) 7 people can be arranged in a line in

$$7 \times 6 \times 5 \times 4 \times 3 \times 2 \times 1 \quad \text{ways};$$

(2) 20 books can be arranged on a shelf in

$$20 \times 19 \times 18 \times \cdots \times 3 \times 2 \times 1 \quad \text{ways};$$

(3) n objects can be arranged in a line in

$$n(n - 1)(n - 2) \cdots 3 \times 2 \times 1 \quad \text{ways};$$

and so on. Once again, note that the dots do not imply that n is greater than 3. The dots indicate that we are to begin with the integer n and continue to multiply factors, each of which is one less than its predecessor, until 1 is reached.

Problems such as the three foregoing may lead to very large numbers or very long sequences of factors. For convenience, therefore, we introduce a special symbol.

2–4 Definition. *n factorial.* The product of all whole numbers from 1 to n is called n factorial, and denoted by $n!$.

Thus,

$$n! = n(n - 1)(n - 2) \cdots 3 \times 2 \times 1 = n \times (n - 1)!.$$

In particular, we have

$$1! = 1,$$
$$2! = 2 \times 1 = 2 \times 1! = 2,$$
$$3! = 3 \times 2 \times 1 = 3 \times 2! = 6,$$
$$4! = 4 \times 3 \times 2 \times 1 = 4 \times 3! = 24,$$
$$5! = 5 \times 4 \times 3 \times 2 \times 1 = 5 \times 4! = 120.$$

Proceeding in this way, we can make the table of $n!$ shown in Table 2–1, or the more extensive Table II in the back of the book. Table II also gives $\log n!$.

TABLE 2–1

n	1	2	3	4	5	6	7	8	9	10
$n!$	1	2	6	24	120	720	5040	40,320	362,880	3,628,800

The task soon becomes laborious, because the factorials increase in size at a fantastic rate. The number of permutations of the letters of the alphabet, 26!, is greater than 4×10^{26}.

The factorial symbol provides a useful notation for representing large numbers of the type encountered in the study of permutations and related topics.

Note that $$20! = 20 \times 19!,$$
$$100! = 100 \times 99!,$$
$$(n + 1)! = (n + 1) \times n!.$$

EXAMPLE 1. From the multiplication principle, we can show (*cf.* Section 2–1) that 50 people can form a line in

$$50 \times 49 \times 48 \times \cdots \times 3 \times 2 \times 1 = 50! \quad \text{ways.}$$

2–5 Theorem. *Permutations of n things, all together.* The number of permutations of a set of n different objects, taken all together, is $n!$.

Proof. The proof is a direct application of the multiplication principle. For, we have n spaces to fill. The first space can be filled with any one of the n objects, and so in n ways. After this has been done in any one of these ways, the second space can be filled with any one of the remaining objects, and so in $n - 1$ ways. Similarly, the third space can be filled in $n - 2$ ways, the fourth space in $n - 3$ ways, and so on. Therefore, by the multiplication principle, the number of ways of filling the n spaces is

$$n(n - 1)(n - 2) \cdots 3 \times 2 \times 1 = n!.$$

The number of permutations of n different objects, taken all together, is denoted by $_nP_n$. Therefore we have

$$\boxed{_nP_n = n!.} \quad \square$$

We now consider permutations of n different objects in which some, but not necessarily all, of the objects are used.

EXAMPLE 2. In how many ways can 3 books be chosen from 7 different books and arranged in 3 spaces on a bookshelf?

Solution. The first space can be filled with any one of the 7 books, and so in 7 ways. After this has been done in any one of these ways, the second space can be filled in 6 ways. Similarly, the third space can be filled in 5 ways. By the multiplication principle, the 3 spaces can be filled in

$$7 \times 6 \times 5 \quad \text{ways.}$$

Factorial symbols can also be used to denote the product $7 \times 6 \times 5$. For,

$$7 \times 6 \times 5 = \frac{7 \times 6 \times 5 \times 4 \times 3 \times 2 \times 1}{4 \times 3 \times 2 \times 1} = \frac{7!}{4!}.$$

The number of permutations of 7 objects, taken 3 at a time, is denoted by $_7P_3$, and its value is $7 \times 6 \times 5$. Thus,

$$_7P_3 = 7 \times 6 \times 5 = \frac{7!}{4!}.$$

NOTE. To evaluate $_7P_3$, we "begin with 7 and proceed for 3 factors."

2–6 Definition. $_nP_r$. An arrangement of r objects, taken from a set of n objects, is called a permutation of the n objects, taken r at a time. The total number of such permutations is denoted by $_nP_r$, $r \le n$.

2–7 Theorem. *Permutations of n things, r at a time.* The number of permutations of a set of n different objects, taken r at a time, without repetitions, is

$$_nP_r = \frac{n!}{(n-r)!}.$$

Proof. Once again, the proof is an application of the multiplication principle. Suppose that we have r spaces to fill and n objects from which to choose. The first space can be filled with any one of the n objects, and so in n ways. After this has been done in any one of these ways, there remain $n - 1$ objects, any one of which can be put in the second space. Thus the second space can be filled in $n - 1$ ways. Similarly, the third space can be filled in $n - 2$ ways, the fourth space in $n - 3$ ways, and so on. The pattern shows that the tenth space can be filled in $n - 9$ ways, the twenty-fifth space in $n - 24$ ways and, in general, the rth space in $n - (r - 1)$ ways. From the multiplication principle, the r spaces can be filled in

$$_nP_r = n(n-1)(n-2) \cdots (n-r+1) \quad \text{ways.} \tag{1}$$

The right-hand member of formula (1) consists of r factors. It takes another convenient form if we multiply by $(n - r)!/(n - r)!$, because then we can write

$$_nP_r = \frac{n!}{(n-r)!}. \quad \square \tag{2}$$

Formula (1) is defined for $r \leq n$. Formulas (1) and (2) agree if $r < n$. But if $r = n$, formula (2) gives

$$_nP_n = \frac{n!}{0!}.$$

By defining 0! to be 1, we make formula (2) hold also for the case $r = n$. The result is then identical with that of Theorem 2–5. Moreover, if $n = 1$, the formula

$$n! = n \times (n - 1)! \tag{3}$$

becomes $$1! = 1(0!).$$

Hence, by defining

$$0! = 1,$$

we make formula (3) hold for $n = 1$.

EXAMPLE 3. How many 5-letter words can be formed from the letters of the word *equations*? (A "word," in this sense, means any arrangement of letters. It does not need to be a word in some language.)

Solution. The problem is that of finding the number of permutations of 9 letters, taken 5 at a time. This number is

$$_9P_5 = 9 \times 8 \times 7 \times 6 \times 5 = 15{,}120.$$

EXAMPLE 4. How many permutations are there of 5 cards, taken from a bridge deck of 52 different cards?

Solution. From Theorem 2–7, the number is

$$_{52}P_5 = 52 \times 51 \times 50 \times 49 \times 48 = 311{,}875{,}200.$$

NOTE. Order counts here. Thus, 2, 3, 4, 5, 6 of hearts differs from 2, 4, 3, 5, 6 of hearts.

EXAMPLE 5. How many words can be formed from the letters of the word *hyperbola*, taken all together? In how many of these words will the letters h and y occur together? In how many will the letters h and y not occur together?

Solution. From Theorem 2–5, the number of ways of arranging 9 different letters, all together, is 9! or 362,880. Therefore, the required number is 9! if there are no restrictions. If the letters h and y must occur together, it is a good idea to consider them as one letter, *hy*. We now have 8 different letters to be arranged all together. This gives 8! arrangements. However, in each of these arrangements, the order hy may be changed to yh, so that each of the 8! arrangements gives rise to two arrangements that satisfy the given restriction. Hence, the total number of words in which the letters h and y occur together is $2(8!) = 80,640$.

The number of words in which the letters h and y do not occur together is the difference $362,880 - 80,640 = 282,240$.

For solving problems involving arrangements of objects in a set, the reader now has available the multiplication and addition principles and some formulas. He must not expect all problems to yield to the direct application of a formula. Flexibility is the key to the situation. Special problems may require formulas, the multiplication or addition principle, some special device, or a combination of these methods.

EXERCISES FOR SECTION 2-2

Note. A "word," as used in these exercises, means any arrangement of letters.

1. Evaluate the following: $_9P_3$, $_mP_1$, $_7P_7$, $_kP_2$.

2. Compute $_nP_0$ and interpret it.

3. How many words can be formed from the letters of the word *fragments* (a) taken all at a time, (b) taken 8 at a time, (c) taken 4 at a time?

4. A student has 4 examinations to write and there are 10 examination periods available. How many possible arrangements are there of his examination program?

5. A musical concert is to consist of 3 songs and 2 violin selections. In how many ways can the program be arranged so that the concert begins and ends with a song, and neither violin selection follows immediately after the other?

6. Prove that the number of 3-letter words that can be formed from the letters of the word *background* is the same as the number of words that can be made by rearranging the letters of the word *ground*.

7. How many automobile license plates bearing 5-digit numbers can be made if no license number starts with 0? If letters of the alphabet are used in place of the first digit and the next digit is not 0, how many plates can be made?

8. A passenger train consists of 2 baggage cars, 4 day coaches, and 3 parlor cars. In how many ways can the train be made up if the 2 baggage cars must come in front, and the 3 parlor cars must come in the rear?

9. If there are 3 roads from town A to town B, and 4 roads from town B to town C, in how many ways can one make a trip from A to C by way of B, and return from C to A by way of B?

10. In how many ways can 7 books be arranged on a shelf (a) if 2 specified books must always be side by side, and (b) if these 2 books must not be side by side?

11. In geometry, polygons are commonly labeled by placing letters at their vertices. How many ways are there of labeling a triangle with letters of the

alphabet? How many ways are there of labeling a pentagon? A decagon? (Do not multiply out the answers.)

12. How many 5-letter words can be made from 10 different letters (a) if any letter may be repeated any number of times, (b) if repetitions of a letter are not allowed? (c) In how many of the words of (a) will repeated letters actually occur?

13. How many 3-letter words can you make from the letters in your last name, if the words must begin and end with different consonants and have a vowel in the middle?

2–3. COMBINATIONS

In order to study the distinction between a permutation and a combination, we shall consider an example.

EXAMPLE 1. In how many ways can a reader select 3 books, without regard to their order, from a set of 4 different books denoted by A, B, C, and D?

Solution. We have seen that the number of *permutations* of 4 different books, taken 3 at a time, is

$$_4P_3 = 4 \times 3 \times 2 = 24.$$

In these permutations, or arrangements, the *order* of the books counts.

An entirely different problem arises if we wish to make a *selection* of 3 books from A, B, C, and D without taking order into account. There are then only 4 possible selections:

$$ABC, \quad ABD, \quad ACD, \quad BCD. \tag{1}$$

For example, we do not list ACB because the selection ACB is the same selection as ABC, since order does not count.

The word "selection" is a good, everyday word that describes the outcome of the operation we are considering. However, since we are dealing with a special kind of selection that is not concerned with the order of objects, we need a special word. (A similar situation occurred in connection with the word "arrangement" as used to describe a permutation.) Each selection in the list (1) is called a *combination* of the 4 books taken 3 at a time. The total number of such combinations is denoted by

$$_4C_3, \quad \text{or by} \quad \binom{4}{3},$$

each of which is read "number of combinations of 4 things taken 3 at a time." The symbol $\binom{4}{3}$ has no bar in the middle; it is not a fraction. By counting items in the list (1), we see that

$$_4C_3 = \binom{4}{3} = 4.$$

The foregoing example underlines the difference between a permutation and a combination:

In a permutation, order counts;

in a combination, order does not count.

Practical considerations. Ordinarily, we must decide from the nature of the problem whether permutations or combinations are involved. The decision hinges on the answer to the question: *Does order count or doesn't it?* For example, if we are *arranging* 3 books on a shelf, it is natural to regard ABC and ACB as different arrangements, and to take order into consideration; permutations are involved. But if we are *selecting* 3 books for weekend reading, ABC and ACB are regarded as the same selection; order does not count, and combinations are involved. Likewise two men, X and Y, can line up in 2 ways: XY or YX. But these two men can form a committee of two in only one way, because XY and YX yield the same committee. Order counts in a line-up; order does not count in a committee of the usual type, unless it matters which member is chairman.

Subsets of a given set. The language of sets can be used in discussing Example 1. We talk about subsets of 3 elements that can be formed from the set

$$\{A, B, C, D\}.$$

For brevity, we sometimes call a subset of 3 elements a 3-subset. Thus we say that the number of 3-subsets in the given 4-set is 4.

2-8 Definition. *Combinations.* A combination is a selection of objects considered without regard to their order. A subset of r objects selected without regard to their order from a set of n different objects is called a combination of the n objects, taken r at a time. The total number of such combinations is denoted by

$$_nC_r, \quad \text{or by} \quad \binom{n}{r}, \quad \text{where} \quad r \leq n.$$

Alternatively, we say that the number of r-subsets in a given n-set is $_nC_r$, or $\binom{n}{r}$. We must now find out how to evaluate these symbols.

Evaluation of $_nC_r$, or $\binom{n}{r}$. Consider (1), the list of possible selections of 3 books from 4. By rearranging, we get 6 permutations from each of the 4 selections

$$ABC, \qquad ABD, \qquad ACD, \qquad BCD,$$

since each 3-subset can be arranged in 3! ways. This operation yields a total of 4(3!) or 24 permutations, as listed in Table 2–2.

TABLE 2–2

$_4C_3$ AND $_4P_3$. EACH COMBINATION HAS $3! = 6$ PERMUTATIONS.

Combinations	Permutations
ABC	$ABC, ACB, BAC, BCA, CAB, CBA$
ABD	$ABD, ADB, BAD, BDA, DAB, DBA$
ACD	$ACD, ADC, CAD, CDA, DAC, DCA$
BCD	$BCD, BDC, CBD, CDB, DBC, DCB$

It is evident that all 24 permutations of the 4 books, taken 3 at a time, are obtained by thus rearranging the combinations. In other words,

(number of combinations) $\times$ 3! $=$ (number of permutations).

Or, in symbols:

$$_4C_3 \times 3! = {}_4P_3,$$

$$\binom{4}{3} \times 3! = 4 \times 3 \times 2.$$

Thus

$$_4C_3 = \binom{4}{3} = 4.$$

A generalization of the foregoing reasoning enables us to evaluate $_nC_r$ or $\binom{n}{r}$.

2–9 Theorem. *Combinations of n things, r at a time.* The number of combinations of a set of n different objects, taken r at a time, is

$$_nC_r = \binom{n}{r} = \frac{n!}{r!(n-r)!}. \tag{2}$$

Proof. Each combination of r objects can be arranged in $r!$ ways, and therefore gives rise to $r!$ permutations. Hence, $r!$ permutations of each of the $_nC_r$ combinations yield $_nC_r \times r!$ permutations. Moreover, the number $_nC_r \times r!$ is the total number of permutations, since each permutation of r objects arises from some combination of r objects. Therefore,

$$_nC_r \times r! = _nP_r = \frac{n!}{(n-r)!}.$$

Or, dividing by $r!$, we get

$$_nC_r = \binom{n}{r} = \frac{n!}{r!(n-r)!}. \qquad \square \qquad (2)$$

By direct application of formula (2), we obtain

$$_{100}C_2 = \frac{100!}{2!98!} = \frac{100 \times 99}{1 \times 2} = 4950,$$

$$\binom{n}{1} = \frac{n!}{1!(n-1)!} = n,$$

$$\binom{n}{n} = \frac{n!}{n!(n-n)!} = \frac{1}{0!} = 1.$$

2–10 Corollary. The number of combinations of n things taken $n-r$ at a time is the same as the number taken r at a time:

$$\binom{n}{n-r} = \frac{n!}{(n-r)!r!} = \binom{n}{r}. \qquad (3)$$

Proof. The denominator of the middle term of Eq. (3) can be rearranged to give $\binom{n}{r}$. $\square$

Discussion. That the number of combinations of n objects taken $(n-r)$ at a time is the same as the number taken r at a time is not surprising. For whenever we select r objects from the n, we leave $(n-r)$ objects behind. Thus,

$$\binom{9}{5} = \binom{9}{4} \quad \text{and} \quad \binom{50}{5} = \binom{50}{45}.$$

EXAMPLE 2. In how many ways can a hand of 13 cards be selected from a standard bridge deck of 52 cards?

Solution. The number of ways of selecting 13 cards from a deck of 52 different cards is given by formula (2):

$$\binom{52}{13} = \frac{52!}{13!39!} = 635{,}013{,}559{,}600.$$

EXAMPLE 3. In how many ways can a committee of 3 be chosen from 4 married couples (a) if all are equally eligible, (b) if the committee must consist of 2 women and 1 man, (c) if a husband and wife cannot both serve on the same committee?

Solution. (a) In a committee order does not count, so the problem is that of selecting 3 people from 8 in all possible ways. From formula (2), the total number is

$$\binom{8}{3} = \frac{8!}{3!5!} = \frac{8 \times 7 \times 6}{1 \times 2 \times 3} = 56.$$

(b) The 2 women can be selected in $\binom{4}{2}$ or 6 ways, and after they have been selected in any one of these ways, the 1 man can be selected in $\binom{4}{1}$ or 4 ways. Hence, by the multiplication principle of Section 2–1, the number of ways of selecting 2 women and 1 man is

$$\binom{4}{2} \times \binom{4}{1} = 6 \times 4 = 24.$$

(c) If a husband and wife cannot both serve on the committee, then 3 couples must be represented on the committee. Three couples can be selected from 4 in $\binom{4}{3}$ ways. After the 3 couples have been selected, two choices can be made from the first couple (husband or wife), two from the second couple, and two from the third couple. By the multiplication principle, the total number of committees is

$$\binom{4}{3} \times 2 \times 2 \times 2 = 32.$$

Alternatively, there are 4 ways to select a couple, and 6 ways to select the remaining member or, in all, $6 \times 4 = 24$ ways to select a committee with a couple. Subtracting 24 from the total ways, 56, gives 32 committees without a couple. Frequently, counting unwanted cases and taking complements is easier than a direct count.

EXAMPLE 4. In how many ways can a selection of one or more books be made from 5 identical algebra books and 4 identical geometry books?

Solution. Let us first deal with the algebra books. We can select 1 or 2 or 3 or 4 or 5 or none of them. Hence the algebra books can be dealt with in 6 ways. After dealing with them in any one of these 6 ways, we can similarly deal with the geometry books in 5 ways. By the multiplication principle, we can make a selection from both kinds of books in 6 × 5, or 30 ways. These 30 ways include the case in which we take no algebra book and no geometry book. If we must take at least one book, then the number of selections is $30 - 1 = 29$.

2-11 Theorem. *Pascal's Rule.*

$$\binom{n+1}{r} = \binom{n}{r-1} + \binom{n}{r}, \qquad \text{for } 1 \leq r \leq n.$$

Proof. The formula may be proved by substituting factorial symbols and simplifying. Another method of proof depends on the meanings of the symbols, as follows.

The number of selections of r objects that can be made from a given set of $n + 1$ objects, without restrictions, is $\binom{n+1}{r}$. Consider some specified object in the given set. If this specified object is included in the selection, the remaining $r - 1$ objects can be selected from the remaining n objects in $\binom{n}{r-1}$ ways. If the specified object is not included, the r objects must be selected from the remaining n objects, and this can be done in $\binom{n}{r}$ ways. The total number of selections is obtained by adding the number in which the specified object occurs to the number in which the specified object does not occur, since no other cases are possible. Therefore, the total number is

$$\binom{n}{r-1} + \binom{n}{r} = \binom{n+1}{r}. \quad \square$$

NOTE. The foregoing proof is an application of the addition principle, not of the multiplication principle. The problem presents us with two operations, either of which is admissible separately, but not both simultaneously. It is a question of *either* this operation *or* that operation. Such operations are *mutually exclusive;* they cannot both occur together. Each operation forms the basis of a separate problem, and the final result is obtained by addition, not by multiplication.

TABLE 2-3. PASCAL'S TRIANGLE FOR $\binom{n}{r}$, $0 \le r \le n \le 10$.

$$\binom{n+1}{r} = \binom{n}{r-1} + \binom{n}{r}, \quad 1 \le r \le n.$$

r \ n	0	1	2	3	4	5	6	7	8	9	10
0	1										
1	1	1									
2	1	2	1								
3	1	3	3	1							
4	1	4	6	4	1						
5	1	5	10	10	5	1					
6	1	6	15	20	15	6	1				
7	1	7	21	35	35	21	7	1			
8	1	8	28	56	70	56	28	8	1		
9	1	9	36	84	126	126	84	36	9	1	
10	1	10	45	120	210	252	210	120	45	10	1

Pascal's rule gives a simple way of building a table of values of $\binom{n}{r}$, known as *Pascal's triangle*. Table 2-3 shows the part of Pascal's triangle for values of n from 0 through 10. The rows of the table correspond to values of n; the columns, to values of r. The first and last entries in each row are 1 because $\binom{n}{0} = \binom{n}{n} = 1$. The entry other than the first or last in each row is the sum of the entry immediately above it and the entry to the left of that one, by Pascal's rule. Thus, for example, the entry for $n = 3$, $r = 2$ appearing in the fourth row and third column of the body of the table is the sum of the entry in the third row and third column and that in the third row and second column because $\binom{3}{2} = \binom{2}{2} + \binom{2}{1}$.

EXERCISES FOR SECTION 2-3

1. Evaluate the following: $\binom{9}{3}$, $\binom{9}{6}$, $\binom{m}{3}$, $\binom{k}{1}$, $\binom{5}{5}$.
2. Show that $\binom{n}{0} = 1$, and interpret it in terms of selections.
3. Solve the following equations for n:

(a) $\binom{n}{2} = 45$;   (b) $\dfrac{_nP_4}{\binom{n-1}{3}} = 60$;   (c) $\binom{n}{8} = \binom{n}{12}$.

4. In how many ways can a committee of 5 be chosen from 8 people?

5. A contractor needs 4 carpenters and 10 apply for the jobs. In how many ways can he pick out 4?

6. In how many ways can a selection of fruit be made from 7 plums, 4 lemons, and 9 oranges? (Assume that the 7 plums are indistinguishable. Likewise for the lemons and for the oranges.)

7. How many selections of 1 or more letters can be made from 2 A's, 5 B's, and 9 C's?

8. Ten points are taken on the circumference of a circle. How many chords can be drawn by joining them in all possible ways? With these 10 points as vertices, how many triangles can be drawn? How many hexagons?

9. In how many ways can a selection of 4 books be made from 9? If a certain book must be chosen, in how many ways can the selection be made? In how many ways can it be made if a certain book must be left?

10. A company of 20 men is to be divided into 3 sections so that there are 3 men in the first, 5 in the second, and 12 in the third. In how many ways can this be done? (Don't multiply out.)

11. Find the number of ways in which at least one book can be selected from 4 identical cook books and 8 identical novels.

12. Write a symbol for the number of combinations of 20 objects taken 4 at a time, and for the number of combinations of 100 objects taken 98 at a time. Compute the numerical value of each symbol, and find which is the greater.

13. A pack of playing cards contains 52 different cards. If a hand is made up of 5 cards, use the factorial notation to express the number of possible hands. (Disregard order in the hands.)

14. In how many ways can 2 booksellers divide between them 300 copies of one book, 200 copies of another, and 100 copies of a third, if neither bookseller is to get all the books? (Don't multiply out.)

15. A bridge deck of cards is made up of 13 spades, 13 hearts, 13 diamonds, and 13 clubs. How many different hands can be formed if each hand contains 5 spades, 4 hearts, 2 diamonds, and 2 clubs? (Don't multiply out.)

16. Six candidates contest an election for two similar offices. If a voter may mark his ballot either for one or for two candidates, in how many ways can he cast his vote?

17. How many 5-letter words, each consisting of 3 consonants and 2 vowels, can be formed from the letters of the word *equations*?

18. Twenty persons are to travel in a double-decker bus that can carry 12 passengers inside and 8 outside. If 4 of the persons will not travel inside, and 5 will not travel outside, in how many ways can the passengers be seated (a) if the arrangement of the passengers inside, or outside, is not considered, and (b) if the arrangement inside and outside is considered?

19. In how many ways can 4 persons be selected from 5 married couples (a) if the selection must consist of 2 women and 2 men, and (b) if a husband and wife cannot both be selected?

20. Verify that the entries for $n = 4$ in Table 2–3 satisfy the conditions $\binom{4}{0} = \binom{4}{4} = 1$ and $\binom{4}{r} = \binom{3}{r} + \binom{3}{r-1}$ for $1 \leq r \leq 3$.

21. Write out the entries that would be in the rows for $n = 11$ and $n = 12$ in Pascal's triangle, Table 2–3.

EXERCISES ON PERMUTATIONS AND COMBINATIONS

A.

1. In how many ways can a man choose 3 gifts from 10 different articles?

2. A railway has 50 stations. If the names of the point of departure and the destination are printed on each ticket, how many different kinds of single tickets must be printed? How many kinds are needed if each ticket may be used in either direction between two towns?

3. In how many ways can 15 different objects be divided among A, B, and C, if A must receive 2 objects, B must receive 3 objects, and C must receive 10 objects?

4. Given 20 points, no three of which are in a straight line, find the number of straight lines that can be drawn by joining pairs of these points.

5. Given 4 non-coplanar points in space, how many planes can be determined by selecting triples of these points?

6. A ring of 8 boys is to be enlarged by the addition of 5 girls. In how many ways can this be done if no two girls are to stand beside each other? (Note that order counts here because people are distinguishable.)

7. A town council is made up of a mayor and 6 aldermen. How many different committees of 4 can be formed, (a) if the mayor is on each committee, and (b) if the mayor is on no committee?

8. How many 4-letter words can be made from the letters of the word *zephyr*? How many of these words will not contain the letter r? How many will contain r? How many will begin with z and end with r?

9. In how many ways can a coach choose a team of 5 from 10 boys (a) if 2 specified boys must be included, and (b) if there are no restrictions?

10. A man has 8 different pairs of gloves. In how many ways can he select a right-hand glove and a left-hand glove that do not match?

11. A 35-mm colored slide is mounted in a $2'' \times 2''$ square holder. How many wrong ways are there of inserting the mounted slide into a projector?

B.

12. In how many numbers between 1000 and 9999 inclusive does the digit 3 occur?

13. How many words, each of 2 vowels and 2 consonants, can be formed from the letters of the word *involute*?

14. How many quadrilaterals can be formed, each having as its vertices 4 of the vertices of a given regular polygon of 20 sides, if no 2 of the selected 4 are opposite vertices of the given polygon?

15. Prove $\binom{n}{r} + \binom{n}{r-1} = \binom{n+1}{r}$ (Pascal's Rule) by using factorials to replace the symbols on the left, and simplifying.

16. There are 10 chairs in a row. In how many ways can 2 persons be seated? In how many of these ways will the 2 persons be sitting in adjacent chairs? In how many will they have at least one chair between them?

17. How many diagonals has a 20-sided polygon? How many sides has a polygon with 35 diagonals?

18. Four jobs of one kind can be held by women only, 5 jobs of another kind by men only, and 3 jobs of a third kind by either men or women. In how many ways can these jobs be filled from 18 applicants of whom 8 are women and 10 are men?

19. Fifteen points lie in a plane in such a way that 5 of the points are on one straight line and, apart from these, no 3 points are collinear. Find the total number of straight lines that can be obtained by joining pairs of the 15 points.

20. How many 6-digit numbers can be formed from the digits 1, 2, 3, 4, 5, 6, 7, 8, 9 if each number has 3 odd and 3 even digits and no two digits are alike?

21. In how many ways can one assign to 2 soldiers different 3-digit numbers? In how many ways can this be done if the 3-digit numbers are composed of even digits only (zero being considered even)?

22. In a set of 10 examinations, 2 are in mathematics. In how many different orders can the examinations be given if those in mathematics are not consecutive?

23. A stamp collector has 8 different Canadian stamps and 10 different United States stamps. Find the number of ways in which he can select 3 Canadian stamps and 3 United States stamps and arrange them in 6 numbered spaces in his stamp album.

24. A symphony is recorded on 4 discs, both sides of each disc being used. In how many ways can the 8 sides be played on a phonograph so that some part of the symphony is played out of its correct order?

25. A railway coach has 10 seats facing backward and 10 facing forward. In how many ways can 8 passengers be seated, if 2 refuse to ride facing forward and 3 refuse to ride facing backward?

26. From a company of 20 soldiers, a squad of 3 men is chosen each night. For how many consecutive nights could a squad go on duty without two of the squads being identical? In how many of these squads would a given soldier serve?

27. Find the number of ways in which 8 persons can be assigned to 2 different rooms, if each room must have at least 3 persons in it.

2-4. PERMUTATIONS OF THINGS THAT ARE NOT ALL DIFFERENT

In Sections 2–1 through 2–3, we considered arrangements of sets of objects that were different from each other. How will the number of possible permutations be affected if some objects in the given set are alike? A little thought will doubtless convince you that if some of the objects in a set cannot be distinguished from others, the number of possible permutations is decreased. For example, the letters A, B, and C yield 3! or six 3-letter words; but the letters A, A, A yield only one 3-letter word.

EXAMPLE 1. In how many ways can the letters of the word *assess* be arranged, all at a time?

Solution. The problem would be easy if the four *s*'s were different from one another. For we know that there are 6! permutations of 6 *different* letters taken all together. We shall relate this familiar problem (letters all different) to our new problem (letters not all different) by making the four s's *temporarily* different, as described in the following.

Let the unknown total number of permutations of the letters of the word *assess* be x. Now consider any one of these permutations; for example,

$$s \quad s \quad s \quad s \quad a \quad e.$$

In this arrangement, if we replace the four s's by

$$s_1, \ s_2, \ s_3, \ s_4,$$

the original arrangement gives rise to 4! arrangements by permuting the four s's with subscripts (now different) without disturbing the other letters. In the same way, each of the original x permutations gives rise to 4! permutations. Thus the total number of permutations is $x(4!)$. Since the 6 letters

$$s_1, \ s_2, \ s_3, \ s_4, \ a, \ e$$

are now all different, $x(4!)$ is the number of permutations of 6 different letters, taken all together. Therefore,

$$x(4!) = 6!$$

or

$$x = \frac{6!}{4!}.$$

Recall that a similar type of reasoning was used to evaluate $\binom{n}{r}$. We can at once generalize this reasoning to show that the number of permutations of a set of n objects, taken all together, where r of the objects are alike and the rest are different, is $n!/r!$. Repeated applications of this principle yield the following theorem.

2–12 Theorem. *Permutations of objects that are not all different.* Given a set of n objects having n_1 elements alike of one kind, and n_2 elements alike of another kind, and n_3 elements alike of a third kind, and so on for k kinds of objects; then the number of permutations of the n objects, taken all together, is

$$\boxed{\frac{n!}{n_1! n_2! \cdots n_k!},} \tag{1}$$

where $\qquad n_1 + n_2 + \cdots + n_k = n.$

2–13 Corollary. *Permutations for two kinds of objects.* If a set of n objects consists of r elements of one kind and $n - r$ elements of another, then the number of permutations of the n objects, taken all together, is

$$\frac{n!}{r!(n-r)!} = \binom{n}{r} = \binom{n}{n-r}. \tag{2}$$

Proof. (a) The proof follows at once from Theorem 2–12, when we set $n_1 = r$ and $n_2 = n - r$. Alternatively, this corollary can be proved as follows.

(b) Suppose there are r A's and $n - r$ B's to be arranged in order. We think of n blank spaces to be filled, r with A's, and the rest with B's. The number of ways of selecting the r spaces for the A's is $\binom{n}{r}$ and, after this has been done, the A's can be arranged in the spaces in just one way. Next, the B's can be arranged in the remaining $n - r$ spaces in just $\binom{n-r}{n-r} \times 1$, or 1, way. Hence the total number of arrangements is $\binom{n}{r}$. $\square$

REMARK. The number of *permutations* of n objects, r alike of one kind and $n - r$ alike of another kind, is equal to the number of *combinations* of n different objects (the n blank spaces), taken r at a time. The foregoing proof shows why this particular equivalence between permutations and combinations occurs.

EXAMPLE 2. How many arrangements can be made of the letters of the word *Mississippi*, taken all together?

Solution. We have 11 letters in all, with one m, four i's, four s's, and two p's $\{m \ iiii \ ssss \ pp\}$. Thus, $n_1 = 1$, $n_2 = 4$, $n_3 = 4$, and $n_4 = 2$. By Theorem 2–12, the total number of permutations of the 11 letters, taken all together, is

$$\frac{11!}{1!4!4!2!} = 34{,}650.$$

EXAMPLE 3. How many arrangements can be made from the letters of the word *equations*, provided that the vowels must always remain in the order e, u, a, i, o?

Solution 1. Since the order of the vowels relative to one another cannot be changed, it follows that the vowels cannot be permuted among themselves and so for the purposes of this problem may be considered as identical. Hence the problem is that of finding the number of permutations of 9 letters, taken all together, where 5 of the letters are identical. By Theorem 2–12, the number is

$$\frac{9!}{5!(1!)^4} = 3024.$$

Solution 2. The 9 letters are to be arranged to fill 9 spaces. The spaces for the vowels can be selected in $\binom{9}{5}$ ways and, once they are selected, the vowels can be arranged in them, in the order e, u, a, i, o, in just one way. The consonants can be arranged in the remaining 4 spaces in 4! ways. Hence the total number of arrangements is

$$\binom{9}{5} \times 1 \times 4! = \frac{9!}{5!4!} \times 4! = \frac{9!}{5!} = 3024.$$

EXAMPLE 4.   Given $n + r$ letters, of which n are A's and r are B's, how many different sequences can be formed from the A's and B's, if each sequence must contain all n A's?

Solution. There are $r + 1$ mutually exclusive cases because we may have n A's and no B's, or n A's and one B, or n A's and two B's, and so on. The $r + 1$ alternative cases are listed in Table 2–4, together with the number of sequences to which each case gives rise. For each case, the number of sequences is calculated by formula (2) of Corollary 2–13.

Since the cases are mutually exclusive, we get the total number of sequences by applying the addition principle. The number is

$$\binom{n}{0} + \binom{n+1}{1} + \binom{n+2}{2} + \cdots + \binom{n+r}{r}. \quad \square$$

TABLE 2–4

Mutually exclusive cases	Number of sequences
n A's, no B's	$\binom{n}{0}$
n A's, one B	$\binom{n+1}{1}$
n A's, two B's	$\binom{n+2}{2}$
n A's, three B's	$\binom{n+3}{3}$
$\vdots$	$\vdots$
n A's, r B's	$\binom{n+r}{r}$

REMARK. This sum equals $\binom{n+r+1}{r}$, as can be shown by successive applications of Pascal's Rule (Theorem 2–11, Section 2–3). For we have

$$\binom{n}{0} + \binom{n+1}{1} = \binom{n+1}{0} + \binom{n+1}{1} = \binom{n+2}{1};$$

$$\binom{n+2}{1} + \binom{n+2}{2} = \binom{n+3}{2};$$

$$\binom{n+3}{2} + \binom{n+3}{3} = \binom{n+4}{3};$$

and so on. Finally, the rth step gives

$$\binom{n+r}{r-1} + \binom{n+r}{r} = \binom{n+r+1}{r}. \quad \square$$

EXERCISES FOR SECTION 2–4

1. Find the number of arrangements of the letters of the word *committee*, using all the letters in each arrangement.

2. How many different numbers can be obtained by arranging the digits 2233344455, all together, in all possible ways?

3. How many permutations can be made using the letters of the word *institution*, taken all at a time? How many of these begin with t and end with s?

4. In how many ways can 13 different cards be arranged in a row, if a certain 10 of them must always be in a specified order relative to each other?

5. Find the number of ways in which 6 plus signs and 4 minus signs can be arranged in a row.

6. Find the number of ways in which nine 3's and six 5's can be placed in a row so that no two 5's come together.

7. How many different numbers can be obtained by arranging the digits 123456789, all at a time, if the even digits must always remain in ascending order and the odd digits likewise?

8. Find the number of arrangements of the letters of the word *engineering*, taken all together. In how many of these are three e's together? In how many are exactly two e's together?

9. A class consists of 12 girls and 10 boys. In how many ways can the class form a line, if the girls always remain in ascending order of height, and the boys likewise?

10. In how many ways can one take a walk for 9 blocks, if he always walks 5 blocks west and 4 blocks north?

11. How many numbers greater than 3,000,000 can be formed from the digits 1, 1, 1, 2, 2, 3, 3?

12. In how many ways can 5 red balls, 4 black balls, and 4 white balls be placed in a row so that the balls at the ends of the row are of the same color?

REVIEW EXERCISES

1. A rat runs a branching maze, so constructed that he first must choose one of a pair of doors, beyond each of these he must choose one of 3 doors, and beyond each of these he must choose one of 4 doors. After passing through a door he cannot return. How many paths are there from start to finish?

2. A metallurgist, studying alloys, wants to study the effect of 3 different temperatures, 6 different heating times, and 4 different amounts of a copper compound. One experiment has one level for each variable. How many different experiments must he perform if every triple of temperature level, heating time, and amount of copper is to be represented?

3. A dial safe has 100 positions on its dial and 3 settings are required for a combination. However, no setting can be fewer than 10 positions from the immediately preceding setting. How many combinations are there?

4. A keymaker has 12 types of blanks. Each blank has 5 different positions where metal can be removed and there are 3 cutting depths at each position except the first, which has only 2. How many possible keys are there?

5. A soil chemist has 6 different treatments to study, and he can apply 3 different treatments, simultaneously, in a single experiment. How many experiments must he do to exhaust all triples of treatments?

6. If the soil chemist in the preceding exercise cannot have triples in which treatments A and B appear simultaneously, how many experiments are there?

7. A computing machine is used for the study of problem-solving. It has 10 different steps it can use, and it does not use one it has previously used in the same attempt to solve a problem. The problems it solves require 4 different steps taken in the correct order. What is the largest number of attempts the computer may have to make before it solves a given problem?

8. An experimenter studying problem-solving has designed a problem whose correct solution requires 6 steps taken in order. There are two steps of type A, two of type B, and two of type C. He has made a list of the possible orders

$$AABBCC, \qquad AABCBC, \qquad \ldots, \qquad CCBBAA$$

and he has 88 such orders in his list. Has he found them all?

9. In the World Series, the American League team A, and the National League team N, play until one team wins 4 games. If the sequence of winners is designated by letters ($NAAAA$ means National League won the first game and lost the next 4), how many different sequences of winners are possible?

2-5. THE BINOMIAL THEOREM

Expansions of positive, integral powers of the binomial $(a + x)$, such as

$$(a + x)^2 = a^2 + 2ax + x^2,$$
$$(a + x)^3 = a^3 + 3a^2x + 3ax^2 + x^3,$$

are of frequent use in algebra. Moreover, expansions of this kind are important for our future studies in this book, and are related to results already obtained in this chapter. We are presently interested in finding a law or formula by which such expansions can be readily obtained.

Of course, we can always obtain them by ordinary multiplication. But the process soon becomes laborious. After we have shown by multiplication that

$$(a + x)^4 = a^4 + 4a^3x + 6a^2x^2 + 4ax^3 + x^4,$$

we may well begin to wonder if there isn't some better method of getting the result. If we study the expansions for $(a + x)^2$, $(a + x)^3$, and $(a + x)^4$, we soon note that part of the solution is easily guessed. The terms in the expansions, *apart from their coefficients*, can be written by inspection. For example, the expansion of $(a + x)^5$ has $5 + 1$, or 6 terms; without their coefficients, the terms are

$$a^5, \quad a^4x, \quad a^3x^2, \quad a^2x^3, \quad ax^4, \quad x^5.$$

Note that each of these terms is the product of 5 factors, where each factor is a or x. We say that such terms are of *degree* 5 in a and x. (In general, the *degree* of a term in a and x equals the number of factors a or x that the term contains.)

Proceeding along these lines, we see that the expansion of $(a + x)^n$ has $n + 1$ terms; without their coefficients, the terms are

$$a^n, \quad a^{n-1}x, \quad a^{n-2}x^2, \quad \cdots, \quad a^{n-r}x^r, \quad \cdots, \quad x^n,$$

where each term is of degree n in a and x. But there remains the question: How do we find the coefficients of these terms? Why, in the expansion of $(a + x)^4$, do we have $4a^3x$ and $6a^2x^2$? To answer such questions, let us examine the multiplication process.

Products of distinct binomials. The use of subscripts may help to illuminate what is going on when we multiply binomials. Consider the following products:

$$(a_1 + x_1)(a_2 + x_2) = a_1a_2 + a_1x_2 + x_1a_2 + x_1x_2;$$

$$(a_1 + x_1)(a_2 + x_2)(a_3 + x_3)$$

$$= a_1a_2a_3 + \boxed{a_1a_2x_3} + \boxed{a_1x_2a_3} + \boxed{x_1a_2a_3} + a_1x_2x_3$$

$$+ x_1a_2x_3 + x_1x_2a_3 + x_1x_2x_3.$$

The foregoing expansions illustrate three principles of multiplication:

(1) the *degree*, in a and x, of each term in a product equals the number of factors multiplied;

(2) the terms are obtained by *selecting exactly one* letter from each of the factors (note the subscripts on the right-hand sides);

(3) the expansion consists of the sum of such terms *obtained in all possible ways.*

In these products of distinct binomials, if we drop subscripts and collect like terms, we obtain the expansions of $(a + x)^2$ and $(a + x)^3$, respectively. Note that principles (2) and (3) are the keys to the discovery of the coefficients. If, for example, we can select two a's and one x in 3 different ways, as shown by the boxes, then the term a^2x will occur 3 times and so have the coefficient 3 in the expansion.

Let us apply the three principles above to obtain the expansion of $(a + x)^4$. Since

$$(a + x)^4 = (a + x)(a + x)(a + x)(a + x),$$

the terms of the expansion are of degree 4 in a and x. The possibilities are listed once more for reference:

$$a^4, \qquad a^3x, \qquad a^2x^2, \qquad ax^3, \qquad x^4.$$

Each term is obtained by selecting exactly one letter from each of the 4 factors. To get the first term, a^4, we select no x's and four a's from the 4 factors. Because this can be done in $\binom{4}{0}$ or 1 way, a^4 occurs only once in the expansion, and its coefficient is 1. To get the second term, a^3x, we select an x from one of the factors and three a's from the remaining three factors. This can be done in $\binom{4}{1}$ or 4 ways. Thus the term a^3x occurs 4 times and has the coefficient 4. Similarly, the term a^2x^2 is obtained in $\binom{4}{2}$ or 6 ways; the term ax^3 in $\binom{4}{3}$ or 4 ways; and the term x^4 in $\binom{4}{4}$ or 1 way. These last three terms therefore have the coefficients 6, 4, and 1, respectively. The complete expansion is the *sum* of all these terms:

$$(a + x)^4 = \binom{4}{0} a^4 + \binom{4}{1} a^3 x + \binom{4}{2} a^2 x^2 + \binom{4}{3} ax^3 + \binom{4}{4} x^4$$

$$= a^4 + 4a^3 x + 6a^2 x^2 + 4ax^3 + x^4.$$

We now proceed to generalize the foregoing reasoning.

2–14 Theorem. *The binomial theorem.* If n is a positive integer, then

$$(a + x)^n = \binom{n}{0} a^n + \binom{n}{1} a^{n-1} x + \binom{n}{2} a^{n-2} x^2 + \cdots$$

$$+ \binom{n}{r} a^{n-r} x^r + \cdots + \binom{n}{n} x^n. \tag{1}$$

Proof. Each term in the expansion of $(a + x)^n$ is of degree n in the variables a and x. Thus, if we ignore the coefficients, each term has the general pattern

$$a^{n-r} x^r, \qquad \text{where} \qquad r = 0, 1, 2, 3, \ldots, n.$$

The term $a^{n-r} x^r$ is obtained by selecting x from r of the factors and a from the remaining $n - r$ factors. This selection can be made in $\binom{n}{r}$ ways. (Cf. Theorem 2–9, Section 2–3.) Hence the term $a^{n-r} x^r$ occurs $\binom{n}{r}$ times and its coefficient is $\binom{n}{r}$. Therefore the complete general term is

$$\binom{n}{r} a^{n-r} x^r,$$

and the expansion is that shown in (1). In summation notation (see Appendix II), this expansion may be written

$$(a + x)^n = \sum_{r=0}^{n} \binom{n}{r} a^{n-r} x^r. \quad \square$$

The coefficients $\binom{n}{r}$ are often called *binomial coefficients*.

Binomial formula with expanded coefficients. Since

$$\binom{n}{0} = 1, \qquad \binom{n}{1} = n, \qquad \binom{n}{2} = \frac{n(n-1)}{2!},$$

$$\binom{n}{3} = \frac{n(n-1)(n-2)}{3!}, \qquad \text{etc.,}$$

the binomial expansion (1) may also be written as

$$(a+x)^n = a^n + \frac{n}{1!}a^{n-1}x + \frac{n(n-1)}{2!}a^{n-2}x^2 + \cdots + x^n. \tag{2}$$

EXAMPLE 1. Expand $(2+x)^4$.

Solution. Use formula (2), to obtain

$$(2+x)^4 = 2^4 + \frac{4}{1}(2^3)x + \frac{4\cdot 3}{1\cdot 2}(2^2)x^2 + \frac{4\cdot 3\cdot 2}{1\cdot 2\cdot 3}(2)x^3 + \frac{4\cdot 3\cdot 2\cdot 1}{1\cdot 2\cdot 3\cdot 4}x^4$$

$$= 16 + 32x + 24x^2 + 8x^3 + x^4.$$

EXAMPLE 2. Expand $(1 - 2x^2)^5$.

Solution. From formula (2), we obtain

$$(1 - 2x^2)^5 = \left(1 + (-2x^2)\right)^5$$

$$= 1 + \frac{5}{1}(-2x^2) + \frac{5\cdot 4}{1\cdot 2}(-2x^2)^2 + \frac{5\cdot 4\cdot 3}{1\cdot 2\cdot 3}(-2x^2)^3$$

$$+ \frac{5\cdot 4\cdot 3\cdot 2}{1\cdot 2\cdot 3\cdot 4}(-2x^2)^4 + (-2x^2)^5$$

$$= 1 - 10x^2 + 40x^4 - 80x^6 + 80x^8 - 32x^{10}.$$

NOTE. The signs of the terms in this expansion alternate because of the negative sign of the second term of the binomial $(1 - 2x^2)$. For the same reason, the signs in the formal expansion of $(a - x)^n$ alternate.

EXAMPLE 3. Prove that $\binom{n}{0} + \binom{n}{1} + \binom{n}{2} + \cdots + \binom{n}{n} = 2^n$.

Solution. Since formula (1) is valid for all values of a and x, we may set $a = x = 1$. This gives

$$(1 + 1)^n = \binom{n}{0} + \binom{n}{1} + \binom{n}{2} + \cdots + \binom{n}{n},$$

which proves the proposition. $\square$

EXAMPLE 4. If nx is near zero, prove that

$$(1 + x)^n \approx 1 + nx.$$

Solution. The proof follows at once from formula (2) if we set $a = 1$ and ignore terms with x^2, x^3, and higher powers. These neglected terms are

$$\frac{n(n - 1)}{2!} x^2, \qquad \frac{n(n - 1)(n - 2)}{3!} x^3, \qquad \text{and so on.}$$

Their absolute values are respectively less than the absolute values of

$$\frac{n^2 x^2}{2!}, \qquad \frac{n^3 x^3}{3!}, \qquad \text{and so on,}$$

because

$$n(n - 1) < n^2, \qquad n(n - 1)(n - 2) < n^3, \qquad \text{and so on.}$$

If nx is near zero, these higher powers of nx are small compared with the first power. Therefore, we have

$$\boxed{(1 + x)^n \approx 1 + nx. \quad \square} \qquad\qquad (3)$$

In Exercise 39 of this section, you are asked to show that when $|nx| < 1$ the approximation (3) is in error by an amount that is less than $(nx)^2$. This estimate of the error shows that the nearer nx is to zero, the better the approximation. For example, consider

$$(1 + 0.003)^{20}.$$

Since $x = 0.003$ and $n = 20$, it follows that

$$(nx)^2 = (0.06)^2 = 0.0036.$$

Consequently, formula (3) gives a two-decimal approximation for 1.003^{20}:

$$1 + 20(0.003) = 1.06.$$

For nx near zero, the formula

$$(1 + x)^n \approx 1 + nx$$

holds for nonintegral values of n as well as for integral values. For example,

$$(1 + x)^{1/2} \approx 1 + \tfrac{1}{2}x, \qquad \text{if } x \text{ is near zero.} \tag{4}$$

EXAMPLE 5. Find $\sqrt{4.02}$, approximately.

Solution. Transforming the radical and using (4), we get

$$\sqrt{4.02} = 2\sqrt{1.005} = 2(1 + 0.005)^{1/2} \approx 2(1 + 0.0025) = 2.005.$$

EXERCISES FOR SECTION 2–5

1. In the expansion of $(p + q)^7$, what is the degree of each term in p and q? Write, in ascending powers of q, the terms of this expansion without their co-efficients. What is the general form of these partial terms?

2. How many terms are there in the expansion of $(m + n)^{100}$? Write the first three terms of this expansion, without their coefficients, in ascending powers of n.

3. In the expansion in ascending powers of x of $(1 + x)^{1000}$, what is (a) the 200th term? (b) the coefficient of the 375th term? (c) the coefficient of x^{625}?

4. In the expansion of $(a + x)^{100}$, write, in unsimplified form, the 50th term. What is the 20th term? What is the term that contains x^{60}?

5. Expand $(q + p)^4$. If $p = \tfrac{1}{2}$ and $q = \tfrac{1}{2}$, find the values of the terms.

Use the binomial formula to expand the following:

6. (a) $(1 + b)^5$; (b) 1.01^5 7. (a) $(1 - b)^5$; (b) 0.98^5

8. $(1 + p)^7$ 9. $(1 - 3a)^4$ 10. $(1 - x^2)^5$

11. $(2 + 4m)^4$ 12. $(x + y)^6$ 13. $(3 - 6c)^5$

14. $(\tfrac{1}{2}a + 1)^4$ 15. $(p + q)^7$ 16. $(a + ax)^6$

17. $(1 - x^3)^5$ 18. $(x^2 - x^3)^6$ 19. $(x - y)^5$

Expand each of the following to 3 terms:

20. $(p + q)^{50}$ 21. $(x - y)^{100}$ 22. $(1 - a^2)^{40}$ 23. $(2x - 3y)^8$

Use the binomial formula to find approximations for the following:

24. 1.002^{10} 25. 0.997^{20} 26. 1.004^5 27. 0.9998^{10}

28. $\sqrt{9.09}$ 29. $\sqrt[3]{8.024}$ 30. $\sqrt{26}$ 31. $\sqrt[3]{999}$

32. $600^{3/4}$ 33. $1/\sqrt[5]{3120}$

Find approximations for the following, given that $|x|$ is small:

34. $\sqrt{1 - 2x}$ 35. $\sqrt[3]{1 + 6x}$ 36. $\sqrt{4 + 8x}$ 37. $\sqrt[3]{8 - 24x^2}$

38. If n is even, use formula (1) to prove that

$$\binom{n}{0} + \binom{n}{2} + \binom{n}{4} + \cdots + \binom{n}{n} = \binom{n}{1} + \binom{n}{3} + \binom{n}{5} + \cdots + \binom{n}{n - 1}.$$

39. If $|nx| < 1$, prove that the approximation formula

$$(1 + x)^n \approx 1 + nx,$$

is in error by an amount less than $(nx)^2$. (*Hint.* $1/r! \leq 1/2^{r-1}, r \geq 1$.)

40. How many different terms are there in the expansion of $(a + b + c)^n$: for $n = 1$? for $n = 2$? for $n = 3$? for general n?

3

A FIRST LOOK AT PROBABILITY: EQUALLY LIKELY OUTCOMES

3–1. INTRODUCTION. SOME EXPERIMENTS

One of the earliest notions in probability was that of equally likely cases, or equally likely outcomes. The words "equally likely" are meant to convey the notion of "equally probable." The idea is essentially an intuitive one. For example, if a coin is tossed it seems reasonable to assume that the coin is just as likely to fall "heads" as to fall "tails": the two outcomes, heads and tails, are considered to be equally likely. In other words, we say that heads and tails have *equal chances*.

A "die" (plural, *dice*) is a homogeneous cube whose faces are marked with dots as follows:

$$\cdot \;\; , \;\; \overset{\displaystyle \cdot}{\cdot} \;\; , \;\; \overset{\displaystyle \cdot}{\cdot} \;\; , \;\; \overset{\displaystyle \cdot\,\cdot}{\cdot\,\cdot} \;\; , \;\; \overset{\displaystyle \cdot\,\cdot}{\cdot\;\cdot} \;\; , \;\; \overset{\displaystyle \cdot\;\cdot}{\cdot\;\cdot} \;\; \cdot$$

If a die is thrown, most people find it reasonable to assume that when the die stops, one face is as likely to be on top as another: the six faces have equal chances. Thus, the throw of a die gives rise to six "equally likely" outcomes: the upper face shows one dot, or two dots, or three dots, and so on. We say that each of these outcomes has "one chance in six" of occurring.

Cards in an ordinary bridge deck are made so as to be indistinguishable from one another when they are placed face down. Suppose that we shuffle such a deck and draw one card. We then say that each card has the same chance of being drawn as every other card: one chance in fifty-two.

What makes us feel, in the tossing of a coin, that the two sides are equally likely, that in the throwing of a die the six faces are equally likely, and that in the drawing of a card the fifty-two cards are equally likely? It is the symmetry and homogeneity of the coin and the die, and the similarity of the cards. If the die were heavily loaded on one side, then the opposite side would be more likely to appear on top, and the six faces would not be equally likely. Experience with ordinary coins, dice, and cards confirms the notion that heads and tails appear about equally often when coins are tossed, that one face of a die appears on top about as often as another when dice are thrown, and that one card appears about as often as another when cards are drawn. Thus both reasoning based on symmetry and similarity, and experience with actual physical objects support the idea of equally likely outcomes for such experiments.

J. E. Kerrich* designed a coin-tossing experiment while he was interned during World War II. In ten sets of 1000 tosses, he found that the numbers of heads were

$$502, \ 511, \ 497, \ 529, \ 504, \ 476, \ 507, \ 528, \ 504, \ 529.$$

We see that these numbers cluster around 500, although none is exactly 500. To check that theory fits the facts, it is important to examine the results of such experiments with physical objects and to compare these results with theory. It is even more important to experience at first hand the relation between mathematical theory and events in the real world. For this reason, we have suggested and we shall continue to suggest experiments for you to perform.

To appreciate the importance of experimental verification as well as clear reasoning, consider the experiment of tossing two coins. It is said that the mathematician D'Alembert reasoned that there are three possible ways the coins can fall: (a) both heads, (b) one head and one tail, and (c) both tails. He thought these three outcomes were equally likely. If that were true, we should expect each of them to occur about $\frac{1}{3}$ of the time in actual experiments. Before reading further, you are urged to do Exercise 1 at the end of this section.

Table 3–1 shows another analysis of the two-coin problem. This analysis leads to four possible outcomes instead of three. If these four cases were equally likely, we should expect one head and one tail to occur about twice as often as two heads (or two tails), because cases 2 and 3 both contribute to the "one head and one tail" count.

Would reason alone enable us to decide which analysis of the two-coin problem is correct? Possibly so. But intelligent people have disagreed,

---

* J. E. Kerrich, *An Experimental Introduction to the Theory of Probability.* Belgisk Import Co. Copenhagen.

TABLE 3–1. POSSIBLE WAYS 2 COINS CAN LAND.

Case	First coin	Second coin
1	head	head
2	head	tail
3	tail	head
4	tail	tail

some choosing the "three equally likely cases" and others the "four equally likely cases." As we learn more about the theory of probability, we shall discover that the "four equally likely cases" corresponds to the assumption that the outcome on either coin is independent of the outcome on the other—an assumption that most experts nowadays believe fits the facts for coins.

Four major uses of the "equally likely cases" approach in probability are:

(1) To describe a physical experiment such as the tossing of a coin.

(2) To offer a "baseline" for comparison with empirical results. We may not believe that a phenomenon can be described by "equally likely cases," but we see where such an assumption leads, and then we check the consequences experimentally. For instance, the experiment of tossing 2 coins 50 times furnishes evidence for deciding in favor of three or of four equally likely cases.

(3) To give a satisfactory approximation to a process where we know very well that the cases are not equally likely. For example, even though more boys than girls are born, we often assume that every new baby has an equal chance of being a boy or a girl, and for many purposes this assumption is adequate.

(4) To achieve random sampling in sample surveys and other experimental investigations. The analysis of data from random samples is a relatively straightforward matter, but the analysis of data from samples not based on randomness requires difficult judgments.

The idea of an experiment. We have used the word *experiment* to describe such things as the throwing of one or more coins, the tossing of a die, or the drawing of a card from a bridge deck. Many more serious experiments are associated with every medical and scientific research campaign, such as the search for a polio vaccine, the study of the cause and cure of cancer, the studies of genetics by Gregor Mendel,* the psychological experiments of Pavlov, and the synthesis of penicillin by Sheehan. In the experiments of such campaigns, it is difficult to imagine all possible outcomes and it is not to be expected that these outcomes would be equally likely.

Nearly all serious experiments produce observations or measurements whose interpretation may well use an application of probability or of statistical reasoning. We shall use the word "experiment" to describe any act that can be repeated under given conditions. Usually the exact result of the act cannot be predicted with certainty. We focus attention on experiments that have only a finite number of possible outcomes and, in this chapter, we usually deal with outcomes that are equally likely.

For example, selecting a sample of 3 persons from a population of 30 persons is an "experiment" that may result in the choice of any one of the $\binom{30}{3}$ or 4060 different combinations of 30 people, selected 3 at a time. To select such a sample "at random" means that each combination has 1 chance in 4060 of being selected.

Probability: a measure of chance. Although we used the word loosely earlier, we now introduce the word "probability" as a technical word that we shall define and use when dealing with experiments involving "chance."

The experiments discussed to this point suggest a method of assigning numbers to the chances of certain events. Consider, for example, the throwing of a coin. In everyday language, we say that "the coin has 1 chance in 2 of falling heads"; in technical language, we say that "the probability of heads is $\frac{1}{2}$." In symbols, we write

$$P \text{ (head)} = \tfrac{1}{2}.$$

Similarly, in the tossing of a die, the face with six dots has 1 chance in 6 of landing on top; thus, we say that "the probability of 6 dots on top is $\frac{1}{6}$." In symbols:

$$P \text{ (6 dots on top)} = \tfrac{1}{6}.$$

Likewise, when we draw a card from a shuffled bridge deck, we have

$$P \text{ (ace of hearts)} = \tfrac{1}{52};$$

and when we select at random a sample of 3 people from a population of

---

* See "Mathematics of Heredity" by Gregor Mendel, *World of Mathematics*, vol. 2, pp. 937–949.

30, the probability of selecting three specified persons A, B, and C is

$$P\ (A,\ B,\ \text{and}\ C) = \tfrac{1}{4060}.$$

In general, we use

$$\text{``}P\ (\_\ \_\ \_\ \_)\text{''}$$

to denote "the probability of $\_\ \_\ \_\ \_$," where the blank may be filled with the name of any outcome.

As a further example, consider a 10-ticket draw for a prize. A name is written on each of 10 tickets, the tickets are then thoroughly mixed in a bag, and one ticket is drawn at random. The person whose name appears on the ticket so drawn is the winner.

Now if John's name appears on just one ticket, his chance of winning the prize is 1 in 10, since all outcomes in the drawing are equally likely. Therefore we say

$$P\ (\text{John wins}) = \tfrac{1}{10}.$$

Similarly, if John's name appears on 7 tickets, his chances of winning are 7 in 10, and

$$P\ (\text{John wins}) = \tfrac{7}{10}.$$

The general idea is that of separating from the whole set of equally likely outcomes the special subset of "favorable" outcomes. Then we assign the probability of a favorable outcome by the following rule:

$$P\ (\text{favorable outcome}) = \frac{\text{number of favorable outcomes}}{\text{number of possible outcomes}}.$$

This method of assigning to a favorable outcome a measure, or number, called its probability has an immediate consequence; for if there are no favorable outcomes in the set of possible outcomes, then

$$P\ (\text{favorable outcome}) = 0;$$

and, if all possible outcomes are favorable, then

$$P\ (\text{favorable outcome}) = 1.$$

It follows that

$$0 \leq P\ (\text{favorable outcome}) \leq 1.$$

This is consistent with our intuitive feeling. If John's name is on no ticket, he has no chance of winning and P (John wins) $= 0$; if his name is on all the tickets, his winning is a sure thing and P (John wins) $= 1$.

The number assigned to the probability of a favorable outcome also measures what we feel would be the long-run proportion of occurrences of the outcome in many repetitions of the experiment.

EXAMPLE 1. Four faces of an ordinary six-sided die are painted red, and the other two faces are painted green. If the die is rolled once, what is the probability that the top face is (a) red, (b) green?

Solution. Since the six faces are equally likely, the probability that the top face is red is given by

$$\frac{\text{number of favorable outcomes}}{\text{number of possible outcomes}} = \frac{4}{6} = \frac{2}{3}.$$

Thus we have

$$P \text{ (red)} = \tfrac{2}{3}.$$

Similarly,

$$P \text{ (green)} = \tfrac{2}{6} = \tfrac{1}{3}.$$

Note that the answer is not $\tfrac{1}{2}$. The two outcomes "red" and "green" are not equally likely.

The idea of an event. Sometimes it is convenient to regard a set of outcomes as corresponding to a single *event*. In Example 1, we may think of any one of the 4 red faces landing on top (4 outcomes) as corresponding to the event "top face red." The foregoing method of assigning probabilities can be defined in terms of events.

3–1 Definition. *Probability of an event.* If an experiment can result in any one of n different, equally likely outcomes, and if exactly m of these outcomes correspond to event A, then the probability of event A is

$$P(A) = \frac{m}{n}. \tag{1}$$

REMARK. We denote the event not-A by $\overline{A}$. It follows at once from the foregoing definition that the probability of event not-A is given by

$$P(\overline{A}) = \frac{n - m}{n} = 1 - \frac{m}{n} = 1 - P(A). \tag{2}$$

Odds. The relative chances for A and for $\overline{A}$ are often expressed in terms of the *odds in favor of A:*

$$\text{odds in favor of } A = \frac{P(A)}{P(\overline{A})} = \frac{m/n}{(n-m)/n} = \frac{m}{n-m}. \qquad (3)$$

Thus for the die with 4 red faces and 2 green faces, the odds in favor of red are $\frac{4}{2}$ or $\frac{2}{1}$. If we know the probabilities of the events A and $\overline{A}$, Eq. (3) gives the odds in favor of A. Sometimes these are also called the odds *against* $\overline{A}$.

On the other hand, if we know that the odds in favor of A are a/b, then

$$P(A) = \frac{a}{a+b}, \qquad P(\overline{A}) = \frac{b}{a+b}. \qquad (4)$$

EXAMPLE 2. A card is drawn at random from an ordinary bridge deck. Find the probability and the odds that the card is an "honor" (that is, an ace, king, queen, jack, or ten).

Solution. The number of possible outcomes is 52. There are 5 honor cards in each of the 4 suits—a total of 20 honor cards. We may regard the 20 different outcomes in which an honor card is drawn as corresponding to the event "honor card drawn." If the cards are well shuffled, and one card is drawn at random from the deck, we assume that each of the 52 cards is equally likely to appear. Hence

$$P \text{ (honor card)} = \frac{m}{n} = \frac{20}{52} = \frac{5}{13}.$$

The odds in favor of an honor card are 5 to 8, since

$$P \text{ (non-honor card)} = 1 - \frac{5}{13} = \frac{8}{13} \quad \text{and} \quad \frac{5/13}{8/13} = \frac{5}{8}.$$

Alternatively, the odds *against* an honor card are 8 to 5. We get the same results by observing that

$$\text{odds in favor of honor card} = \frac{\text{number of honor cards}}{\text{number of non-honor cards}}$$

$$= \frac{20}{32} = \frac{5}{8},$$

and then computing

$$P \text{ (honor card)} = \frac{5}{5+8} = \frac{5}{13}.$$

EXERCISES FOR SECTION 3-1

1. Perform the following experiment. Toss 2 coins 50 times, keeping a careful tally of the possible outcomes—two heads, one head and one tail, two tails. Compute the proportion of occurrence for each of the three outcomes. Do your results appear to support the reasoning of D'Alembert that the three outcomes are equally likely?

2. If a die is thrown, what is the probability that the upper face shows 3? More than 3? Less than 3? An even number? An odd number?

3. In a throw of two ordinary dice, what is the probability that the numbers on their upper faces add up to 3? to 4? to 11?

4. When two coins are tossed, what is the probability that both show heads? That they show one head and one tail?

5. From a class of 40 students with 25 girls, one student is chosen by lot. What is the probability that a boy is chosen?

6. A bag contains 10 white marbles and 8 black marbles. If one marble is drawn from the bag at random, what is the probability that it is black? That it is white?

7. In a family of three children, what is the probability that all three are boys? Assume that boys and girls have an equal chance of being born.

8. Toss a coin 100 times, keeping a record of the number of heads; or use the results of Exercise 1 for 50 tosses of 2 coins. Compute the relative frequency of heads. How does your result compare with the probability of getting a head on one toss of a single coin?

9. One card is drawn at random from a well-shuffled bridge deck of 52 cards. What is the probability of drawing a heart? An ace? A black card?

10. What is wrong with the following procedure? To find the probability that an American citizen chosen at random was born in a given state, divide the number of favorable cases (1) by the total number of states (50), and obtain the answer $\frac{1}{50}$.

11. A letter is chosen at random from the word *equations*. What is the probability that the letter is a vowel? A consonant? The letter m?

12. A person holds a ticket in a lottery that offers 10 prizes and sells 120 tickets. What is the probability that the person will win a prize? That he will not win a prize?

13. Ten balls, numbered 1 to 10, are placed in a bag and two of the balls are drawn at random. What is the probability that balls numbered 3 and 7 are drawn?

14. The numbers 1 to 9 inclusive are written on slips of paper, and the slips are placed in a bag and thoroughly mixed. One slip is drawn from the bag at random. What is the probability that the number on the slip is odd? Even? Prime? (*Note.* We do not count the number 1 as a prime.) A multiple of 3?

15. Five balls, numbered 1 to 5, are placed in a bag, mixed, and drawn out, one at a time. What is the probability that the balls are drawn in the order 1, 2, 3, 4, 5?

16. A six-volume encyclopedia is placed at random on a bookshelf. What is the probability that one or more of the volumes is out of its correct order?

17. A 3-digit number is formed by randomly choosing three of the digits 1, 2, 3, 4, 5, without repetition. What is the probability that the number is even? Odd? A multiple of 5?

3–2. A SAMPLE SPACE OF AN EXPERIMENT

We have discussed the notion of an experiment and examined a number of simple experiments with equally likely outcomes. We now introduce an important related idea: "a sample space of an experiment." We approach this idea with the aid of an illustrative example.

Consider the experiment of tossing two coins: a dime and a quarter. How shall we list the possible outcomes of this experiment? It may be done in a number of ways, and the particular method preferred depends upon what our interest is centered on. Suppose, for example, that we are interested in whether each coin falls heads (H) or tails (T). Then the set

$$S = \{HH,\ HT,\ TH,\ TT\} \tag{1}$$

provides a list that represents the possible outcomes of one toss, if we understand that the first letter in a pair designates the outcome for the dime, and the second letter that for the quarter. Thus HT means that the dime fell heads and the quarter fell tails. Every outcome of the experiment corresponds to exactly one element of the set (1).

Alternatively, we may be interested only in the *number* of heads or tails that appear. If we agree to denote a heads and b tails by the ordered pair (a, b), then the set

$$S_1 = \{(2, 0),\ (1, 1),\ (0, 2)\} \tag{2}$$

lists all possible outcomes of the experiment. And every outcome of the experiment corresponds to exactly one element of the set (2).

Again, we may be concerned only with whether the coins fall alike (A) or different (D). We could then list all possible outcomes with the set

$$S_2 = \{A,\ D\}. \tag{3}$$

As before, every outcome of the experiment corresponds to exactly one element of the set (3).

Hence each of the sets (1), (2), and (3) provides a list that includes all possible outcomes of the experiment. Each such set is called "a sample space of the experiment"; that's why we talk about "a" sample space of an experiment, rather than "the" sample space. More than one sample space can be used to list the possible outcomes.

NOTE. S is a more fundamental sample space than S_1 or S_2 because it offers more information. If we know which element of S occurs, we can tell which outcomes occur in S_1 and S_2; but the reverse is not always true.

3–2 Definitions. *Sample space; sample point.* A sample space of an experiment is a set S of elements such that any outcome of the experiment corresponds to exactly one element in the set. An element in a sample space is called a sample point.

EXAMPLE 1. *Three-child families.* To study the distribution of boys and girls in families having three children, a survey of such families is made. What is a sample space for the experiment of drawing one family from a population of three-child families?

Solution. Let B stand for "boy," and G stand for "girl." If we use a triple of letters to represent the oldest, the second, and the youngest child, in that order, then the following set is a sample space for a single family:

$$\{BBB, \ BBG, \ BGB, \ GBB, \ BGG, \ GBG, \ GGB, \ GGG\}.$$

The triple GBB, for instance, represents the outcome "oldest child is a girl, second and third are boys." Another sample space is obtained by listing the number of boys in families with three children:

$$\{0, \ 1, \ 2, \ 3\}.$$

Another useful way of listing the possibilities in this example is the "tree" method shown in Fig. 3–1.

EXAMPLE 2. The numbers 1, 2, 3, and 4 are written separately on four slips of paper. The slips are then put into a hat and stirred. A blindfolded person draws two slips from the hat, one after the other, without replacement. Describe a sample space for the experiment.

Solution. We may consider that each outcome of the experiment is represented by an ordered pair of numbers (x, y), where x is the number on the first slip and y is the number on the second. The restrictions on

x and y are as follows:

$$1 \le x \le 4, \qquad 1 \le y \le 4, \qquad x \ne y.$$

Table 3–2 shows a sample space.

First child   Second child   Third child   Sample space

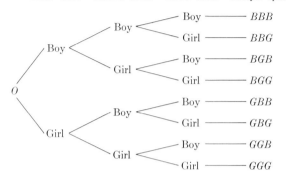

Fig. 3–1.   Tree for three-child families.

TABLE 3–2. SAMPLE SPACE FOR 2 NUMBERED SLIPS.

y: number on second slip

x \ y	1	2	3	4
1		(1, 2)	(1, 3)	(1, 4)
2	(2, 1)		(2, 3)	(2, 4)
3	(3, 1)	(3, 2)		(3, 4)
4	(4, 1)	(4, 2)	(4, 3)	

x: number on first slip

EXERCISES FOR SECTION 3-2

1. A coin is tossed and then a die is thrown. List a sample space for this experiment. Illustrate with a tree graph.

2. Three coins are tossed. List two sample spaces for this experiment.

3. Two letters are randomly chosen, one after another, from the word *tack*. List a sample space.

4. A boy has in his pocket a penny, a nickel, a dime, and a quarter. He takes two coins out of his pocket, one after the other. List a sample space. Illustrate with a tree graph.

5. Suppose you plan to make a survey of families having two children. You want to record the sex of each child, in the order of their births. For example, if the first child is a boy and the second a girl, you record (boy, girl). This is one point in the sample space. List all the sample points.

6. If the survey in Exercise 5 is undertaken for families having four children, list an appropriate sample space. How many sample points does it have? How many of these points correspond to families having 3 boys and 1 girl? How many correspond to families in which the first child is a girl?

7. Two dice, one black and one red, are tossed and the numbers of dots on their upper faces are noted. List a sample space for the experiment. (*Note.* A tabular arrangement is convenient.)

8. An engineer's ruler has a cross section that is an equilateral triangle. Two such rulers, one red and one green, have their faces numbered 1, 2, and 3. The rulers are tossed onto the floor and the numbers on the bottom faces are read when they come to rest. Set up a table for the sample space of outcomes.

9. An experiment consists of selecting 3 radios from a lot of 25 and testing them. The test shows that a radio is defective (D), or nondefective (N). List a sample space for this experiment.

10. From five different books, A, B, C, D, and E, three are selected. List a suitable sample space of outcomes. In your sample space: (a) How many sample points correspond to a selection including A? (b) How many correspond to a selection without A? (c) How many correspond to a selection including both B and C? (d) How many correspond to a selection including either D or E?

11. Two marbles, one red and one blue, are to be placed in two boxes numbered 1 and 2. List an appropriate sample space (a) if one box may be left empty; (b) if neither box may be left empty.

12. A letter is chosen at random from the word *ground*. Which of the following sets are acceptable as sample spaces for the experiment and which are not?

(a) $\{g, r, o, u, n, d\}$;

(b) $\{$vowel, $g, r, n, d\}$;

(c) $\{r, o, u, n, d\}$;

(d) $\{$vowel, consonant$\}$;

(e) $\{$consonant, $u\}$.

13. A bag contains a number of marbles, identical in every way except that some are red, some white, and some blue. Two marbles are drawn, one after the other, without replacement. What is a sample space for this experiment? How many points of the sample space correspond to drawing two marbles of the same color? How many points correspond to drawing marbles of different colors? How many correspond to drawing a red *and* a blue marble? How many correspond to drawing a red *or* a blue marble?

14. In the sample space of Exercise 7, how many sample points correspond to a total of more than 10 dots? To a total of less than 5 dots? To an even total? To the black die showing more than 5 dots? To the red die showing less than 3 *and* the black die showing more than 5? To the red die showing an even number *or* the black die showing 3?

3–3. PROBABILITIES IN A FINITE SAMPLE SPACE

When an experiment is performed, we may want to know the probabilities of various outcomes or events associated with the experiment. Often such probabilities can be computed by setting up a sample space of equally likely outcomes and counting the sample points. The following examples illustrate the method. Since we shall be making considerable use of these examples throughout the remainder of this chapter, they should be studied with special care.

EXAMPLE 1. *Two dice.* An experiment consists of throwing two ordinary six-sided dice and observing the numbers of dots on their upper faces.

Discussion. For the purposes of this experiment, we assume that the dice are distinguishable: one die is *red*, and the other die is *clear*. It would serve our purpose just as well to throw a single die twice, the first throw corresponding to the red die, the second throw corresponding to the clear die. Table 3–3 shows a sample space that lists the possible outcomes of the experiment.

In the rest of the chapter, Table 3–3 is referred to repeatedly, so inserting a bookmark here may speed your reading.

TABLE 3–3. SAMPLE SPACE FOR TWO-DICE EXPERIMENT.

Clear die outcome (c)

	c \ r	1	2	3	4	5	6
	1	(1, 1)	(1, 2)	(1, 3)	(1, 4)	(1, 5)	(1, 6)
Red die outcome	2	(2, 1)	(2, 2)	(2, 3)	(2, 4)	(2, 5)	(2, 6)
(r)	3	(3, 1)	(3, 2)	(3, 3)	(3, 4)	(3, 5)	(3, 6)
	4	(4, 1)	(4, 2)	(4, 3)	(4, 4)	(4, 5)	(4, 6)
	5	(5, 1)	(5, 2)	(5, 3)	(5, 4)	(5, 5)	(5, 6)
	6	(6, 1)	(6, 2)	(6, 3)	(6, 4)	(6, 5)	(6, 6)

Each *row* of the table corresponds to a fixed value of r, the outcome for the *red* die; and each *column* corresponds to a fixed value of c, the outcome for the *clear* die. For instance, the entry (2, 4) in the second row and the fourth column represents the event "red die shows 2, clear die shows 4." The entire sample space, S, is the set of ordered pairs (r, c) with r and c each taking the values 1, 2, 3, 4, 5, or 6:

$$S = \{(r, c): 1 \leq r \leq 6, \ 1 \leq c \leq 6\}. \tag{1}$$

Even without making the list, we can see from (1) that there are 6×6, or 36, possible outcomes of the experiment. We assume that the dice are well balanced and fairly thrown, so that these outcomes are equally likely to occur. We therefore attach probability $\frac{1}{36}$ to each point in the sample space.

Once the sample space of the experiment has been set up and probabilities assigned to the sample points, we can answer questions such as the following:

(1) What is the probability of throwing a double?

(2) What is the probability that the number on the clear die is at least 3 greater than the number on the red die?

(3) What is the probability that the sum $r + c$ is 10?

When an event is described by a verbal expression (for example, "throwing a double"), we often find it helpful to translate the verbal expression into an algebraic condition such as "$c = r$." Then we focus attention on the subset of the sample space whose members satisfy this algebraic condition, which is usually an equation or an inequality. Count-

TABLE 3–4. EVENTS AND PROBABILITIES FOR THE
TWO-DICE EXPERIMENT.

Question number	Verbal description	Algebraic condition	Solution set (subset of S)	Probability
1	throwing a double	$c = r$	(1, 1), (2, 2), (3, 3), (4, 4), (5, 5), (6, 6)	$\dfrac{6}{36} = \dfrac{1}{6}$
2	clear score at least 3 greater than red score	$c \geq r + 3$	(1, 4), (1, 5), (1, 6), (2, 5), (2, 6), (3, 6)	$\dfrac{6}{36} = \dfrac{1}{6}$
3	sum equal 10	$c + r = 10$	(4, 6), (5, 5), (6, 4)	$\dfrac{3}{36} = \dfrac{1}{12}$

ing does the rest. For example, consider the three questions just posed in connection with the two-dice experiment. We list, in Table 3–4, the verbal descriptions, the corresponding algebraic conditions, the solution sets, and the required probabilities.

REMARK. The foregoing procedure is useful for finding the probabilities of various outcomes of an experiment. We list the steps in the method:

(1) *Set up a sample space S of all possible outcomes.* The sample space may be listed as in Table 3–3, or it may be indicated by the set-builder notation as in Eq. (1).

(2) *Assign probabilities to the elements of the sample space (sample points).* In a sample space of n equally likely outcomes, we assign probability $1/n$ to each sample point. The sum of the probabilities of all the sample points in a given sample space must equal 1.

(3) *To obtain the probability of an event E, add the probabilities assigned to the elements of the subset of S that corresponds to E.* Since the empty set has no elements, its probability is zero. (For "empty set," see Appendix I–3, just before Theorem I–3.)

EXAMPLE 2. For a chronic disease, there are five standard ameliorative treatments: a, b, c, d, and e. A doctor has resources for conducting a comparative study of three of these treatments. If he chooses the three treatments for study at random from the five, what is the probability that (a) treatment a will be chosen, (b) treatments a and b will be chosen, (c) at least one of a and b will be chosen?

Solution. In Table 3–5, we list the $\binom{5}{3}$, or 10, possible selections of the 5 treatments, taken 3 at a time. For reference, the sample points are numbered.

TABLE 3–5. S FOR STUDY OF TREATMENTS.

1	2	3	4	5	6	7	8	9	10
abc	abd	abe	acd	ace	ade	bcd	bce	bde	cde

Next, we assign probability $\frac{1}{10}$ to each sample point, since we assume that all 10 selections are equally likely. Then the probability that treatment a is chosen is $\frac{6}{10}$, because there are 6 selections corresponding to the event "treatment a is chosen."

Similarly, the probability that treatments a and b are both chosen is $\frac{3}{10}$, because there are exactly 3 selections containing both a and b. Finally, the probability that at least one of the treatments a and b is chosen is $\frac{9}{10}$; only the tenth sample point contains neither a nor b.

REMARK. Alternatively, we can reach the foregoing conclusions by using the facts of Chapter 2. For example, there are $\binom{5}{3}$ ways of choosing three treatments from five without restrictions, and $\binom{4}{2}$ ways of choosing them if treatment a must be included. Therefore,

$$P(a \text{ chosen}) = \frac{m}{n} = \frac{\binom{4}{2}}{\binom{5}{3}} = \frac{6}{10}.$$

The other cases can be dealt with similarly.

EXERCISES FOR SECTION 3–3

Exercises 1 through 7 refer to the two-dice experiment. Consult the sample space in Table 3–3.

1. What is the probability of not throwing a double?

2. What is the probability that the number on one die is double the number on the other?

3. What is the probability that one die gives a 5 and the other die a number less than 5?

4. What is the probability that the clear die gives a number less than 3 and the red die a number greater than 3?

5. Evaluate: (a) $P(r + c = 6)$ (b) $P(r + c = 8)$ (c) $P(r + c < 5)$
(d) $P(r + c > 9)$ (e) $P(r \geq c + 4)$

6. Give algebraic descriptions of the following verbally described events: (a) not throwing a double, (b) red die shows two less than clear die, (c) clear die shows number at least 2 greater than red die, (d) number on red die twice that on clear die.

7. Give verbal descriptions of the following algebraically described events:

(a) $r = 3c$ (b) $r - c = 1$ (c) $r \neq c$
(d) $r + c > 8$ (e) $c = r^2$ (f) $r \geq c$

8. For the sample space of Exercise 4 at the end of Section 3–2, answer the following: (a) What is the probability that both coins are silver? (b) What is the probability that the value of the coins selected is less than 20 cents? Less than 15 cents? More than 15 cents? A prime number? A number divisible by 10?

9. In Exercise 6, Section 3–2, assume that all points in the sample space have the same probability. What is the probability that in a family of four children the first two are girls? What is the probability that three are boys and one is a girl? That there are two boys and two girls?

10. In Exercise 8, Section 3–2, assume that all points of the sample space have equal probabilities. Let r denote the number on the red ruler, and g the number on the green. Evaluate: (a) $P(r = g)$, (b) $P(r + g > 3)$, (c) $P(r > g)$, (d) $P(r \neq g)$, (e) $P(r = g^2)$.

11. In the ancient Indian game of Tong, two players simultaneously show their right hands to each other, exhibiting either one or two or three extended fingers. If each player is equally likely to extend one, two, or three fingers, what is the probability that the total number of fingers extended is even? Odd? Greater than 4? Less than 2? Prime? (*Note.* Set up a sample space as a first step.)

12. Two rods, one black and one white, have square cross sections. Each rod has its faces numbered 1, 2, 3, and 4. The rods are rolled on the floor, and the numbers on their upper faces are read after they come to rest. Set up a table for a sample space of outcomes. If b is the number on the upper face of the black rod, and w that on the upper face of the white rod, evaluate:

(a) $P(b + w = 5)$ (b) $P(b = w)$ (c) $P(b > w + 1)$

(d) P (black 1 or 3 and white 2 or 4)   (e) P (sum of numbers even)

(f) P (larger number shown is a 4)

13. Repeat the experiment of Exercise 8 at the end of Section 3–2 for three engineer's rulers. (The third ruler is blue.) What is the probability that exactly one of the rulers shows a 2? That exactly two rulers show a 2? That all three rulers show a 2? That the sum of the numbers shown is at least 7?

14. Suppose that you have a black rod from Exercise 12 and a red engineer's ruler from Exercise 13. Rod and ruler are rolled on the floor, and the number on the top face of the rod and that on the bottom face of the ruler are noted. Set up a sample space and find the probability that the number on the black rod is greater than that on the red ruler. What is the probability that both numbers are the same? That the sum of the numbers is prime?

15. In the sample space of Exercise 10 at the end of Section 3–2 assume that all points are equally likely. What is the probability that B will be included in the selection? That both A and B will be included? That either A or B will be included? That the selection will be C, D, and E?

REVIEW EXERCISES FOR SECTIONS 3–1, 3–2, AND 3–3

1. The numbers from 1 through 15 are painted on 15 balls, one number per ball. If one of these balls is drawn at random, what is the probability that the number on it is: (a) Divisible by 5? (b) Even? (c) Odd? (d) A perfect square? (e) A 2-digit number? (f) A prime number? (g) A prime number that is 2 more than another prime?

2. A bag contains 5 times as many red marbles as black marbles (identical except for color). One marble is drawn at random. What is the probability that it is red?

3. A regular *icosahedron* is a symmetrical solid with 20 faces. Some of the faces of such a solid are painted red and the rest are painted blue. If, when the icosahedron is thrown onto the floor, the probability of a red face landing on the bottom is 4 times the probability of a blue face, how many faces are painted red?

4. A poll is taken among 70 residents of a suburb of Boston on the question of an ordinance to prohibit motorboats on the upper Mystic Lake. The results of the poll are tabulated as follows:

	Own motorboat only	Own sailboat only	Own motorboat and sailboat	Own neither	Totals
Favor ordinance	0	7	1	18	26
Oppose ordinance	20	2	3	5	30
No opinion	0	1	1	12	14
Totals	20	10	5	35	70

If one of the 70 persons is chosen at random, what is the probability that he: (a) Favors the ordinance? (b) Opposes the ordinance? (c) Favors the ordinance or has no opinion on it? (d) Owns a boat? (e) Owns a sailboat? (f) Owns a motorboat?

5. A committee of two persons is to be selected from three men (Archer, Baker, Connor) and two women (Davis and Eads). Describe two different sample spaces for the experiment.

6. You ask a friend to "think of a number." Describe a sample space for the experiment.

7. A teacher asks each member of his class to count the number of pencils that he (or she) has brought to class. Describe a sample space for the experiment.

8. Cards are dealt one after another from an ordinary bridge deck until the first ace appears. Describe two different sample spaces for the experiment.

9. A coin is tossed repeatedly until a head first appears, or until tails appear four times in succession. Describe a sample space for the experiment.

10. A die is thrown until a "2" appears. Describe a sample space for the experiment.

11. You ask each of 25 different people to tell you their birthdays. Describe a sample space for the experiment.

12. A plant breeder crosses two parent strains, each possessing a gene pair of type aA. Each parent contributes one-half of this gene pair (either a or A) to the offspring, where the two halves are combined. Describe a sample space for the genetic type of the offspring.

13. Suppose that m places are to be filled from n candidates, where $n \geq m$. (a) How many ways are there of selecting m candidates from among the n available? (b) In how many of the different ways of part (a) is a particular candidate A included in the selection? (c) Assuming all selections of m from among the n are equally likely, what is the probability that candidate A is included? Discuss your result. Does it seem to be reasonable?

14. Two cards are drawn from an ordinary bridge deck, one after the other, and without replacement. (a) If order counts, how many different ordered pairs (x, y) are there in a sample space of the experiment, where x denotes the first card drawn and y denotes the second card? (b) What is the probability of each point in this sample space? (c) What is the probability that the first card is an ace and the second card is a jack? (d) That one of the cards is an ace and the other is a jack?

3–4. EVENTS AND SETS

As already indicated in Sections 3–1 and 3–3, when used as a technical word an "event" is a subset of a sample space S of an experiment. We have seen that subsets, or "events," may be described either verbally or by algebraic equations and inequalities. Such descriptions define subsets of S corresponding to the "events" under consideration.

A note on "or" and "and." In everyday English, expressions of the form "A or B" use the word "or" in two different ways:

(1) in the *exclusive* sense, which connotes "A or B but not both" (for example, a coin falls "heads or tails");

(2) in the *inclusive* sense, which connotes "A or B or both" (for example, consider the statement: "I may visit France or Italy this summer.").

Ordinarily, the context is a sufficient guide to the intended meaning. However, when we use the expression "A or B" in referring to *events*, the meaning is never in doubt because we *always* use the inclusive "or"; in other words, "A or B" means "A or B or both."

The foregoing usage agrees with the definition of $A \cup B$, that is, the *union* of sets A and B. For,

$A \cup B$ is the set of all points belonging to A or to B or to both.

Thus, in this book, "the probability of A or B" always means

$$P(A \cup B).$$

The idea of simultaneous membership in two sets is connoted in our use of "and" when we talk about events. Thus if events A and B are subsets of a sample space, then "A and B" is their *intersection; that is,* the event "A and B" contains those sample points that belong to *both* A and B. For,

> the intersection of A and B, $A \cap B$, is the set of all elements belonging to both A and B.

When we use the verbal description "the probability of A and B," we mean

$$P(A \cap B).$$

We shall illustrate these ideas with further examples based on Table 3–3.

EXAMPLE 1. In the two-dice experiment, what is the probability that $r \leq 3$ or $c \leq 2$?

Solution. For the outcome $r \leq 3$, the red die must show either 1 or 2 or 3. The corresponding set A consists of the 18 points in the first three rows of Table 3–3. For $c \leq 2$, the clear die must show either 1 or 2, and the corresponding set B consists of the 12 points in the first two columns. The points in the union of A and B correspond to the event $r \leq 3$ or $c \leq 2$. To find the number of points in $A \cup B$, we must not add the number in A to the number in B, because there are 6 points that are in both sets and we must not count these twice. The correct count of points in $A \cup B$ is

$$18 + 12 - 6 = 24. \tag{1}$$

Therefore the probability of $r \leq 3$ or $c \leq 2$ is $\frac{24}{36}$, or $\frac{2}{3}$.

We notice in the above calculation that 18 is the number of points in A, 12 is the number in B, and 6 is the number in their intersection $A \cap B$. Dividing all terms of Eq. (1) by 36, we get

$$\frac{18}{36} + \frac{12}{36} - \frac{6}{36} = \frac{24}{36}. \tag{2}$$

Thus, in this example, we may say that

$$P(A) + P(B) - P(A \cap B) = P(A \cup B); \tag{3}$$

for,

$$P(A) = \tfrac{18}{36}, \qquad P(B) = \tfrac{12}{36},$$

$$P(A \cap B) = \tfrac{6}{36}, \qquad P(A \cup B) = \tfrac{24}{36}.$$

In the next section, we show that Eq. (3) is true in general.

EXERCISES FOR SECTION 3-4

Exercises 1 through 7 refer to the sample space for the two-dice experiment of Table 3–3.

1. What is the probability that $r > 2$ or $c > 3$?
2. What is the probability that $r > 2$ and $3c > 3$?
3. What is the probability that $r < 2$ or $c < 4$?
4. What is the probability that $r < 2$ and $c < 4$?
5. What is the probability that $r + c = 5$ or $r + c = 7$?
6. What is the probability that $r + c = 5$ and $r + c = 7$?
7. If A is the event "r is greater than 4" and B is the event "c is greater than 2," prove that

$$P(A) + P(B) - P(A \cap B) = P(A \cup B).$$

Exercises 8 through 14 refer to the sample space for Example 2, Section 3–3 (Table 3–5).

8. What is the probability that treatments a or c are chosen?
9. What is the probability that treatments a and c are chosen?
10. What is the probability that a and b or b and c are chosen?
11. What is the probability that a and b and b and c are chosen?
12. What is the probability that e is chosen or that b and c are chosen?
13. What is the probability that e is chosen and that also b and c are chosen?
14. If A is the event "a is chosen" and B is the event "b is chosen," show that

$$P(A) + P(B) - P(A \cap B) = P(A \cup B).$$

3–5. MUTUALLY EXCLUSIVE EVENTS

If two events cannot happen at the same time, they are said to be *mutually exclusive*. The computation of probabilities is especially simple when an event consists of other mutually exclusive events.

EXAMPLE 1. In the two-dice example of Section 3–3, what is the probability that the sum $r + c$ is 7 or 10?

Solution. (Refer to Table 3–3.) There are 6 sample points with $r + c = 7$, and 3 with $r + c = 10$. Since the corresponding sets do not overlap, there are 9 points with sum 7 or 10. Hence the probability is $\frac{9}{36}$, or $\frac{1}{4}$.

In set language, if A is the set of points with $r + c = 7$, and B is the set with $r + c = 10$, then, *for this example*, we have

$$P(A) + P(B) = P(A \cup B). \tag{1}$$

The equality follows because

$$P(A) = \tfrac{6}{36}, \quad P(B) = \tfrac{3}{36}, \quad \text{and} \quad P(A \cup B) = \tfrac{9}{36}.$$

Equation (1) is like Eq. (3) of the previous section, with $P(A \cap B) = 0$.

3–3 Definition. *Mutually exclusive events.* If two events have no points in common, they are called mutually exclusive, or disjoint. And *n* events are mutually exclusive if no two of them have any points in common (Fig. 3–2).

We note a consequence of this definition: *the intersection of two or more mutually exclusive events is the empty set.*

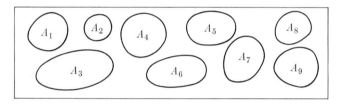

FIG. 3–2.   Graph of mutually exclusive or disjoint subsets.

3–4 Theorem. *Probability of $A \cup B$.* If A and B are events in a finite sample space S (Fig. 3–3), then

$$P(A \cup B) = P(A) + P(B) - P(A \cap B). \tag{2}$$

Proof. The probability of $A \cup B$ is the sum of the probabilities of the points in $A \cup B$. Now $P(A) + P(B)$ is the sum of the probabilities of points in A plus the sum of the probabilities of points in B. Therefore $P(A) + P(B)$ includes the probabilities of points in the intersection $A \cap B$ twice. If we subtract this probability $P(A \cap B)$ once, we shall have the sum of the probabilities of all points in $A \cup B$, each taken just once. Hence

$$P(A \cup B) = P(A) + P(B) - P(A \cap B). \ \square \tag{3}$$

3–5 Corollary. If A and B are disjoint, then

$$P(A \cup B) = P(A) + P(B). \tag{4}$$

Equation (4) follows at once from Eq. (3) since, if A and B are disjoint, $A \cap B = \phi$, the empty set, and $P(A \cap B) = P(\phi) = 0$.

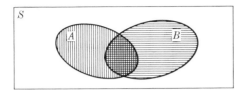

FIG. 3–3.   Events in S.

3–6 Corollary. *Several disjoint events.*   Let A_1, A_2, A_3, ..., A_m be mutually exclusive events.   Then

$$P(A_1 \cup A_2 \cup \cdots \cup A_m) = P(A_1) + P(A_2) + \cdots + P(A_m). \qquad (5)$$

In words, the probability of A_1 or A_2 or ... or A_m is the *sum* of their probabilities, provided the events are mutually exclusive.

Proof.   (Cf. Fig. 3–4.)   The probability of the union of A_1, A_2, and so on, is the sum of the probabilities of its points.   The sum

$$P(A_1) + P(A_2) + \cdots + P(A_m)$$

is the sum of the probabilities of the points in A_1, plus the sum for A_2, and so on.   Since the sets do not overlap, this sum includes the probabilities of the points in the union, once and only once for each point. $\square$

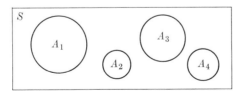

FIG. 3–4.   Disjoint sets.

3–7 Definition. *Partition.*   If the events A_1, A_2, ..., A_m are mutually exclusive and exhaustive (i.e., their union contains all the sample points of S), then we say that the m events form a partition of the sample space S into m subsets.

For example, Fig. 3–5 illustrates a partition of S into 8 subsets:

$$S = A_1 \cup A_2 \cup A_3 \cup A_4 \cup A_5 \cup A_6 \cup A_7 \cup A_8.$$

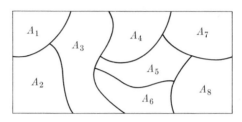

FIG. 3–5.   A partition of S.

3–8 Theorem.   *Probabilities under a partition.*   If $A_1, A_2, \ldots, A_m$ form a partition of a finite sample space S, then

$$P(A_1) + P(A_2) + \cdots + P(A_m) = 1.$$

Proof. From Corollary 3–6, we have

$$P(A_1) + P(A_2) + \cdots + P(A_m) = P(A_1 \cup A_2 \cup \cdots \cup A_m)$$

$$= P(S)$$

$$= 1. \ \square$$

EXAMPLE 2. A high-school basketball coach has available three complimentary tickets to a professional basketball game. He decides to give the tickets to three players chosen at random from the five players of his first string team: Art (a), Bob (b), Chuck (c), Dick (d), and Ed (e). What is the probability that both Art and Bob are chosen, or both Chuck and Ed are chosen, or Bob, Chuck, and Dick are chosen?

Solution. A sample space consists of the $\binom{5}{3}$, or 10, possible selections of the 5 players, taken 3 at a time:

$$S = \{abc,\ abd,\ abe,\ acd,\ ace,\ ade,\ bcd,\ bce,\ bde,\ cde\}.$$

We now select subsets of S that correspond to the three events in which we are interested. These subsets and their verbal descriptions are tabulated as follows:

Verbal description	Event
Art and Bob are chosen	$A_1 = \{abc, abd, abe\}$
Chuck and Ed are chosen	$A_2 = \{ace, bce, cde\}$
Bob, Chuck, and Dick are chosen	$A_3 = \{bcd\}$

Since the three players are chosen at random, we assign to each sample point of S probability $\frac{1}{10}$. Then, because the events A_1, A_2, and A_3 are mutually exclusive, we have

$$P(A_1 \cup A_2 \cup A_3) = P(A_1) + P(A_2) + P(A_3)$$
$$= 0.3 + 0.3 + 0.1 = 0.7.$$

EXAMPLE 3. In the two-dice example of Section 3–3, what is the probability of *not* getting a double?

Solution. There are 6 points in Table 3–3 that correspond to the event "throwing a double." Denote this set by A. Then

$$P(A) = \tfrac{6}{36} = \tfrac{1}{6}.$$

The desired probability of not getting a double is

$$P(\overline{A}) = 1 - P(A) = \tfrac{5}{6}.$$

The event "getting a double" and the event "not getting a double" are mutually exclusive. They are also said to be "complementary." The two events, getting a double and not getting a double, together exhaust all possible outcomes.

3–9 Definition. *Complementary events.* An event A and the event $\overline{A}$, consisting of all points of the same sample space not in A, are called *complementary events.*

Thus any event A and its complementary event $\overline{A}$ are mutually exclusive, and their union is the whole sample space. In other words, events A and $\overline{A}$ form a partition of S into two subsets.

3–10. Theorem. *Complementary events.* If A and $\overline{A}$ are complementary events, then

$$\boxed{P(\overline{A}) = 1 - P(A).}$$ (6)

Proof. Since A and $\overline{A}$ are disjoint, formula (4) gives

$$P(A \cup \overline{A}) = P(A) + P(\overline{A}).$$

Since $A \cup \overline{A}$ is the entire sample space S, it follows that

$$P(A \cup \overline{A}) = P(S) = 1.$$

Therefore

$$P(\overline{A}) = 1 - P(A). \quad \Box$$

This formula was obtained in Section 3–1 as a consequence of the definition of probability of an event for sample spaces with equally likely outcomes. The present proof is also valid for more general sample spaces that will be studied in Chapter 4.

EXERCISES FOR SECTION 3–5

1. A die is rolled. Let E be the event "die shows 4," and F be the event "die shows even number." Are events E and F mutually exclusive?

2. A die is rolled. Let E be the event "die shows even number," and F be the event "die shows odd number." Are events E and F complementary? Are they mutually exclusive?

3. What is the probability of throwing a one or a two or a three with a single fair die?

4. If the probability that A wins a game is 0.6, what is the probability that A loses? Are the two events "A wins" and "A loses" mutually exclusive? Are they complementary? (What about a tie?)

5. Two coins are tossed. E is the event "getting two heads," and F is the event "getting two tails." Are events E and F mutually exclusive? Are they complementary? Evaluate $P(E \cup F)$.

Exercises 6 through 16 refer to the two-dice experiment of Example 1 in Section 3–3. Find the probability that:

6. The sum of the spots is not 11.

7. The two dice show only 3 or 4 or both.

8. Neither 3 nor 4 appears.

9. Each die shows 3 or more spots.

10. At least one die shows fewer than 3 spots.

11. Both dice show fewer than 3 spots.

12. Only one die shows fewer than 3 spots.

13. $r + c$ is even or $r + c$ is odd.

14. $r + c = 4$ or $r + c = 11$.

15. $r \leq 2 + c$.

16. $r \neq c$.

17. Refer to Example 2 of this section. If E is the event "Dick and Ed are chosen," F is the event "Bob and Chuck are chosen," and G is the event "Chuck, Dick and Ed are chosen," find $P(E \cup F \cup G)$.

18. If the probability of Jim's winning a race is $\frac{1}{3}$ and the probability of Tom's winning is $\frac{1}{5}$, what is the probability that either Jim or Tom will win if they are in the same race?

19. Three coins are tossed. Find the probability of getting (a) no heads, (b) at least one head.

20. The integers $1, 2, 3, \ldots, 20$ are written on slips of paper which are placed in a bowl and thoroughly mixed. A slip is drawn from the bowl at random. What is the probability that the number on the slip is either prime or divisible by 3?

3–6. INDEPENDENT EVENTS

The present discussion introduces the notion, and leads to the definition, of *independent events*. When we say, in everyday language, that two events "have nothing to do with each other," we are describing what, in technical language, are called "independent events." We begin with an illustrative example.

EXAMPLE 1. In the two-dice experiment of Section 3–3, what is the probability that $r \leq 3$ *and* $c \geq 5$?

Solution. The event that concerns us requires that two conditions be satisfied simultaneously. If A is the set of points with $r \leq 3$ and B is the set with $c \geq 5$, then we want to know the number of points that these sets have in common—in short, their intersection, $A \cap B$. This intersection is the 3×2 array of points in the first three rows and the last two columns of Table 3–3. Hence we have

$$P(A \cap B) = \tfrac{6}{36} = \tfrac{1}{6}.$$

By counting, we find that

$$P(A) = \tfrac{18}{36} = \tfrac{1}{2} \quad \text{and} \quad P(B) = \tfrac{12}{36} = \tfrac{1}{3},$$

since A has 18 points and B has 12. Using these probabilities and the answer for $P(A \cap B)$, we verify that, *for this example,*

$$P(A \cap B) = P(A) \cdot P(B). \tag{1}$$

This multiplication formula, (1), agrees with the results obtained by an intuitive approach to the problem. For, consider a very long series of throws of the two dice. We expect to find $r \leq 3$ in about half of these throws. Let us restrict our attention to this half of the throws. Of these throws, how many have $c \geq 5$? Since what happens on the red die does not affect the clear die, it seems reasonable that about $\frac{1}{3}$ of the throws with $r \leq 3$ will also have $c \geq 5$. Thus the fraction of throws with *both* $r \leq 3$ *and* $c \geq 5$ is about $\frac{1}{3}$ of $\frac{1}{2}$, or $\frac{1}{6}$.

Is formula (1) true in general? The answer is "no," as we shall see in Example 4. When formula (1) holds, the events A and B are called *independent events;* otherwise they are called dependent events. Our intuition suggests that the fall of the red die is independent of the fall of the clear die. For it seems evident that the fall of the red die has nothing to do with the fall of the clear die, and our everyday usage of the word "independent" implies just that. Moreover, it turns out that when two everyday events "have nothing to do with each other," the probability that both events occur is obtained by the multiplication of their separate probabilities, as we have just seen in Example 1.

For technical purposes, however, we need a definition that frees us from the vagueness of the expression "have nothing to do with each other." Such a technical definition, suggested by the results of problems similar to Example 1, is now given.

3–11 Definition. *Independent events.* Events A and B are independent if and only if

$$\boxed{P(A \cap B) = P(A) \cdot P(B).} \tag{1}$$

The foregoing definition provides us with a clean-cut meaning for "independent events"; if two events A and B do not satisfy Eq. (1), the events are dependent.

3–12 Theorem. If A and B are independent events with nonzero probabilities, then sets A and B have a common sample point.

Proof. Let ϕ represent the empty set. Either $A \cap B = \phi$ or $A \cap B \neq \phi$. If $A \cap B = \phi$, then $P(A \cap B) = 0$, and from (1) it follows that $P(A) = 0$ or $P(B) = 0$. Since this contradicts the hypothesis of the theorem, it follows that $A \cap B \neq \phi$. $\square$

EXAMPLE 2. *Independent events: coins.* Two coins are tossed. Show that event "head on first coin" and event "coins fall alike" are independent.

Solution. A sample space for the experiment is

$$S = \{HH,\ HT,\ TH,\ TT\}.$$

Let event A be "head on first coin" and event B be "coins fall alike." Since the four outcomes in S are equally likely, we assign to each the probability $\frac{1}{4}$. Therefore we have

$$A = \{HH,\ HT\}, \qquad P(A) = \tfrac{2}{4} = \tfrac{1}{2},$$
$$B = \{HH,\ TT\}, \qquad P(B) = \tfrac{2}{4} = \tfrac{1}{2},$$
$$A \cap B = \{HH\}, \qquad P(A \cap B) = \tfrac{1}{4}.$$

Hence it follows that

$$P(A \cap B) = P(A) \cdot P(B),$$

and events A and B are independent, by Definition 3–11.

In the following examples, we exhibit first a case in which the definition of independence is satisfied, and second a case in which events do not satisfy the definition of independence.

EXAMPLE 3. *Independent events: dice.* In the two-dice experiment of Section 3–3, what is the probability that the red die shows even and the clear die shows odd?

Solution. Let us count points in the sample space S (see Table 3–3). There are 18 points (3 rows) with r even and 18 points (3 columns) with c odd. These two 18-point sets have 9 points in common—the 9 points where the three rows intersect the three columns. Hence there are 9 points with r even *and* c odd, and we have

$$P\ (r \text{ even } and\ c \text{ odd}) = \tfrac{9}{36} = \tfrac{1}{4}.$$

Since

$$P\ (r \text{ even}) = \tfrac{18}{36} = \tfrac{1}{2},$$

and

$$P\ (c \text{ odd}) = \tfrac{18}{36} = \tfrac{1}{2},$$

the events "r even" and "c odd" are independent, by Definition 3–11.

EXAMPLE 4. *Dependent events: dice.* In the two-dice experiment of Section 3–3, what is the probability that the sum on the two dice is 11 ($r + c = 11$) and, at the same time, $r \neq 5$?

Solution. There are two points in Table 3–3 with $r + c = 11$: $(5, 6)$ and $(6, 5)$. If we denote this set of two points by E, then

$$P(E) = \tfrac{2}{36} = \tfrac{1}{18}.$$

Let F be the set defined by $r \neq 5$. Then F has 30 points and

$$P(F) = \tfrac{30}{36} = \tfrac{5}{6}.$$

Since the simultaneous event E *and* F has only the single point $(6, 5)$, we have

$$P(E \cap F) = \tfrac{1}{36}.$$

Since $\tfrac{1}{36}$ is not equal to the product of $\tfrac{1}{18}$ and $\tfrac{5}{6}$, E and F are dependent events, by Definition 3–11.

REMARK. When three or more events are independent, the probability of their simultaneous occurrence is the product of their probabilities. Thus, for example, if E, F, and G are independent, then

$$P(E \cap F \cap G) = P(E) \cdot P(F) \cdot P(G). \tag{2}$$

WARNING

There is a danger of confusing *mutually exclusive events* with *independent events.* A source of this confusion is the common expression "have nothing to do with each other." This expression provides a useful description of independence when applied to everyday events. But when applied mistakenly to *sets*, it suggests nonoverlapping; and nonoverlapping sets are mutually exclusive and are *not* independent. Indeed, in dealing with independent events A and B in a sample space, we know that the sets A and B must have a point in common if both A and B have nonzero probabilities. (Cf. Theorem 3–12.)

EXERCISES FOR SECTION 3–6

1. In the two-dice experiment of Example 1, Section 3–3, show that the event "$r > 4$" and the event "$c < 3$" are independent.

2. Three coins are tossed. Show that the event "heads on the first coin" and the event "tails on the last two" are independent. Show that the event "two coins heads" and the event "three coins heads" are dependent.

3. If a coin is thrown four times, what is the probability that it will fall heads on the first throw, tails on the next two throws, and heads on the fourth throw?

4. A pair of dice is tossed twice. What is the probability that, on the second toss, each die shows spots different from those it showed on the first toss? Assume independence of the outcomes of the two tosses.

5. A die is tossed three times. What is the probability that the first toss will show odd, the second toss even, and the third toss a six? Assume independence of the outcomes of the three tosses.

6. In a certain school, examination results showed that 10% of the students failed mathematics, 12% failed English, and 2% failed both mathematics and English. A student is selected at random from the school roll. Are the event "student failed mathematics" and the event "student failed English" independent?

7. If E is any event in sample space S, show that E and S are independent. Are E and ϕ independent?

8. A bag contains 5 black marbles, 4 red marbles, and 3 white marbles. Three marbles are drawn in succession, each marble being replaced before the next one is drawn. What is the probability that the first marble is black, the second red, and the third white?

3–7. CONDITIONAL PROBABILITY

Often we deal with probabilities for part rather than all of a sample space. The probability that a person randomly selected from a population has blue eyes differs from the probability of blue eyes for a person randomly selected from the blondes in this population. For a set of students about to take a mathematics course, the probability that a randomly selected one will get an honor grade is lower than the probability for those who made honor grades in their last two mathematics courses. The chance of a serious fire in the next year in a warehouse selected at random from those in a large city differs from that in the subpopulation consisting only of fireproofed warehouses. Each of these examples focuses attention on the probability of an event in a subset of the original sample space, and emphasizes that the probability in the subset may differ from that in the whole space. The subpopulations are defined by extra conditions beyond those for the whole population, and probabilities associated with events in these subpopulations are called *conditional probabilities.*

To introduce the idea of conditional probability, we discuss the following example, based on the two-dice experiment of Section 3–3. Refer to Table 3–3.

EXAMPLE 1. Given that $r + c < 4$, find the probability that $r = 1$.

Discussion. First, we need some idea of what such a probability means. Among all throws of two dice, some produce a sum $r + c$ that is less than 4, and others do not. We ignore all that do not and obtain a *reduced sample space*, S', consisting of three points:

$$\{(1, 1), (1, 2), (2, 1)\}.$$

Since these three outcomes were equally likely in the original sample space S, we assign them equal probabilities in the reduced sample space S'. Since they are the only points in S', we assign to each of them probability $\frac{1}{3}$. The event defined by $r = 1$ consists of the two points

$$(1, 1) \quad \text{and} \quad (1, 2).$$

Therefore the probability of $r = 1$ in the reduced sample space S' is $\frac{2}{3}$. We call this result the *conditional probability* that $r = 1$, given that $r + c < 4$.

To study conditional probability further, consider, in the original sample space S, the sets that correspond to $r + c < 4$ and to $r = 1$. For convenience, these are tabulated in Table 3–6.

TABLE 3–6

Condition	Event
$r + c < 4$	$B = \{(1, 1), (1, 2), (2, 1)\}$
$r = 1$	$A = \{(1, 1), (1, 2), (1, 3), (1, 4), (1, 5), (1, 6)\}$

Since we want to know the chances of A *given* B, we naturally are interested in the event $A \cap B$ corresponding to the set of points that are simultaneously in A and B. We have:

$$A \cap B = \{(1, 1), (1, 2)\}.$$

What are the probabilities of events A, B, and $A \cap B$ in the *original* sample space S? They are

$$P(A) = \tfrac{6}{36}, \quad P(B) = \tfrac{3}{36}, \quad P(A \cap B) = \tfrac{2}{36}.$$

(Note that we purposely do not reduce these fractions to lowest terms. Sometimes such reduction obscures the pattern that we hope to discover.)

The usual notation for "the probability of A, given B" is

$$P(A|B).$$

The vertical bar is read "given."

In the foregoing example, our first solution led us to the result

$$P(A|B) = \tfrac{2}{3}.$$

We now observe that, *in this example*, we also have

$$P(A \cap B) = P(B) \cdot P(A|B), \tag{1}$$

since

$$\tfrac{2}{36} = \tfrac{3}{36} \cdot \tfrac{2}{3}.$$

Formula (1) suggests an alternative way of getting $P(A|B)$. For Eq. (1) implies

$$P(A|B) = \frac{P(A \cap B)}{P(B)}.$$

It is also interesting to consider the result obtained by interchanging A and B on both sides of Eq. (1). The event $A \cap B$ is the same as the event $B \cap A$. Thus, for this example, we wonder if it is also true that

$$P(A \cap B) = P(B \cap A) = P(A) \cdot P(B|A). \tag{2}$$

(See Exercise 2 at the end of this section.)

EXAMPLE 2. Two a's and two b's are arranged in order. All arrangements are equally likely. Given that the last letter, in order, is b, find the probability that the two a's are together.

Solution. A sample space of possible orders of the four letters is as follows:

$$S = \{aabb,\ abab,\ abba,\ baab,\ baba,\ bbaa\}.$$

Consider a reduced sample space, B, whose elements have b as the last letter:

$$B = \{aabb,\ abab,\ baab\}.$$

Since we want to know the probability that b is the last letter *and* that the two a's are together, we look for the points in B that contain aa. The required points are the intersection of B and A, where A is the set of all points that include aa:

$$A = \{aabb, \ baab, \ bbaa\}.$$

Therefore

$$A \cap B = \{aabb, \ baab\}.$$

If we treat all points of B as equally likely and as constituting a reduced sample space, we assign probability $\frac{1}{3}$ to each of them. Since two points of B contain aa, it follows that

$$P(A|B) = \tfrac{2}{3}.$$

Is Eq. (1) also satisfied in this example? In the original sample space S, we have

$$P(B) = \tfrac{3}{6}, \qquad P(A \cap B) = \tfrac{2}{6}.$$

Hence, *in this example,*

$$P(A \cap B) = P(B) \cdot P(A|B),$$

since

$$\tfrac{2}{6} = \tfrac{3}{6} \cdot \tfrac{2}{3}.$$

In Exercise 2 at the end of this section, you are asked to verify that Eq. (2) also holds for this example.

REMARK. Example 2 can be solved by making direct use of the ideas of Chapter 2. For if b is in the last position, the remaining three letters a, a, b can be arranged in $3!/2!$ or 3 ways. Of these three arrangements, only 2 ($aabb$ and $baab$) have the two a's together. Since the three possible arrangements with b in the last place are equally likely, we have

$$P \ (a\text{'s together}|b \text{ in last place}) = \tfrac{2}{3}.$$

The foregoing examples, and others like them, lead us to adopt the following definitions.

   3–13 Definitions. *Conditional probability and reduced sample space.* The conditional probability of A, given B, is denoted by $P(A|B)$, and is defined by the equation

$$P(A|B) = \frac{P(A \cap B)}{P(B)}, \quad \text{if} \quad P(B) \neq 0. \tag{3}$$

The *reduced sample space* is B, the given event.

All probabilities are referred to some sample space, and $P(A)$ is an abbreviation for $P(A|S)$, where S is the whole sample space. But the S is ordinarily dropped as understood. When some subset of S, such as B, is known to contain all the outcomes of the experiment, then we need to be explicit and write $P(A|B)$. In particular, $P(B|B) = 1$.

REMARK 1. The probabilities in the fraction on the right side of Eq. (3) are probabilities of the events in the *original* sample space S. Of course, we get the same result if we first convert to the *reduced* sample space, which is B. For we then increase the total probability in B to 1; and, if we compute the probabilities on the right side of Eq. (3) in sample space B, the denominator is 1 while the numerator is the probability of $A \cap B$ in B.

REMARK 2. The restriction $P(B) \neq 0$ in Eq. (3) means that the *given* event B must not have probability zero. In finite sample spaces of equally likely outcomes, there must be a nonzero probability for B before it is useful to talk about the probability of A, given B.

In more advanced work with infinite sample spaces, events of probability zero can occur, and conditional probabilities, given such events, can be sensibly interpreted.

REMARK 3. Equations (3) and (1) are essentially the same. We get (1) by multiplying both sides of (3) by $P(B)$. Conversely, assuming $P(B) \neq 0$, we get (3) by dividing both sides of (1) by $P(B)$.

REMARK 4. Even if we know $P(A)$ and $P(B)$, there isn't any formula for computing $P(A \cap B)$ from them unless A and B are independent. We must treat A, B, and $A \cap B$ as three individual sets in S. It may not be a trivial matter to construct $A \cap B$ from the separate sets A and B unless the sets are small and we can list all the elements.

WARNINGS

(1) $P(A|B)$ is rarely the same as $P(A \cap B)$. Indeed, the conditional probability of A, given B, may be entirely different from $P(A)$ or from $P(A \cap B)$.

(2) $A|B$ is *not* a symbol for a set.

For example, in connection with warning (1), consider sample space S of the two-dice experiment. (Cf. Table 3–3.) Let A denote the event "red die even," and let B denote the event "clear die 2." By counting sample points in S, we see that

$$P(A \cap B) = \tfrac{3}{36} = \tfrac{1}{12},$$

and

$$P(A|B) = \tfrac{3}{6} = \tfrac{1}{2}.$$

EXAMPLE 3. In the two-dice experiment (cf. Table 3–3), if $r + c = 11$, what is the probability that the clear die shows 4?

Solution. The probability is zero; it is impossible to have $c = 4$ if $r + c = 11$.

EXAMPLE 4. In the two-dice experiment of Section 3–3, given that the red die shows 4, what is the probability that the clear die shows a number greater than 4?

Solution. Let B be the event described by $r = 4$, and A the event described by $c > 4$. Then B contains 6 sample points (cf. Table 3–3), A contains 12, and their intersection $A \cap B$ contains 2 points, $(4, 5)$ and $(4, 6)$.

Therefore we have

$$P(B) = \tfrac{6}{36}, \qquad P(A \cap B) = \tfrac{2}{36},$$

whence Eq. (3) gives

$$P(A|B) = \frac{2/36}{6/36} = \frac{1}{3}.$$

Note that we obtain the result more directly by counting: 2 equally likely cases ($c = 5$ or 6) out of 6 equally likely cases in B yield a probability of $\tfrac{2}{6}$, or $\tfrac{1}{3}$.

Since A has 12 sample points, we also have

$$P(A) = \tfrac{12}{36} = \tfrac{1}{3}.$$

Thus, *in this example*, the conditional probability of A, given B, is the same as the probability of A. In other words, the information that the red die shows 4 does not change the probability that the clear die will show 5 or 6. The latter probability is $\tfrac{1}{3}$, regardless of the outcome on the red die.

The foregoing example illustrates a general theorem.

3–14 Theorem. *Conditional probability of independent events.* If A and B are independent events having nonzero probabilities, then

$$P(A|B) = P(A) \quad \text{and} \quad P(B|A) = P(B). \tag{4}$$

Proof. Since A and B are independent, and since $A \cap B = B \cap A$, we have from Eq. (2), Section 3–6,

$$P(A \cap B) = P(B \cap A) = P(A) \cdot P(B).$$

Since neither $P(A)$ nor $P(B)$ is zero, we may use them as divisors. Equation (3) gives

$$P(A|B) = \frac{P(A \cap B)}{P(B)} = \frac{P(A) \cdot P(B)}{P(B)} = P(A).$$

The proof that $P(B|A) = P(B)$ is left as an exercise.

EXERCISES FOR SECTION 3–7

1. In the two-dice example of Table 3–3, given that $r + c \geq 10$, find the probability that $r = 5$. Given that $r + c = 8$, find the probability that $c \geq 4$.

2. For Example 2, show that

$$P(A \cap B) = P(B \cap A) = P(A) \cdot P(B|A).$$

3. Five-digit numbers are formed by permuting the digits 44433. All arrangements are equally likely. Given that a number is even, what is the probability that the two 3's are together?

4. Two dice are tossed. If the first die shows 5, what is the probability that the second die shows even?

Exercises 5 through 16 are based on the following data. Six boys (Joe, Sam, Tom, Dick, Harry, and Pete) form a club. They decide to select from their number a committee of three. The selection process is to be by lot, so that all twenty possible committees are equally probable.

5. Verify that the number of committees of 3 that can be selected from 6 boys is 20.

6. Describe a process of selecting such a committee by lot.

7. Set up a sample space of 20 points to represent the 20 possible committees.

8. What is the probability that Sam is on the committee? That Sam is not on the committee?

9. What is the probability that Sam is on the committee and Tom is not?

10. What is the probability that neither Sam nor Tom is on the committee?

11. Given that Sam is on the committee, what is the probability that Tom is also on it?

12. What is the probability that Tom, Dick, and Harry are not all on the committee?

13. Given that Tom and Dick are on the committee, what is the probability that Harry is not?

14. What is the probability that Joe or Pete or both are on the committee?

15. Suppose that Joe and Sam are brothers, Tom and Dick are brothers, and Harry and Pete are brothers. What is the probability that the committee has two brothers on it?

16. Instead, suppose that Joe, Sam, and Pete are the only brothers. What is the probability that the committee has no two or more brothers on it?

17. If p is the probability that an event will happen in one trial, show that the probability of its happening in each of n independent trials is p^n.

18. If 2 persons are chosen from 10 and all choices are equally likely, what is the probability that two specified persons will both be chosen? That they will not both be chosen? That neither of them will be chosen?

19. Of 100,000 persons living at age 20, statistics show that 47,773 will be alive at 70. What is the probability that a person aged 20 will live to be 70? That he will die before he is 70?

20. The probability that A will die within the next 20 years is 0.025, and that B will die within the next 20 years is 0.030. What is the probability that both A and B will die within the next 20 years? That A will die and B will not die? That neither A nor B will die?

21. Seven persons form a line at random. What is the probability that two specified persons are next to each other? That these persons are not next to each other?

22. A basketball player has a probability of $\frac{1}{2}$ of scoring on a free throw. How many free throws would he have to take in order to make his probability of scoring one or more times at least 0.99?

23. If p is the probability that an event will happen in one trial, show that the probability that it will happen at least once in n independent trials is $1 - (1 - p)^n$.

24. A bag contains 3 white marbles and 4 black ones. In succession, three persons each draw a marble, without replacing it in the bag. The first person who draws a white marble wins. What are the respective chances of the person drawing first, the person drawing second, and the person drawing third? (They continue until someone wins.)

25. If you stop 3 people at random on the street, what is the probability that all were born on Friday? That two were born on Friday and the other on Tuesday? That none were born on Monday?

26. Two numbers are selected at random from 1, 2, 3, . . . , 10. What is the probability that the sum of the two numbers is even?

27. A buyer will accept a lot of 10 radios if a sample of 2, picked at random, contains no defectives. What is the probability that he will accept a lot of 10 if it contains 4 defectives?

28. A committee of 3 is chosen from a group of 20 people. What is the probability that a specified member of the group will be on the committee? That this specified member will not be on the committee?

29. A committee of 4 is chosen at random from 5 married couples. What is the probability that the committee will not include a husband and wife?

30. Seven-digit numbers are formed by permuting the digits 1, 2, 3, 4, 5, 6, 7. If all permutations are equally likely, what is the probability that, in a permutation selected at random, the odd digits will occur in ascending order?

3–8. SAMPLE SPACES WITH MANY ELEMENTS

When the number of elements in a sample space is very large, it is inconvenient to make a list. However, even without a list, the methods of counting developed in Chapter 2 may enable us to calculate probabilities for sample spaces with equally likely outcomes. The following examples illustrate the methods.

EXAMPLE 1. *The first ace.* An ordinary bridge deck of 52 cards is thoroughly shuffled. The cards are then dealt face up, one at a time, until an ace appears. What is the probability that the first ace appears (a) at the fifth card? (b) at the kth card? (c) at the kth card or sooner?

Solution. (a) There are several possible sample spaces for this experiment. We choose one as follows. Once the cards are shuffled and in position in the deck, the only feature of each card that concerns us is whether it is an ace (A) or a non-ace (N). There are 48 non-aces and 4 aces, so we consider all possible arrangements of 48 N's and 4 A's in 52 numbered positions. There are

$$\frac{52!}{48!4!} = \binom{52}{4}$$

permutations of 48 N's and 4 A's, and each of these is a point in our sample space S. We assume that all points are equally likely and assign probability $1/\binom{52}{4}$ to each point.

Consider now an event E in sample space S, where E is described as "the first ace appears at the fifth card." If the first ace is in fifth place, then the first five symbols of every sample point in E are

$$N\,N\,N\,N\,A,$$

in that order. The number of points in E is, therefore, the number of ways of arranging the remaining 44 N's and 3 A's in the remaining 47 places. This number is

$$\frac{47!}{44!3!} = \binom{47}{3}.$$

Hence

$$P(E) = \frac{\binom{47}{3}}{\binom{52}{4}} = \frac{16,215}{270,725} \approx 0.060.$$

(b) Similarly, if the first ace appears in the kth place in the row, then the remaining 3 aces and $48 - (k - 1)$ or $49 - k$ non-aces can be arranged in the last $52 - k$ positions in $\binom{52-k}{3}$ ways. Hence,

$$P \text{ (first ace in } k\text{th place)} = \frac{\binom{52-k}{3}}{\binom{52}{4}}, \qquad k = 1, 2, \ldots, 49.$$

(c) Denote by F the event "first ace at kth card or sooner." Then the complementary event $\overline{F}$ is the event "4 aces after kth card." The first k symbols of every sample point in $\overline{F}$ are all N's. Therefore the number of sample points in $\overline{F}$ is the number of ways of arranging 4 A's and $48 - k$ N's in the remaining $52 - k$ places. This number is

$$\frac{(52 - k)!}{(48 - k)!4!} = \binom{52 - k}{4}.$$

Hence

$$P(\overline{F}) = \frac{\binom{52-k}{4}}{\binom{52}{4}},$$

and

$$P(F) = 1 - P(\overline{F}) = 1 - \frac{\binom{52-k}{4}}{\binom{52}{4}}, \qquad k = 1, 2, \ldots, 49.$$

If $k = 9$, we obtain

$$P(F) \approx 1 - 0.46 = 0.54.$$

Thus there is a better than even chance that the first ace appears at or before the ninth card.

REMARK. The foregoing example affords an instance in which the so-called "maturation of chance" operates. In the light of this example, the student may wish to re-read the discussion in Section 1–6.

EXAMPLE 2. *The birthday problem.* There are k people in a room. What is the probability that at least two of these people have the same birthday, that is, have their birthdays on the same day and month of the year? What is the smallest value of k such that the probability is $\frac{1}{2}$ or better that at least two of the people have the same birthday? (Write down your guess.)

Solution. We shall neglect February 29 and deal with a 365-day year. There are 365 possibilities for each person's birthday, and hence 365^k possibilities for the birthdays of k people. Thus our sample space S has 365^k points, each of which is an ordered k-tuple

$$(x_1, x_2, x_3, \ldots, x_k),$$

where x_1 represents the birthday of a first person, x_2 represents the birthday of a second person, ... , and x_k represents the birthday of the kth person. We assume that all of the 365^k possible outcomes are equally likely, and assign to each sample point probability $1/365^k$.

Consider now an event E in sample space S, where E is described thus: "no two of the k people have the same birthday." Under this restriction, the birthday of a first person has 365 possible values, that of a second person 364 possible values, that of a third person 363 possible values, ... , and that of the kth person $365 - (k - 1)$, or $365 - k + 1$ possible values. Therefore, by the multiplication principle, the number of possible sets of k birthdays with no two birthdays alike is

$$365 \cdot 364 \cdot 363 \cdots (365 - k + 1),$$

and this number is the number of sample points in E.

It follows that

$$P(E) = \frac{365 \cdot 364 \cdot 363 \cdots (365 - k + 1)}{365^k}.$$

Finally,

$$P \text{ (at least 2 birthdays are the same)} = 1 - P(E).$$

Probabilities for specific values of k yield some rather startling information. Some results are given in Table 3–7. With as few as 23 people in the room, there is a better than even chance that two people have identical birthdays!

TABLE 3–7

Number of people in room	5	10	20	23	30	40	60
Probability that at least two birthdays are the same	0.027	0.117	0.411	0.507	0.706	0.891	0.994

REMARK. Although in examples such as the foregoing no list is made, it is a good idea to think carefully about the nature of the individual points in the sample space, their number, and the subset that corresponds to a particular event whose probability is desired.

At times, it is advisable to split an event A into simpler subsets that are mutually exclusive, such as

$$A_1, A_2, A_3, \ldots, A_k.$$

In such a case, we have

$$A = A_1 \cup A_2 \cup A_3 \cup \cdots \cup A_k,$$

and (since these subsets are disjoint)

$$P(A) = P(A_1) + P(A_2) + \cdots + P(A_k). \tag{1}$$

As Example 3 illustrates, it sometimes happens that the subsets have equal probabilities; if so, Eq. (1) becomes

$$P(A) = kP(A_1).$$

EXAMPLE 3. A small boy is playing with a set of 10 colored cubes and 3 empty boxes. If he puts the 10 cubes into the 3 boxes at random, what is the probability that he puts 3 cubes in one box, 3 in another box, and 4 in the third box?

Solution. Imagine that the boxes have been lettered a, b, c to enable us to tell them apart. To help construct a sample space for the experiment, let us watch the boy perform the experiment and write down, in order, the letters of the boxes as he puts in the cubes, one after another. The result is a string of 10 letters; for example,

$$bbcaaaccba. \tag{2}$$

The particular sequence (2) corresponds to first cube in box b, second cube in box b, third cube in box c, fourth, fifth, and sixth cubes in box a, and so on. Thus the points of our sample space S [of which sequence (2) is one example] consist of all possible sequences of 10 letters, where each letter in the sequence may be a, or b, or c. From the multiplication principle of Chapter 2, we find that the number of points in this sample space is

$$n = 3 \times 3 \times 3 \times \cdots \times 3 = 3^{10}.$$

We assign probability $1/n$ to each sample point, since the boy puts the cubes into the boxes at random.

We next consider the event A described by saying that 3 cubes go into one box, 3 into another, and 4 into the third. Let us split this event into three mutually exclusive and exhaustive subsets, as follows:

A_1 is the event "3 cubes in box a, 3 cubes in box b, and 4 cubes in box c";

A_2 is the event "3 cubes in box a, 4 cubes in box b, and 3 cubes in box c";

A_3 is the event "4 cubes in box a, 3 cubes in box b, and 3 cubes in box c."

Since no two of these events can occur simultaneously, they are disjoint. Hence

$$P(A) = P(A_1) + P(A_2) + P(A_3).$$

Now let us focus attention on one of these subsets, say A_1. The points of S that are in A_1 have 3 a's, 3 b's, and 4 c's arranged in some order. By Theorem 2–12, Section 2–4, the total number of possible different arrangements of 3 a's, 3 b's, and 4 c's is

$$\frac{10!}{3!3!4!}. \tag{3}$$

Therefore the probability of A_1 is this number times $1/n$:

$$P(A_1) = \frac{10!}{3!3!4!} \times \frac{1}{3^{10}}.$$

Finally, it is clear that formula (3) also gives the number of points in A_2 or in A_3. Therefore the three events A_1, A_2, and A_3 have equal probabilities, and

$$P(A) = 3P(A_1) = 3 \times \frac{10!}{3!3!4!} \times \frac{1}{3^{10}} = \frac{1400}{3^8} \approx 0.213.$$

EXAMPLE 4. *Sampling problem.* A school staff consists of 30 teachers: 20 women and 10 men. A random sample of 5 teachers is drawn for the discussion of school problems. What is the probability that the sample (a) is composed entirely of women, (b) has exactly 2 men?

Solution. (a) The number of possible equally likely samples is

$$\binom{30}{5}, \quad \text{or} \quad 142{,}506.$$

A sample composed entirely of women can be selected in

$$\binom{20}{5}, \quad \text{or} \quad 15{,}504 \text{ ways.}$$

Thus, 15,504 points of S correspond to the event "sample composed entirely of women." Hence

$$P \text{ (5 women)} = \frac{\binom{20}{5}}{\binom{30}{5}} = \frac{15{,}504}{142{,}506} \approx 0.109.$$

(b) A sample composed of exactly 2 men and 3 women can be selected in

$$\binom{10}{2} \times \binom{20}{3}, \quad \text{or} \quad 51{,}300 \text{ ways.}$$

Therefore

$$P \text{ (2 men and 3 women)} = \frac{\binom{10}{2}\binom{20}{3}}{\binom{30}{5}} = \frac{51{,}300}{142{,}506} \approx 0.360.$$

NOTE. The following generalization of the foregoing example is important. Suppose that we have a group of n objects, m A's and w $\bar{A}$'s

$(m + w = n)$. From the n objects, we choose a sample of r. What is the probability that the sample contains exactly x A's? The data are collected in Table 3–8.

TABLE 3–8

	A	$\overline{A}$	Totals
In sample	x	$r - x$	r
Not in sample	$m - x$	$w - r + x$	$n - r$
Totals	m	w	n

We have $\binom{n}{r}$ possible samples. Of these, $\binom{m}{x}\binom{w}{r-x}$ have exactly x A's. Therefore

$$P(x \ A\text{'s}) = \frac{\binom{m}{x}\binom{w}{r-x}}{\binom{n}{r}}.$$

The formula just calculated tells how the probability is distributed among the possible 2-by-2 tables represented by Table 3–8. Each value of x gives a different table. The distribution of probabilities for such a set of 2-by-2 tables has a name: the *hypergeometric* distribution.

EXERCISES FOR SECTION 3-8

1. Refer to Example 1 of this section. What is the probability that the first ace appears at the 4th card? At the 47th card?

2. In the first-ace problem (Example 1, Section 3–8), what is the probability that the first ace appears at the 5th card or sooner? At the 49th card or sooner?

3. Refer to the birthday problem (Example 2, Section 3–8). Forty people are in a room. What is the probability that at least two of them have the same birthday? Ten people are accosted at random on the street and their birthdays noted. What is the probability that at least two of them have the same birthday? Estimate the probability that at least two members of the United States Senate have identical birthdays. (See Table 3–7.)

4. There are k people in a room. What is the probability that at least two of them have the same birthmonth? (Assume that all birthmonths are equally likely.)

5. Repeat Exercise 4 for the case in which $k = 5$.

6. Eight commuters drive their cars to the city each day and park at one of three parking lots. If the lots are selected at random, what is the probability

that, on a given day, there will be 5 of these 8 cars in one parking lot, 2 in another, and 1 in the third?

7. From a lot of 20 radios a sample of 3 is randomly selected for inspection. If there are 6 defective radios in the lot, what is the probability that the sample (a) is composed entirely of defectives, (b) is composed entirely of nondefectives, (c) is composed of one defective and two nondefectives?

8. A class is made up of 35 students, 20 girls and 15 boys. It is decided to distribute 4 complimentary tickets by lot to 4 members of the class. What is the probability that (a) the tickets go to 4 girls, (b) the tickets go to 2 boys and 2 girls?

9. Show that

$$\binom{52-k}{4} + \sum_{j=1}^{k}\binom{52-j}{3} = \binom{52}{4}, \qquad k = 1, 2, \ldots, 49.$$

[*Hint.* Use Pascal's Rule to combine $\binom{52-k}{4}$ and $\binom{52-k}{3}$, etc.]

10. There were 33 different presidents of the United States from 1789 to 1960. Before looking up their birthdays, what are the odds in favor of your finding that some pair of them had the same birthday? Now look in the *World Almanac*, or elsewhere, and determine the facts.

11. Visitors to historical sites often read inscriptions on tombstones. If a visitor selects a random sample of 30 tombstones, what is the probability of finding two dates of death that are the same month and day? Compare the dates of death of deceased United States presidents. Are any two of them the same month and day?

3-9. RANDOM DRAWINGS

In the early part of this chapter, we have seen that certain physical considerations—fair tossing of symmetrical objects such as coins or dice, or thorough shuffling of identical cards with blindfold drawing—make it reasonable to assign equal probabilities to the points of the sample space. The fair tossing, the thorough shuffling, and the blindfold drawing are physical processes that we use in trying to achieve what is called "randomness,"*; that is, in trying to give all outcomes equal chances or, mathematically, to give all points of the sample space equal probabilities.

In addition to the simple experiments presented above, there are more serious experiments where it is desirable to assign some chosen set of probabilities over the sample space of outcomes, and to make the outcomes

---

* The expressions "random," "at random," and "randomness" are not exclusively used for situations where equal probabilities are desired, but in everyday language this is usually what is meant. We use these expressions with the everyday meaning unless the text specifically states otherwise.

occur in accordance with these assigned probabilities. In some of these experiments, such as the famous drawing of draft numbers in the fall of 1940, only one trial of the experiment may be made. In others, the experiment may be repeated many times, as in the simulation of the random-walk problem in Chapter 1.

In this section and in the next two, we give examples of such experiments. We discuss ways of achieving desired probabilities, whether equal or unequal, by physical processes, and traps to be avoided in attempting to produce probabilities by these processes. In Section 3–11, we present some physically sound processes for approximating required probability assignments.

EXAMPLE 1. *Door prize.* At a school dance, a door prize is offered to the couple holding the winning ticket. The sample space consists of the k ticket numbers. The dance committee wants to give all couples an equal chance at the door prize, and therefore wishes each ticket to have the probability $1/k$ of being drawn. The tickets are placed in a bowl and stirred. Then a blindfolded person reaches into the bowl and draws out the winning ticket.

Criticism. For the purpose at hand, the procedure seems adequate. If k is large, say 100 or more, the physical stirring is probably rather ineffective, because slips of paper in a bowl are very difficult to stir thoroughly. One might wonder whether early, middle, and late arriving couples had equal chances, but an investigation of such a question by many repeated trials at successive dances is inappropriate. Each ticket may not have probability $1/k$ of being drawn, but we can only guess about the direction of bias, if one exists.

EXAMPLE 2. *Selective Service numbers.* During World War II, it became necessary to choose an order in which to draft men into military service. Each man in a Selective Service District was given a number from 1 to 9000. (The significance of the number 9000 is that it was larger than the number of men in any one Selective Service District.)

Each number was placed in an opaque capsule, and the capsules were put into a bowl and stirred. The capsules were then drawn, one at a time, from the bowl until the supply of capsules was exhausted. A sample space of this experiment is the set of 9000! permutations of the numbers. No doubt the intention was to make each permutation have probability 1/9000!. After the stirring, high officials drew the numbers from the bowl, and the early numbers were announced by radio as they were drawn.

There is some question as to the effectiveness of the stirring. The resulting sequence of numbers had surprising properties, and some scientific papers have been written to prove that the drawing was not random.

But from our previous discussion of the physical conditions under which we assign equal probabilities to sample points, we recognize that the real issue is whether or not the stirring was thorough. Only thorough stirring gives us confidence in the assignment of equal probabilities.

Here is the frequency distribution of the first 50 numbers drawn:

Numbers between	Frequency
1 — 1000	5
1001 — 2000	0
2001 — 3000	3
3001 — 4000	1
4001 — 5000	7
5001 — 6000	8
6001 — 7000	11
7001 — 8000	7
8001 — 9000	8
	Total 50

Note that there are rather few numbers between 1 and 4000. We expect about $\frac{4}{9} \times 50$, or about 22, as opposed to the 9 observed. The actual finding is consistent with the notion that the capsules were in layers and not thoroughly stirred. It is also remarkable that among the first 50 drawn, all 5 numbers below 2000 were between 100 and 199. Of course, every set of 50 numbers drawn from 9000 would be remarkable in some way. It is the correspondence between the special remarkableness of these numbers and the special kind of outcome that we expect from inadequate stirring that raises doubts about the assignment of equal probabilities to the sample space. Better evidence would be a first-hand knowledge of the original mixing process. The moral, as every cook knows, is that thorough mixing is not as easy as it sounds.

EXAMPLE 3. *Medical experiment.* A doctor proposes a new treatment for a certain disease. It is desired to compare the new treatment with the old. Of 20 patients available for the study, half will be given the new treatment and half the old. The 20 patients are grouped into 10 pairs, each pair consisting of two patients who have the disease in a similar state of advancement. The doctor plans to give one patient in each pair the new treatment, and the other patient the old. (This helps guard against the possibility that the half chosen for the new drug will be mainly severe cases or mainly light cases.)

So far so good. But how does the doctor pick from a pair the patient who is to receive the new treatment? One might think that the doctor's choice is immaterial, but he knows that the matching of pairs, though carefully done, is not perfect, and that he may, from his knowledge of the patients, subconsciously choose for the new treatment the patient who has the better chance of recovery from the disease. This would systematically bias the test in favor of the new drug. How can the doctor defend the experiment from this kind of bias?

The sample space consists of the $2^{10} = 1024$ possible ways of choosing one patient from each of the 10 pairs. Since there is no medical reason for preferring some of these choices to others, the doctor wants each to have probability $\frac{1}{1024}$. What physical process can he use to make his choices? One way is to list the 1024 choices on slips of paper and, after thorough mixing, draw one of the slips. Alternatively, he could arbitrarily assign to one patient of each pair the letter H and to the other, T, and for each pair toss a coin. If the coin falls heads, patient H gets the new drug; if it falls tails, patient T gets the new drug.

Empirically checking or solving a probability problem. Sometimes, after working out a complicated problem in applied probability theory, the worker has some uneasiness in his mind about the accuracy of his solution. If the problem does not provide suitable special cases to give an adequate mathematical check, he may turn to random sampling as a check.

We illustrate with an easy problem. Two distinct numbers are drawn in order from the integers 1, 2, 3, ..., 10, all ordered pairs being equally likely. What is the probability that the larger number of the ordered pair exceeds 5? After you have worked out your answer, check it by actually drawing two cards from 10 properly numbered cards, and then repeating this experiment a large number of times. Compare the empirical results with your theoretical answer.

Some probability problems are so complicated and mathematically intractable that to obtain numerical answers to a single problem, thousands of repetitions of an experiment are executed on high-speed computers. The numerical answer obtained from averaging, or otherwise analyzing, the many results is the one used for practical work. This technique is called the *Monte Carlo* method.

Random drawings for solving nonprobabilistic problems. The Monte Carlo method is not reserved for problems in probability. An applied mathematician often finds it convenient to transform a nonprobabilistic problem into a probabilistic one. He then uses experimental methods not unlike those we have described. In other words, he uses empirical probabilistic methods to solve nonprobabilistic problems.

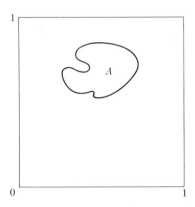

FIG. 3–6. Irregularly shaped region A, whose area is to be determined by a probabilistic process.

The following example illustrates this type of thinking. Suppose that we wish to approximate the area contained in the irregularly shaped region A of Fig. 3–6. Assume that it is possible to drop a point "at random" into the unit square. By "at random" we mean that every rectangular region of area p in the square has probability p of having the point fall in it. Thus the region of unknown area A has probability A that the point falls inside it.

When a point is dropped into the square, it either falls into the special region A, or it does not. Envisage dropping hundreds of points at random into the unit square. The fraction of points that fall inside A is a good estimate of its area. A rough and ready method of performing a suitable experiment is as follows. Draw the figure so that the unit square has sides of 2 inches, and then stand 8 or 10 feet away and throw darts at it. Only count throws where the dart hits the square. The area A is estimated by the ratio of the number of hits in A to the number of hits in the square.

3–10. RANDOM NUMBERS

After one has tossed coins, drawn cards, thrown dice, and so on, for a large number of times, he begins to wish for faster and better methods of performing mathematically equivalent experiments. If we wish to draw 500 sets of three cards from a pack, the shuffling is slow and tiresome, and fatigue leads to poor shuffling and lack of randomness. Cards, marbles, and slips of paper are all very well if there are only a few to handle. If there are hundreds or, as often happens, thousands, the task gets out of hand. As a result of such considerations—slowness of handling

TABLE 3–9

BRIEF TABLE OF RANDOM NUMBERS.*

	Columns	
Rows	1–5	6–10
1	22719	92549
2	17618	88357
3	25267	35973
4	88594	69428
5	60482	33679
6	30753	19458
7	60551	24788
8	35612	09972
9	43713	18448
10	73998	97374

* Reprinted by permission of the publisher, The Free Press of Glencoe, Illinois, from *A Million Random Digits with 100,000 Normal Deviates*, copyright 1955, by The Rand Corporation.

physical objects and lack of randomness—random numbers were invented to provide a basis for mathematical experiments to simulate physical ones.

What are random numbers? Random numbers are formed from ordinary digits successively generated by a random process. The series of digits may be of almost any length desired. Published tables of random numbers have up to 1,000,000 digits.

Construction of a table of random digits. Most tables of random digits are constructed by setting up a sample space consisting of the ten digits 0, 1, 2, 3, 4, 5, 6, 7, 8, 9. Some physical process is devised that gives good positive evidence that each of these digits has probability $\frac{1}{10}$ of occurring on each trial and that the separate trials are independent. Then the process is set in motion, and thousands of digits are generated and written down in the order in which they occur. Table 3–9 is a short table of random digits generated by such a process; Table I at the back of the book is a larger sample. One way to generate such digits is to roll a die and toss a coin, but ignore the two ordered pairs where the 6 appears on the die. Label

$$(H, 1), (H, 2), (H, 3), (H, 4), (H, 5), (T, 1), (T, 2), (T, 3), (T, 4), (T, 5)$$

with the digits

0, 1, 2, 3, 4, 5, 6, 7, 8, 9, respectively.

If the coin and die are true, the probabilities are $\frac{1}{10}$ for each digit.

Persons wishing to make random drawings use these tables as described in Section 3–11. Thus they use the random process behind the table, instead of a process of their own devising. The tables are speedy to use, and are based on a better physical process than one we are likely to construct in a few minutes for ourselves.

It must be emphasized again that a set of digits is not in and of itself random or not random. Thus, if one writes the digits 825 and the digits 999, there is no reason to say that the first set is random and the second, not. We call a set of numbers random if the following conditions hold:

(1) There are known probabilities in the sample space for those numbers; and

(2) there is a physical process that generated the successive numbers with good assurance that each element of the sample space had the probability assigned to it.

The words "random digits" are an abbreviation for "randomly generated digits," where each digit has probability $\frac{1}{10}$.

3–11. USE OF TABLES OF RANDOM DIGITS

Random-digit tables have a great variety of uses. We shall offer a few examples by way of illustration.

To begin drawing random numbers from a random-digit table is sometimes an awkward matter. However, if you own your own table, the difficulty is easily overcome. Merely start at the beginning of the table and continue systematically until you have used as many digits as your problem requires. Then check off the used digits, and start the next problem with the next digit.

EXAMPLE 1. In an earlier example, we wished to draw pairs of distinct numbers with equal probabilities from the 10 digits 1, 2, . . . , 10. In a random-digit table, it is often convenient to consider the digit "0" as "10"; we shall do so in this example.

Let us start by sampling at the top left of Table 3–9 with the five digits 22719. Since the first digit is 2, in our first sample of two numbers the first number is 2. Reading across, we see that the next digit is 2. We ignore it, since the numbers in each of our ordered pairs must be distinct. The next digit is 7. Therefore, our first pair of numbers is (2, 7). Continuing, we note that the next digit in the table is 1, so we record 1 for the first number of our second ordered pair. The next digit in the table is 9, so our second pair is (1, 9).

Our line of five digits is now exhausted, so we proceed to the second row, consisting of the digits 17618. The first of these digits is 1 and the second is 7, so our next pair is (1, 7). We continue in this manner until we get as many pairs as we please.

EXAMPLE 2. *Medical problem.* The doctor designing the medical experiment with 20 patients in pairs (Example 3, Section 3–9) might proceed as follows. He first lists his 10 pairs of patients in order in two columns:

Jones	Smith
Johnson	Williams
Hoffman	Wood
Ross	Farlow
Zanetti	Wilson
⋮	

Suppose that he has used Table 3–9 through the first two sets of five digits. Then he begins with column 1, row 3, and proceeds to choose for the new treatment the patient in the first column if the digit is 0, 1, 2, 3, 4; otherwise, he chooses the patient in the second column. The random digits in the table are 25267. Therefore, in the first five pairs, Jones, Williams, Hoffman, Farlow, and Wilson are to be given the new treatment.

EXAMPLE 3. *Four boat owners.* Suppose that four boys own a boat in shares, with Joe having a 10% share, Bill a 20% share, Tom a 30% share, and Sam a 40% share. On the Fourth of July, they all want to use the boat and they agree to draw lots for it. Sam and Tom argue that since they own larger shares, they should have better chances of winning in the draw. They want their chances to be equal to their fractions of ownership.

Essentially what is desired is a sample space of four points J, B, T, and S to which are assigned probabilities 0.1, 0.2, 0.3, and 0.4, respectively. With a table of random digits, the task is readily accomplished as follows. Blindfold one of the boys and let him jab a pencil at the table of random digits. Note the digit in the table nearest to the pencil point. If this digit is 0, Joe gets the boat; if it is 1 or 2, Bill gets the boat; if it is 3, 4, or 5, Tom gets the boat; and if it is 6, 7, 8, or 9, Sam gets the boat.

EXAMPLE 4. *Not using all digits.* Suppose that we wish a distribution over a sample space of points A, B, and C with probabilities $\frac{1}{6}$, $\frac{2}{6}$, and $\frac{3}{6}$, respectively. A convenient technique is to make the following correspondence:

Digit in table	Point in sample space
0	A
1	B
2	B
3	C
4	C
5	C
6, 7, 8, 9 (ignore)	No point

Thus we ignore the digits 6, 7, 8, 9 when they occur in the table. The only random digits of interest are 0, 1, 2, 3, 4, 5. They have total probability 1 and are equally likely, so each has probability $\frac{1}{6}$.

EXAMPLE 5. *Obtaining finer probabilities.* Suppose that we require samples from a sample space of four points A, B, C, D with probabilities 0.11, 0.25, 0.34, 0.30, respectively. Instead of looking at the sample space of random digits with 10 equally likely points, we could consider two successive digits in the table as one of the 100 equally likely two-digit numbers 00, 01, 02, 03, . . . , 10, 11, . . . , 20, . . . , 99. Each of these has probability $\frac{1}{100}$ of occurring. (Why?)

We then set up a correspondence as follows:

Two-digit random number	Point in sample space
00–10	A
11–35	B
36–69	C
70–99	D

With two-digit numbers, most workers find it easier to read down a column than across a row. For example, if we start in row 4, columns 1 and 2, we read the random digits 88, 60, 30, 60, . . . , so our sample points are D, C, B, C, . . .

EXAMPLE 6. *Drawing a sample from a list.* Suppose that, for survey purposes, we wish to draw a sample of 200 students from the 800 students of a school. One way is to assign to each student one of the three-digit numbers 001, 002, . . . , 800. Then enter the random-digit table and examine successive three-digit numbers. If, in Table 3–9, we start with columns 6, 7, 8 and row 1 and read down, the first three numbers obtained are 925, 883, and 359.

Each three-digit number is either the number of a student in the list, or it is not. If not, ignore the number, and proceed to the next. If the three-digit number belongs to a student in the list, then we check that student's name for the sample unless he has previously been checked, in which case we ignore that number and proceed to the next. The process is continued until 200 students have been checked. These students constitute the random sample from the population of 800 students.

EXERCISES FOR SECTIONS 3–9, 3–10, AND 3–11

1. Describe a physical process for randomly choosing 2 persons from a group of 10. Set up a sample space and assign probabilities to it.

2. Write a description of a random drawing problem of your own, set up a sample space and assign probabilities to it. Then describe a physical process for carrying out the drawings.

3. Compute the probability for the problem described on page 103 and execute the experiment.

4. On a rectangular coordinate system, draw a square with vertices $(0, 0)$, $(0, 1)$, $(1, 1)$, and $(1, 0)$. With center at $(0, 0)$ and radius 1 unit, draw a quarter circle within the square. How can you use the Monte Carlo method, a table of random digits, and the foregoing figure to estimate the value of π?

5. Take a random sample of 30 pages of this book. Record whether or not each page of the sample has a figure or a table on it. Estimate the fraction of pages in the book that have figures or tables.

6. In Example 6 of Section 3–11, what is the sample space and the probability attached to each sample point?

7. For phoning in connection with a TV program, it is desired to draw three names at random from a large telephone book (excluding the yellow pages). How would you draw the three names?

8. Suggest a method of using the random-digit table to obtain selective service numbers. (See Example 2, Section 3–9.)

9. Refer to the example of the four boat owners (Example 3, Section 3–11). How would you modify the scheme if there were three boat owners with shares of 20%, 30%, and 50%, respectively?

10. How would you modify Example 4 of Section 3–11 if the sample points were A, B, C, and D, with probabilities 0.2, 0.3, 0.4, and 0.1, respectively?

11. Modify Example 5, Section 3–11, to accommodate five sample points A, B, C, D, and E with probabilities 0.23, 0.32, 0.35, 0.06, and 0.04, respectively.

3-12. CONCLUSION

In this chapter, the purpose of the intuitive approach to probability and statistics was threefold:

(1) to gain an intuitive feeling for probabilities and some notion of how to work with them;

(2) to make plausible the assumptions that we shall make later in the more formal mathematical treatment; and

(3) to become familiar with concepts and notations to be used later.

By now we should realize that a mathematical theory does not always work out perfectly when applied to real-life situations, and that its value depends upon finding the conditions, if any, under which the theory is a close approximation to real life. Thus, in thinking about probabilities associated with the faces of a die, our mathematical die is a perfect homogeneous cube. Each face has probability $\frac{1}{6}$ of appearing. A brand new physical die bought from a reliable manufacturer is a close approximation to our theoretical cube. We expect the true probabilities for the physical die to be extremely close to, but not exactly equal to, $\frac{1}{6}$. A worn die might have probabilities rather far from $\frac{1}{6}$.

However, if we do not know the probabilities, all is not lost. It is one function of probability theory to state what the frequencies of various outcomes are when the initial probabilities are known. But it is also the function of statistics to make inferences about the values of the true probabilities on the basis of experimental results when the true probabilities are unknown.

All that is lost, as we know less and less about a die, are the values of the probabilities associated with its faces; *we do not lose the mathematical theory or the laws.* Later, we shall develop a more complete theory of probability for unknown probabilities and unequally likely events. From such theories, we can develop statistical methods for important problems.

It is fortunate that these methods work for initially unknown probabilities, because in most scientific and engineering work the probabilities are not known, but must be estimated from observations. When we come to real-life situations, we rarely assume that the ideal probabilities, obtained from counting possibilities, represent the physical situation. For example, we assume that a production process has some true, but unknown, probability of turning out a defective light bulb. We take observations and use them to estimate the unknown probability.

In practical work, idealized probabilities such as those obtained from counting are often treated as hypotheses that are available for a test. One might have the idealized notion that as many males are born as females, that is, that the probability of a male birth is $\frac{1}{2}$. After looking at the records for the United States in the years 1935–1952, one would soon be convinced that, consistently, more boys than girls are born. In 1950, there were 1,823,555 boys and 1,730,594 girls* born. We might then estimate that the probability of a male birth is about 1,823,555/ 3,554,149, or about 0.513. And we would abandon the notion that the true probability is 0.5, except as a rough approximation.

The rest of this book is devoted to a more formal development of the ideas of the theory of probability and statistics.

* *The World Almanac*—1956, New York World Telegram, 1956, p. 302.

4

GENERAL THEORY OF PROBABILITY FOR FINITE SAMPLE SPACES

4–1. INTRODUCTION

In Chapter 3 we discovered some general results in sample spaces with equally likely outcomes. For example, we found that

$$P(A \cup B) = P(A) + P(B) - P(A \cap B), \tag{1}$$

for events A and B.

In this chapter, we adopt a set of axioms and definitions that can be applied even when outcomes in a sample space are not equally likely. The axioms are reasonable and sufficient for proving general results like Eq. (1). But before stating these axioms, we consider a simple experiment to illustrate why some axioms, or assumptions, are needed. The experiment has these properties:

(1) there are exactly two outcomes;

(2) each outcome has a definite probability whose value is between zero and one;

(3) the outcomes are not equally likely;

(4) there is no obvious way to assign probabilities to the two outcomes.

Thumbtack experiment. Imagine that an ordinary thumbtack is tossed or dropped onto a hard surface, where it bounces before coming to rest. When the thumbtack comes to rest, it points up (U) or down (D), as in Fig. 4–1.

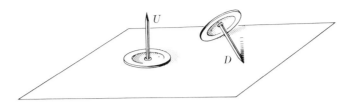

Fig. 4–1.   Thumbtack.

These are the two possible outcomes of the experiment, just as head (H) and tail (T) are the two possible ways a coin can land. Each time the thumbtack is tossed, it seems reasonable to suppose that the outcomes U and D have fixed probabilities $P(U) = p$ and $P(D) = 1 - p$. But we cannot say, just by looking at the thumbtack, exactly what number between 0 and 1 is equal to p. In particular, there is no reason to believe that $p = \frac{1}{2}$, because the two cases U and D need not be equally likely.

How might we get some idea of the value of $P(U)$? Let us specify conditions and toss a thumbtack 50 times, say, then record the data and calculate the proportion of times the thumbtack falls U. This proportion is not $P(U)$: it is an *estimate* of $P(U)$. We cannot hope to get the probability exactly from such experiments. Even for apparently symmetrical coins the proportion that actually falls heads in a sequence of 50 tosses may not be $\frac{1}{2}$. But if we specify that the coin be a thin flat disc, not out of shape like a bent bottle cap, and that it be given a vigorous toss into the air, with a spinning motion that turns it over and over many times before it lands, then it seems reasonable that the two cases, head and tail, are equally likely; $P(H) = P(T) = \frac{1}{2}$. If thumbtack tossing ever becomes a popular indoor sport, some physicist or statistician will no doubt develop a theory that predicts quite well, for a few given dimensions, materials, and tossing specifications, the probability that the tack falls U. The fact that we can arrive at reasonable theoretical probabilities for cards, dice, and coins, and cannot do so easily for a thumbtack does not lessen for us the reality of the probability $P(U)$.

Suppose our thumbtacks fall U about 40 times out of 100. We would estimate $P(U)$ to be 0.4. Now if 0.4 were the true probability, we could apply to this number the ideas we worked out earlier for coins and dice. Instead, let us suppose there is a true but unknown value for $P(U)$, say p.

EXAMPLE 1. *Two tosses.* If we toss the thumbtack twice and its probability of falling U on a single toss is p, what is the probability that it falls U both times?

Solution. We assume the tosses are independent. Our sample space of ordered pairs is represented thus:

Second toss

		U	D
First	U	(U, U)	(U, D)
toss	D	(D, U)	(D, D)

Let event A be U on the first trial, and event B be U on the second trial. The point (U, U), whose probability we want, comprises the event $A \cap B$. Hence the probability that the thumbtack falls U both times is $P(A \cap B)$.

From our experience with sample spaces of equally likely outcomes, we know that in such spaces the probability of the intersection of independent events is the product of the individual probabilities. So we might assume this to be true more generally and assign probability

$$P(A) \cdot P(B) = p^2$$

to the point (U, U). Another line of reasoning that leads to the same result is the following. Consider a long sequence of pairs of tosses of a thumbtack. In this sequence, the proportion where the first toss of a pair results in U is approximately p. And approximately the proportion p of *these* fall U on the second toss as well. Hence we expect the long-run proportion that fall (U, U) to be about p^2. Thus both lines of reasoning suggest that we assign probability p^2 to the outcome (U, U); and we do so:

$$P(\{(U, U)\}) = p^2. \tag{2}$$

Notation. The parentheses and braces in Eq. (2) are used in the following ways: the inside parentheses, in (U, U), are used in the same way we use parentheses to designate a point, say $(3, 4)$, in coordinate geometry. Thus (U, U) is a sample point. Next, the braces, in $\{(U, U)\}$, indicate a set whose only element is the point (U, U). Finally, the outer parentheses are used as they are, for example, in $P(E)$, denoting probability of a set E. However, the weird collection of braces and parentheses in Eq. (2) is almost too frightening to live with, so we shall adopt the logically less accurate, but typographically more pleasing, notation $P(U, U)$, and write simply

$$P(U, U) = p^2.$$

Similarly, we assign to the outcome (U, D) the probability

$$P(U, D) = pq,$$

where

$$q = 1 - p$$

is the probability that a thumbtack lands "point down."

If, for example, we assume that 0.4 is the true probability $p = P(U)$, then

$$P(U, U) = (0.4)(0.4) = 0.16.$$

Similar considerations would give us

$$P(U, D) = P(U) \cdot P(D)$$
$$= (0.4)(0.6) = 0.24,$$

and

$$P(D, D) = (0.6)(0.6) = 0.36.$$

EXERCISES FOR SECTION 4-1

1. In the thumbtack example, find the probabilities of the four possible outcomes on two tosses, assuming that $P(U) = 0.3$.

2. Use the results of Exercise 1 to find the probability that (a) at least one toss falls U; (b) the second toss falls D; (c) the second toss falls D, given that the first toss falls U [compare your answer with the answer to part (b)]; (d) both tosses fall alike.

3. How would you assign the probability that two tosses of a thumbtack fall U, given that both fall alike?

4. Suppose a thumbtack, with $P(U) = p$ and $P(D) = q = 1 - p$, is independently tossed three times in succession. List a sample space for the possible outcomes of this experiment. Assign probabilities to its points.

5. In Exercise 4, take $P(U) = p = 0.4$, and find the probability that the thumbtack fell U twice and D once in the three tosses.

6. A thumbtack with $P(U) = p = 0.2$ is tossed four times. What probabilities would you assign to the following outcomes?

(a) $UUUD$ (b) $UUDU$ (c) $UDUU$ (d) $DUUU$ (e) $UUDD$
(f) $UDUD$ (g) $DUUD$ (h) $UDDU$ (i) $DUDU$ (j) $DDUU$
(k) U three times and D once   (l) U twice and D twice

7. Suppose that the length of the shaft of the thumbtack in Fig. 4–1 varies from 0 to some large positive value L. What would you guess $P(U)$ to be when the length of the shaft is 0? When it is L? Discuss.

8. Do the probabilities you assigned to the sample points in Exercise 4 add up to 1, as they should?

4–2. SAMPLE SPACE AND PROBABILITY

In this section, we develop the axioms of probability in relation to the familiar notion of a *sample space* of an experiment. A sample space, we recall, is a set of elements such that any performance of the experiment produces a result that corresponds to exactly one element in the set. We restrict attention to *finite* sample spaces, i.e., those with a finite number of sample points. In a finite sample space, every set of sample points is called an *event*. An *elementary* event contains exactly *one* sample point.*

If a performance of the experiment produces a result that corresponds to a point in the subset E, we say that the *event E occurs*. The empty set is also an event, but it never occurs, since no sample points are in it.

The next example illustrates events in a sample space of 4 sample points.

EXAMPLE 1. *Bond issue for new school.* A survey is made in connection with the planning for a new high school. Each of 100 voters is asked two questions:

(1) Do you favor a bond issue to finance the building of the school?

(2) Do you own property in the school district?

Discussion. Each voter in the survey belongs to one of the following four categories:

> e_1: favors issue and owns property,
>
> e_2: favors issue and does not own property,
>
> e_3: opposes issue and owns property,
>
> e_4: opposes issue and does not own property.

The experiment of surveying 100 voters and classifying them is the same as 100 performances of the simpler experiment of asking just one voter and classifying him. The set

$$S = \{e_1, e_2, e_3, e_4\}$$

is an appropriate sample space for this single-voter experiment, since each performance must result in exactly one of these four possibilities. This sample space S also provides a scheme for tallying the results of the 100-voter experiment.

---

* So different elementary events are always *mutually exclusive*. All the elementary events together form a *partition* of the sample space.

The nonempty subsets of S are

$$\{e_1\}, \quad \{e_1, e_2\}, \quad \{e_2, e_4\}, \quad \{e_1, e_3, e_4\},$$

$$\{e_2\}, \quad \{e_1, e_3\}, \quad \{e_3, e_4\}, \quad \{e_2, e_3, e_4\},$$

$$\{e_3\}, \quad \{e_1, e_4\}, \quad \{e_1, e_2, e_3\}, \quad \{e_1, e_2, e_3, e_4\}.$$

$$\{e_4\}, \quad \{e_2, e_3\}, \quad \{e_1, e_2, e_4\}.$$

Each of these subsets is an *event*. Technically, the empty set is also an event, though trivial. The subsets

$$E_1 = \{e_1\}, \quad E_2 = \{e_2\}, \quad E_3 = \{e_3\}, \quad \text{and} \quad E_4 = \{e_4\}$$

contain just one sample point apiece; they are the *elementary events*. Every event, other than the empty set, is the union of one or more distinct elementary events. These events can also be described verbally; for example, "favors the bond issue" describes the event $E_1 \cup E_2 = \{e_1, e_2\}$; and "owns property or opposes the issue" describes $\{e_1, e_3, e_4\}$. The event $\{e_1, e_2, e_3, e_4\}$ is the entire sample space S; it may be described by "person in the survey."

Later we shall want to see how we might attach probabilities to the sets in this sample space and continue the example. But we delay this in order to introduce the general idea of assigning probabilities to more general sample spaces.

NOTE. In set theory, a logical distinction is made between a set E_1 that contains a single point e_1, and the point itself. We have made the distinction above by writing $E_1 = \{e_1\}$, to indicate that E_1 is the *set* whose only element is the *point* e_1. This permits us to write the probability of E_1 as $P(E_1)$ rather than as $P(\{e_1\})$. However, we shall not always make such distinctions, and may write this probability simply as $P(e_1)$, without the inner braces. This usage is an abbreviation.

Probability. Given a sample space S, we need to assign probabilities to its events. We assume that the sample space has a finite number n of sample points:

$$S = \{e_1, e_2, \ldots, e_n\}.$$

To each event in S we assign a number, called its *probability*. We now adopt the following axioms, or postulates, about these probabilities.

AXIOMS FOR PROBABILITY IN FINITE SAMPLE SPACES

AXIOM I.   *Positiveness.* The probability assigned to each event is positive or zero.

AXIOM II.   *Certainty.* The probability of the entire sample space is 1.

AXIOM III. *Unions.* If A and B are mutually exclusive events, then $P(A \cup B) = P(A) + P(B)$.

We call the first of these the *positiveness* postulate because probabilities are never negative; they are either positive or zero. For most purposes, events with zero probability, in a finite sample space, can be deleted.

The second postulate is called the *certainty* postulate because it says, in effect, that the probability of an event that is bound to occur is 1. The entire sample space is just such a certain event because it contains all possible outcomes of the experiment.

The third postulate, concerning the probability of the *union* of two mutually exclusive events, permits us to focus attention on the *elementary* events when we are assigning probabilities. For, as the next theorem shows, as soon as we know the probabilities of the elementary events, the probabilities of all other events are uniquely determined by Axiom III.

4–1 Theorem. Let A be an event in a finite sample space S. If A is the empty set, then $P(A) = 0$. If A is nonempty, then $P(A)$ is the sum of the probabilities of the elementary events whose union is A.

Proof. First, suppose $A = \phi$, the empty set. In Axiom III, take $A = \phi$ and $B = S$, the entire sample space. Then A and B are mutually exclusive, because ϕ is empty, so

$$P(\phi \cup S) = P(\phi) + P(S). \tag{1}$$

Also, since S is the entire sample space, the union of ϕ and S is S:

$$\phi \cup S = S.$$

Hence

$$P(\phi \cup S) = P(S). \tag{1'}$$

Subtracting Eq. (1') from (1), we have

$$0 = P(\phi),$$

and therefore $P(A) = 0$ if $A = \phi$.

Next, suppose A is nonempty and is the union of m distinct elementary events $E_1, E_2, \ldots, E_m$, where $E_i = \{e_i\}$, $i = 1, 2, \ldots, m$. For the purpose of the present proof, we assume that the sample points have been labeled in such a way that the m points in A are the first m points of the sample space. This simplifies the notation without affecting the validity of the proof.

If $m = 1$, $A = E_1$ and $P(A) = P(E_1)$. If $m = 2$, $A = E_1 \cup E_2$ is the union of two mutually exclusive events, because E_1 and E_2 are distinct elementary events. Axiom III gives the result

$$P(A) = P(E_1) + P(E_2). \tag{2}$$

If $m = 3$, then $A = (E_1 \cup E_2) \cup E_3$ and, again by Axiom III,

$$P(A) = P(E_1 \cup E_2) + P(E_3).$$

Application of Eq. (2) leads to

$$P(A) = P(E_1) + P(E_2) + P(E_3).$$

The extension to values of $m > 3$ is readily made by mathematical induction. We assume the theorem is true for $m - 1$ elementary events and write A as the union of E_m and $E_1 \cup E_2 \cup \cdots \cup E_{m-1}$. When we apply Axiom III, we get

$$P(A) = P(E_1 \cup E_2 \cup \cdots \cup E_{m-1}) + P(E_m)$$
$$= P(E_1) + P(E_2) + \cdots + P(E_{m-1}) + P(E_m),$$

the desired extension. $\square$

In some applications, we feel that the n sample points are equally likely to occur, and then we assign to each elementary event the probability $1/n$. But in many applications, the elementary events have unequal probabilities. In the school-bond example, we would assign to each category a probability equal to the proportion of voters in the school district who are in that category, if the proportions were known. Thus, if it were known that 40% favor the issue and own property, 20% favor the issue and do not own property, 30% oppose the issue and own property, and 10% oppose the issue and do not own property, we would assign probabilities to the elementary events as follows:

$$P(E_1) = 0.4, \qquad P(E_2) = 0.2, \qquad P(E_3) = 0.3, \qquad P(E_4) = 0.1.$$

We also arrange this information in the form of a two-by-two array giving the sample space and associated probabilities shown in Table 4–1. The purpose of this arrangement is to focus attention on the two attributes or characteristics that the survey is designed to study: namely, the state of property ownership, for one, and the attitude toward the bond issue for the other. Each person in the survey either does or does not own property in the district, and either does or does not favor the bond issue. When we provide for a "yes" or "no" answer to each of the two survey questions, we get the four categories described earlier. Such a two-by-two table is often used to study a possible relationship between two characteristics or attributes.

TABLE 4–1

	Owns property, O	Does not own property, $\overline{O}$
Favors bond issue, F	$E_1, p_1 = 0.4$	$E_2, p_2 = 0.2$
Opposes bond issue, $\overline{F}$	$E_3, p_3 = 0.3$	$E_4, p_4 = 0.1$

EXAMPLE 2. If the probabilities of the elementary events are those given in Table 4–1, what is the probability that a voter selected at random (a) is in favor of the bond issue? (b) favors the bond issue or owns property in the district? (c) opposes the bond issue or does not own property in the district?

Solution. Every event in the sample space can be expressed in terms of the events O and F and their complements $\overline{O}$ and $\overline{F}$, where

$$F = \{e_1, e_2\} = E_1 \cup E_2 \text{ corresponds to "favors bond issue,"}$$

and

$$O = \{e_1, e_3\} = E_1 \cup E_3 \text{ corresponds to "owns property in the district."}$$

The events in question have these probabilities:

$$P \text{ (person favors bond issue)} = P(F) = P(E_1) + P(E_2)$$
$$= 0.4 + 0.2 = 0.6,$$

$$P \text{ (favors bonds or owns property)} = P(F \cup O)$$
$$= P(E_1) + P(E_2) + P(E_3)$$
$$= 0.4 + 0.2 + 0.3 = 0.9,$$

P (opposes bonds or does not own property) $= P(\overline{F} \cup \overline{O})$
$$= P(E_2) + P(E_3) + P(E_4)$$
$$= 0.2 + 0.3 + 0.1 = 0.6.$$

Theorems. In Section 3–5, we proved the following theorems. (Note that their proofs, as given earlier, did not assume that the elementary events in S were equally likely. Those proofs are valid in any finite sample space, so we need not repeat them here. Alternatively, they can easily be proved directly from the axioms.)

4–2 Theorem. *A or B (or both).*

$$P(A \cup B) = P(A) + P(B) - P(A \cap B). \tag{3}$$

4–3 Theorem. *Mutually exclusive events.* If A_1, A_2, ..., A_m are mutually exclusive, then

$$P(A_1 \cup A_2 \cup \cdots \cup A_m) = P(A_1) + P(A_2) + \cdots + P(A_m). \tag{4}$$

4–4 Theorem. *Complementary events.*

$$P(\overline{A}) = 1 - P(A). \tag{5}$$

In the bond example, we used elementary events to find the probability that a voter is in favor of the bond issue or owns property in the district:

$$P(F \cup O) = P(E_1) + P(E_2) + P(E_3) = 0.9.$$

The only sample points not in $F \cup O$ are those that belong neither to F nor to O; they therefore belong to $\overline{F} \cap \overline{O}$. Hence the complement of $F \cup O$ is $\overline{F} \cap \overline{O}$ and, by Theorem 4–4,

$$P(F \cup O) = 1 - P(\overline{F} \cap \overline{O})$$
$$= 1 - 0.1 = 0.9.$$

A third method uses Eq. (3):

$$P(F \cup O) = P(F) + P(O) - P(F \cap O)$$
$$= 0.6 + 0.7 - 0.4 = 0.9.$$

Note that we would get the absurd result 1.3 if we forgot to subtract $P(F \cap O)$ from $P(F) + P(O)$, because the events F and O are *not* mutually exclusive.

EXERCISES FOR SECTION 4–2

1. Let A and B be events in a sample space S, such that

$$P(A) = 0.4, \qquad P(B) = 0.3, \qquad P(A \cap B) = 0.2.$$

Find the probabilities of:

(a) $A \cup B$ (b) $\bar{A}$ (c) $\bar{B}$ (d) $\bar{A} \cap B$ (e) $A \cup \bar{B}$ (f) $\bar{A} \cup \bar{B}$

2. In the two-dice example of Chapter 3, Table 3–3, the sample space is

$$S = \{(r, c): r \text{ and } c \text{ are integers from 1 through 6}\}.$$

Let A be the event described by $r \leq 3$ and B the event described by $c \geq 4$. Find the probabilities of:

(a) A (b) B (c) $A \cap B$ (d) $A \cup B$

(e) $\bar{A}$ (f) $\bar{B}$ (g) $\bar{A} \cup \bar{B}$ (h) $\bar{A} \cap \bar{B}$

3. In Exercise 2 above, describe each of the following events in different mathematical symbols or in words:

(a) $A \cap B$ (b) $A \cup B$ (c) $\bar{A} \cup \bar{B}$ (d) $\bar{A} \cap \bar{B}$

4. *Color blindness.* Assume that 5% of males and 1% of females are color-blind. Assume furthermore that 50% of the population is male and 50% female. A person is to be selected at random from this population, and that person's sex and state of vision (color-blind or not) are to be recorded. List a sample space for the experiment of sampling one person. Assign probabilities to the elements of the sample space. What is the probability that (a) the person is male and color-blind? (b) the person is female and color-blind? (c) the person is color-blind? [Genetic theory suggests that if p is the proportion of color-blind males, p^2 is the proportion of color-blind females, so $\frac{1}{4}\%$ rather than 1% may be a more realistic figure for females in this example.]

5. The true odds in favor of three events that are mutually exclusive, and whose union is the sample space, are in the ratio 3 to 2 to 1. Find the probabilities of the three events.

6. A sample space is composed of n mutually exclusive events, of which $n - 1$ have identical probabilities and the remaining one has probability as large as $r + 1$ of the others. Find the probabilities of the two kinds of events.

7. The probabilities of the mutually exclusive events A and B are related as $P(B) = [P(A)]^2$, and $A \cup B = S$, the sample space. Find $P(A)$, (a) exactly, and (b) to two decimals.

8. The event C is twice as likely as A, and B is as likely as A and C together. The events are mutually exclusive and together they exhaust the sample space. Find their probabilities.

9. If one letter is chosen at random from the word *boot* and one letter from the word *toot*, what is the probability that the two letters are the same? (First, set up a sample space and assign probabilities to its elements.)

10. Two letters are drawn at random, without replacement, from the word *memento*. What is the probability that some arrangement of the two letters spells *me*?

11. Terry is batting in a ball game with no one on base. Assume the possible outcomes of this experiment, and the associated probabilities, to be as follows:

P (striking out) $= 0.35$, P (base on balls) $= 0.21$,
P (flying out) $= 0.17$, P (grounding out) $= 0.10$,
P (getting extra-base hit) $= 0.04$, P (being hit by the pitcher) $= 0.01$,
P (getting a single) $= 0.12$.

Find the following probabilities:

(a) P (getting at least to first base safely),
(b) P (having to hurry toward first base),
(c) P (getting a hit),
(d) P (getting put out).

12. In the school-bond example (Table 4–1), if all the voters who do not own property in the district join the property owners who are opposed to the bond issue in voting against it, and everyone votes, how will the vote on the bond issue turn out?

13. Prove the theorem: If A is a subset of B and $P(B) = 0$, then $P(A) = 0$.

14. The statement "A implies B" means that every occurrence of A is also an occurrence of B. Explain why this is the same as saying that A is a subset of B in the sample space. Prove that if A implies B, then $P(A) \leq P(B)$.

4–3. INDEPENDENT EVENTS

The definitions of independence and dependence in Section 3–6 also apply in sample spaces where the outcomes are not equally likely.

EXAMPLE 1. In the bond-issue example, show that F and O are dependent.

Solution. Recalling that

$$F = \{e_1, e_2\}, \qquad O = \{e_1, e_3\}, \qquad F \cap O = \{e_1\},$$

we have

$$P(F) = 0.6, \qquad P(O) = 0.7, \qquad P(F \cap O) = 0.4$$

and

$$P(F \cap O) \neq P(F) \cdot P(O),$$

since

$$0.4 \neq 0.6 \times 0.7 = 0.42.$$

EXAMPLE 2. A thumbtack with probability $P(U) = 0.4$ is tossed twice. If E is the event "first toss lands up" and F is the event "second toss lands up," show that the following pairs of events are independent:

(a) E and F (b) E and $\overline{F}$ (c) $\overline{E}$ and F (d) $\overline{E}$ and $\overline{F}$

Solution. The possible outcomes and associated probabilities were discussed in Section 4–1. We reorganize the data here for reference.

Outcome of second toss

		F (U)	$\overline{F}$ (D)	Row sums
Outcome of first toss	E (U)	0.16	0.24	0.40
	$\overline{E}$ (D)	0.24	0.36	0.60
Column sums		0.40	0.60	1.00

If E is the event "first toss lands up" and F the event "second toss lands up," then
$$P(E) = P(F) = 0.4$$
and
$$P(E \cap F) = P(U, U) = 0.16 = P(E) \cdot P(F),$$

so the events E and F are independent. It is also easy to verify that E and $\overline{F}$ are independent, as are $\overline{E}$ and F, and $\overline{E}$ and $\overline{F}$:

$$P(E \cap \overline{F}) = P(U, D) = 0.24 = P(E) \cdot P(\overline{F}),$$
$$P(\overline{E} \cap F) = P(D, U) = 0.24 = P(\overline{E}) \cdot P(F),$$
$$P(\overline{E} \cap \overline{F}) = P(D, D) = 0.36 = P(\overline{E}) \cdot P(\overline{F}).$$

We now restate the formal definition of independence, and prove a theorem suggested by the last example.

4–5 Definition. *Independent events.* Two events E and F are *independent* if and only if

$$P(E \cap F) = P(E) \cdot P(F). \tag{1}$$

4–6 Theorem. *Independent events.* Let E and F be independent events in a sample space S. Then E and $\overline{F}$ are independent, as are $\overline{E}$ and F, and $\overline{E}$ and $\overline{F}$.

Proof. Consider the two-way array in Table 4–2. We shall show that the entries in this table correctly give the probabilities of the corresponding compound events.

TABLE 4–2. INDEPENDENT EVENTS.

	F	$\overline{F}$	Row sums
E	$P(E) \cdot P(F)$	$P(E) \cdot P(\overline{F})$	$P(E)$
$\overline{E}$	$P(\overline{E}) \cdot P(F)$	$P(\overline{E}) \cdot P(\overline{F})$	$P(\overline{E})$
Column sums	$P(F)$	$P(\overline{F})$	1

From the assumption that E and F are independent, Eq. (1) says that

$$P(E \cap F) = P(E) \cdot P(F),$$

and the entry in the upper left corner, corresponding to $P(E \cap F)$, is correct. Next, the row sums and column sums must be $P(E)$, $P(\overline{E})$, $P(F)$, and $P(\overline{F})$, as shown in Table 4–3.

TABLE 4–3

	F	$\overline{F}$	
E	$P(E) \cdot P(F)$		$P(E)$
$\overline{E}$			$P(\overline{E})$
	$P(F)$	$P(\overline{F})$	1

From the row sum $P(E)$, we see that

$$P(E \cap \overline{F}) = P(E) - P(E) \cdot P(F) = P(E) \cdot [1 - P(F)]$$
$$= P(E) \cdot P(\overline{F}), \qquad (2)$$

which shows that E and $\overline{F}$ are independent.

Similarly, $\overline{E}$ and F are independent and

$$P(\overline{E} \cap F) = P(\overline{E}) \cdot P(F), \tag{3}$$

but we leave the proof as an exercise. Likewise $\overline{E}$ and $\overline{F}$ are independent:

$$P(\overline{E} \cap \overline{F}) = P(\overline{E}) - P(\overline{E} \cap F) = P(\overline{E}) - P(\overline{E}) \cdot P(F)$$
$$= P(\overline{E}) \cdot [1 - P(F)] = P(\overline{E}) \cdot P(\overline{F}). \tag{4}$$

Therefore, if E and F are independent, the probabilities of the compound events are those shown in the cells of Table 4–2. □

Note that the probability entered in any of the four main cells of Table 4–2 is just the product of the corresponding row and column probabilities. This property of probabilities of independent events is very easy to check when the probabilities are set up in a two-by-two table of this kind. If one entry can be filled in by multiplication of its row sum and its column sum, so can all the others.

EXAMPLE 3. Are the events E and F independent if the probabilities are as shown in the following table?

	F	$\overline{F}$	
E	0.04	0.06	0.10
$\overline{E}$	0.08	0.82	0.90
	0.12	0.88	1.00

The answer is "no," because

$$0.04 \neq (0.12) \cdot (0.10) = 0.012.$$

We also observe that *every* entry is different from the product of its row sum and its column sum.

REMARK. In the bond-issue example, we have discussed ownership status (person owns or does not own property) and attitude toward the bond issue ("for" or "against"). If the events "owns property" and "for bond issue" were independent, then Theorem 4–6 would imply independence between such other pairs of events as "owns property" and "against bond issue," and so on. It would then be convenient to speak of independence of "ownership status" and "attitude on bond issue." So, in general, when independence works for one cell of a 2-by-2 table, we say that the characteristic, or label, associated with the rows is independent of that associated with the columns. And indeed, even in a larger table of m rows and n columns, if the probability in every cell is the product of its row total and column total, we continue to say that the row label is independent of the column label.

Independence of three or more events. If we study three or more events we may represent them by $E_1, E_2, \ldots, E_m$. (In this discussion, the E_i's are not elementary events.) It is natural to say that these m events are *independent* provided the probability of their intersection is equal to the *product* of their probabilities:

$$P(E_1 \cap E_2 \cap \cdots \cap E_m) = P(E_1) \cdot P(E_2) \cdots P(E_m). \qquad (5)$$

But if $m \geq 3$, Eq. (5) alone is not sufficient to guarantee the truth of the equations that we get by replacing some of these events by their complements on both sides of Eq. (5), as is the case when $m = 2$. To achieve this desired goal, we need to require *complete independence*.

4–7 Definition. *Complete independence.* The m events are said to be *completely independent* if and only if every *combination* of these events, taken any number at a time, is independent.

When $m = 3$, *complete independence* of E_1, E_2, E_3 means that the following equations are satisfied:

$$
\begin{aligned}
P(E_1 \cap E_2 \cap E_3) &= P(E_1) \cdot P(E_2) \cdot P(E_3), \\
P(E_1 \cap E_2) &= P(E_1) \cdot P(E_2), \\
P(E_1 \cap E_3) &= P(E_1) \cdot P(E_3), \\
P(E_2 \cap E_3) &= P(E_2) \cdot P(E_3).
\end{aligned}
\qquad (6)
$$

And if equations (6) are satisfied, so is any equation we get by replacing an event by its complement on both sides of one of the original equations. For instance,

$$P(E_1 \cap \overline{E}_2 \cap E_3) = P(E_1) \cdot P(\overline{E}_2) \cdot P(E_3). \qquad (7)$$

Or we may replace any two, or three, events by their complements on both sides of the equation and get a true result.

REMARK. It might be supposed that 3 events are independent if every pair of them is independent. However, such pairwise independence does *not* imply independence of the three events, as the following example shows.

EXAMPLE 4. *Three pairwise independent events that are not independent.*

Discussion. Two coins are tossed. If E_1 is the event "head on first coin," E_2 the event "head on second coin," and E_3 the event "the coins match; both are heads or both tails," then

$$P(E_1) = P(E_2) = P(E_3) = \tfrac{1}{2}$$

and

$$P(E_1 \cap E_2) = P(E_1 \cap E_3) = P(E_2 \cap E_3) = \tfrac{1}{4}.$$

Hence the events are independent in pairs. But

$$P(E_1 \cap E_2 \cap E_3) = \tfrac{1}{4} \neq P(E_1) \cdot P(E_2) \cdot P(E_3),$$

so they are *not* independent when taken all together.

EXAMPLE 5. Independently, a coin is tossed, a card is drawn from a deck, and a die is thrown. What is the probability that we observe a head on the coin, an ace from the deck, and a five on the die?

Solution.

$$P \text{ (head)} = \tfrac{1}{2}, \qquad P \text{ (ace)} = \tfrac{1}{13}, \qquad P \text{ (5 on die)} = \tfrac{1}{6}.$$

$$P \text{ (head and ace and 5)} = \tfrac{1}{2} \times \tfrac{1}{13} \times \tfrac{1}{6} = \tfrac{1}{156}.$$

EXAMPLE 6. *Flawless shoes.* In a shoe factory, uppers, soles, and heels are manufactured separately and randomly assembled into single shoes. Five percent of the uppers, four percent of the soles, and one percent of the heels have flaws. What percent of the pairs of shoes are flawless in these three parts?

Solution. Let U, S, and H stand for unflawed upper, sole, and heel, respectively, and $\overline{U}$, $\overline{S}$, and $\overline{H}$ stand for the flawed parts. For a single shoe,

$$P(U) = 1 - 0.05 = 0.95, \qquad P(S) = 1 - 0.04 = 0.96,$$

$$P(H) = 1 - 0.01 = 0.99,$$

$$P(U \cap S \cap H) = 0.95 \times 0.96 \times 0.99 \approx 0.903.$$

This is the probability that one shoe is unflawed. Assuming that pairs are also randomly assembled, we would have

$$\begin{aligned}
P \text{ (both shoes unflawed)} &= P \text{ (left and right unflawed)} \\
&= P \text{ (left unflawed)} \cdot P \text{ (right unflawed)} \\
&\approx 0.903 \times 0.903 \\
&\approx 0.815.
\end{aligned}$$

EXAMPLE 7. *Light bulbs.* Light bulbs are produced by a sequence of machine operations. When the machine is in good working order, it produces one defective bulb per thousand. The outcomes for successive bulbs are independent. What is the probability that the next two bulbs produced are nondefective?

Solution. Let E be "first bulb nondefective," F be "second bulb nondefective."

$$P(E) = P(F) = 1 - 0.001 = 0.999,$$

$$P(E \cap F) = 0.999 \times 0.999 = (1 - 0.001)^2 \approx 1 - 2(0.001) = 0.998.$$

After this section, when we speak of *independence*, we shall mean *complete independence*.

EXERCISES FOR SECTION 4–3

1. If two events E and F are mutually exclusive and have probabilities different from zero, prove that they are dependent.

2. Give examples of events E and F like those described in Exercise 1, based upon the two-dice example, Table 3–3.

3. Prove that if E and F are independent, then $\overline{E}$ and F are also independent.

4. Prove that if $P(E \cap F) \neq P(E) \cdot P(F)$, then

$$P(\overline{E} \cap F) \neq P(\overline{E}) \cdot P(F), \qquad P(E \cap \overline{F}) \neq P(E) \cdot P(\overline{F}),$$

$$P(\overline{E} \cap \overline{F}) \neq P(\overline{E}) \cdot P(\overline{F}).$$

5. Three ordinary dice are thrown. Assuming the outcomes on the dice are completely independent, what is the probability that the sum of the numbers on the top faces is five?

6. A certain automatic machine makes bolts and fills boxes with them. If 1 box in 100 has at least one defective bolt in it and the outcomes are independent, what is the probability that each of the next 3 boxes has one or more defective bolts? That all have no defective bolts?

7. The probability that a man is hospitalized during the next month is 0.01. If we consider three men who are strangers to each other, what is the probability that during the next month exactly one of them goes to the hospital?

8. There are three traffic lights spaced several miles apart on a highway between towns A and B. The cycles of the three lights are one minute each. The three lights show green 30, 40, and 50 seconds, respectively. Assuming that a car strictly observes traffic-light regulations, what is the probability that the car makes the trip from A to B without being stopped by any of these three traffic lights? That the car will be stopped by exactly one light? By exactly two lights? By all three? (Assume that this is the only car on the road from A to B.)

9. Two ordinary dice are independently thrown and the outcomes on the top faces are observed. Show that the events

$$E_1: \text{ first die shows an even number,}$$

$$E_2: \text{ second die shows an odd number,}$$

$$E_3: \text{ sum of the results is odd}$$

are pairwise independent, but not completely independent.

10. Let $S = \{e_1, e_2, e_3, e_4, e_5, e_6\}$ be the sample space of an experiment. Suppose the probabilities of the elementary events are

$$p_1 = \tfrac{1}{8}, \qquad p_2 = \tfrac{5}{16}, \qquad p_3 = \tfrac{1}{16}, \qquad p_4 = \tfrac{3}{8}, \qquad p_5 = p_6 = \tfrac{1}{16},$$

where $p_i = P(\{e_i\})$. Let $E = \{e_1, e_4\}$, $F = \{e_1, e_2, e_5\}$, $G = \{e_1, e_2, e_3\}$. Show that E, F, and G are independent, but not completely independent.

11. In matches between two teams, teams A, B, and C score points in games, independently of whom they play, according to the following probability table:

Points

Team	0	1	2	3	4	5
A		0.5			0.5	
B	0.2			0.8		
C			0.8			0.2

The team with the most points wins. Show that $P(A \text{ beats } B)$, $P(B \text{ beats } C)$, and $P(C \text{ beats } A)$ are all greater than $\tfrac{1}{2}$. That is, A usually beats B, B usually beats C, and C usually beats A. Thus the relation "usually beats" need not be transitive.

ADDITIONAL EXERCISES FOR SECTION 4–3

World Series Exercises

In a World's Series, teams A and B play until one team has won 4 games. Let p be the probability that team A wins any individual game played with B. Then $q = 1 - p$ is the probability that B wins. Use this information to answer the questions in Exercises 1 through 9:

1. What is the probability that A wins the first 4 games? That B wins the first 4 games? That the series ends at 4 games? [Ans: p^4, q^4, $p^4 + q^4$]

2. What is the probability that A wins the series in the 5th game? That the series ends at 5 games? [Ans: $4p^4q$, $4pq(p^3 + q^3)$]

3. What is the probability that A wins the series in the 6th game? That the series ends at 6 games? [*Ans:* $10p^4q^2$, $10p^2q^2(p^2 + q^2)$]

4. What is the probability that A wins the series in the 7th game? That the series ends at 7 games? [*Ans:* $20p^4q^3$, $20p^3q^3$]

5. Using the results of Exercises 1 through 4, construct a sample space for the experiment of playing a World's Series and assign probabilities to the sample points. What is the probability that team A wins the series? That team B wins? (Express the answer for B's winning in two different ways.) [*Ans:* $P(A \text{ wins}) = p^4(1 + 4q + 10q^2 + 20q^3)$]

6. In Exercise 5, suppose $p = \frac{2}{3}$, $q = \frac{1}{3}$, so that team A is "twice as good" as team B.* Is A's chance of winning the series also twice the probability that B wins? If not, what are the odds in favor of A's winning the series? [*Ans:* $P(A \text{ wins}) = \frac{1808}{2187}$, $P(B \text{ wins}) = \frac{379}{2187}$; $\approx 4.77:1$]

7. If, in Exercise 5, $p = q = \frac{1}{2}$, what is the probability that the series ends in 4 games? 5? 6? 7? [*Ans:* $\frac{2}{16}$, $\frac{4}{16}$, $\frac{5}{16}$, $\frac{5}{16}$]

8. In Exercise 5, assume that $p = \frac{2}{3}$. What is the probability that the series ends in 4 games? 5? 6? 7? [*Ans:* $\frac{153}{729}$, $\frac{216}{729}$, $\frac{200}{729}$, $\frac{160}{729}$]

9. In Exercise 8, with $p = \frac{2}{3}$, which is more likely, that the series is over before the 6th game, or that it is not over then? What are the relative odds?

4–4. CONDITIONAL PROBABILITY

In Section 3–7, conditional probabilities were studied for sample spaces whose sample points have equal probabilities. In this section we extend the notion of conditional probability to more general sample spaces. In the remaining two sections of this chapter, we study two classes of applications of conditional probability:

(a) its use in assigning probabilities in a sample space,

(b) its use in modifying our "degree of belief" in various alternative hypotheses as a result of experimental evidence.

EXAMPLE 1. An irregular tetrahedron is tossed into the air. The four faces, numbered 1, 2, 3, 4, have corresponding probabilities 0.1, 0.2, 0.3, 0.4 of being on the bottom when the tetrahedron comes to rest. Given that face 1 or face 2 is down, what is the probability that it is face 1?

Solution. Since we are *given* that face 1 or face 2 is down, we can ignore the other two possibilities and consider a reduced sample space consisting solely of the outcomes face 1 down and face 2 down. The probability of face 2 is twice that of face 1. Hence, in a large number of performances of the experiment resulting in one of these two faces on the bottom, we

---

* Historical results suggest that these figures approximate the relative strengths of the teams in actual play.

expect face 1 to be down about $\frac{1}{3}$ of the time and face 2 to be down about $\frac{2}{3}$ of the time. Therefore,

$$P \text{ (face 1|face 1 or face 2)} = \frac{1}{3} = \frac{0.1}{0.1 + 0.2}.$$

The result has the form

$$P(A|A \text{ or } B) = \frac{P(A)}{P(A) + P(B)},$$

where A and B are the mutually exclusive events "face 1 down" and "face 2 down."

EXAMPLE 2. *Color blindness.* Assume that 5% of males and 1% of females are color-blind, and that males and females each form 50% of the population. A researcher studying color blindness selects a color-blind person at random. What is the probability that the person so selected is (a) male, (b) female?

Solution. The given data provide us with the probabilities shown in Table 4–4. For instance, 5% of 50% of the population, or 2.5%, is both male and color-blind, so 47.5% is male and not color-blind. Similarly, 1% of 50%, or $\frac{1}{2}$ of 1%, is female and color-blind, and 49.5% is female and not color-blind. A sample of 1000 persons having exactly these percentages would have 25 color-blind males and 5 color-blind females; a total of 30 color-blind persons. Since males are $\frac{25}{30}$ of this group and females are $\frac{5}{30}$, it seems reasonable to say that the probability of selecting a male is $\frac{25}{30}$, and the probability of selecting a female is $\frac{5}{30}$.

TABLE 4–4. COLOR BLINDNESS.

		Color-blind, C	Normal color vision, N	Row sums
Male	M	.025	.475	.500
Female	F	.005	.495	.500
Column sums		.030	.970	1.000

We write the conditional probability of the event "person selected is male," given the event "person is color-blind," as

$$P \text{ (male|color-blind)} = P(M|C) = \tfrac{25}{30} = \tfrac{5}{6}.$$

Note that $\frac{25}{30}$ is also the same as

$$\frac{0.025}{0.030} = \frac{P(M \cap C)}{P(C)},$$

and we have, for this example,

$$P(M|C) = \frac{P(M \cap C)}{P(C)}. \tag{1}$$

Similarly,

$$P(F|C) = \frac{P(F \cap C)}{P(C)} = \frac{0.005}{0.030} = \frac{1}{6}.$$

Since the axioms do not treat conditional probability, we require a definition.

4–8 Definition. *Conditional probability.* The conditional probability of an event A, given B, is denoted by $P(A|B)$ and is defined by

$$P(A|B) = \frac{P(A \cap B)}{P(B)}, \tag{2}$$

where A, B, and $A \cap B$ are events in a sample space S, and $P(B) \neq 0$.

REMARK. If we multiply both sides of Eq. (2) by $P(B)$, we get

$$P(A \cap B) = P(B) \cdot P(A|B). \tag{3}$$

Order is not important in $A \cap B$, because

$$A \cap B = B \cap A.$$

Hence we also have

$$P(B \cap A) = P(B) \cdot P(A|B), \tag{4}$$

and

$$P(A \cap B) = P(A) \cdot P(B|A). \tag{5}$$

Equation (5) is used in Section 4–5 to assign probabilities. It can also be extended to three or more events. For example, the probability of the joint occurrence of three events A, B, and C is

$$P(A \cap B \cap C) = P(A) \cdot P(B|A) \cdot P(C|A \cap B). \tag{6}$$

Another way of looking at Eq. (2) may be helpful. Consider a sample space S and the events, A, B, and their intersection $A \cap B$ (shown shaded in Fig. 4–2). If we are given B, we ignore all other possible outcomes in S, and think of B as constituting a new, reduced, sample space S^*. (See Fig. 4–2.) If we were to assign to points of S^* the same probabilities they

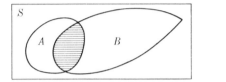 

FIG. 4–2.   New sample space. $S^* = B$.

had in S, these would add up only to $P(B)$. We wish that the total probability in the new sample space S^*, which is just B, were one. We achieve this desired goal by enlarging all probabilities p_i of points in B by multiplying each probability by the constant factor $1/P(B)$. When we assign these new probabilities to points of B,

$$p_i^* = \frac{p_i}{P(B)} , \tag{7}$$

and sum both sides of Eq. (7) over all values of i corresponding to sample points in $B = S^*$, we find that the total probability in S^* is

$$\sum p_i^* = \frac{\sum p_i}{P(B)} = \frac{P(B)}{P(B)} = 1,$$

as desired.

Finally, to get the probability of any event A, given B, we add the p^* probabilities of the points of A that are in the reduced sample space $S^* = B$. These are the points in the intersection $A \cap B$; we denote their probabilities in S by $p_1, p_2, \ldots, p_m$. Then, summing both sides of Eq. (7) for values of i from 1 through m, we get

$$P(A|B) = \sum_{i=1}^{m} p_i^* = \sum_{i=1}^{m} \frac{p_i}{P(B)} = \frac{P(A \cap B)}{P(B)} \cdot$$

Note that the conditional probability of A, given B, is proportional to the probability of $A \cap B$, the proportionality factor being $k = 1/P(B)$, just as it is in Eq. (7) for individual points.

EXAMPLE 3. A coin is tossed until a head appears, or until it has been tossed three times. Given that the head does not occur on the first toss, what is the probability that the coin is tossed three times?

Solution. A sample space is given by

$$S = \{H, TH, TTH, TTT\},$$

with associated probabilities

$$P(H) = \tfrac{1}{2}, \qquad P(TH) = \tfrac{1}{4}, \qquad P(TTH) = P(TTT) = \tfrac{1}{8}.$$

These add to 1. Let B be the given event, "no head on first toss." Then

$$B = \{TH, TTH, TTT\}$$

and

$$P(B) = \tfrac{1}{4} + \tfrac{1}{8} + \tfrac{1}{8} = \tfrac{1}{2}.$$

Next, let A be the event "coin is tossed three times." Then

$$A = \{TTH, TTT\}, \qquad P(A) = \tfrac{1}{4},$$

and

$$A \cap B = A, \qquad P(A \cap B) = \tfrac{1}{4}.$$

Hence

$$P(A|B) = \frac{P(A \cap B)}{P(B)} = \frac{1/4}{1/2} = \frac{1}{2}.$$

EXAMPLE 4. The integers from 1 through n are assigned probabilities proportional to their sizes. (a) Find the probabilities. (b) Find the conditional probability of 1, given that 1 or n occurs.

Solution. (a) The total probability must be 1, and the probability of any integer i from 1 through n is proportional to i:

$$P(i) = k \times i; \qquad i = 1, 2, \ldots, n.$$

Then

$$\sum_{i=1}^{n} ki = k[1 + 2 + 3 + \cdots + n] = 1.$$

But

$$1 + 2 + 3 + \cdots + n = \frac{n(n + 1)}{2}.$$

Hence

$$k = \frac{2}{n(n + 1)}$$

and

$$P(i) = \frac{2i}{n(n + 1)}.$$

(b) $$P(1|1 \text{ or } n) = \frac{P(1 \cap 1 \text{ or } n)}{P(1 \text{ or } n)} = \frac{P(1)}{P(1) + P(n)}$$

$$= \frac{k \times 1}{k \times 1 + k \times n} = \frac{1}{1 + n}.$$

Note that we did not need to know the value of the proportionality factor k to solve part (b).

EXERCISES FOR SECTION 4–4

1. If A and B are *mutually exclusive* and $P(B)$ is not zero, what can you say about $P(A|B)$? Interpret your result.

2. If A always occurs when B does, then every sample point in B is also in A; B is a subset of A. What can you say about $P(A|B)$ in such circumstances? Interpret your result.

3. If A and B are independent and $P(B) \neq 0$, what can you say about $P(A|B)$? Does this seem reasonable?

4. In Example 1, what is the probability that face 3 is down, given that face 4 is not down?

5. In Example 2, a person is selected at random from the population of people with normal color vision. What is the probability that the selected person is (a) male? (b) female?

6. In Example 3, given that the coin was tossed at most two times, what is the probability that it was tossed exactly twice?

7. A coin is tossed until a head first appears, or until it has been tossed 4 times. Given that a head did not appear on either of the first two tosses, find the probability that (a) the coin was tossed 4 times, and (b) it was tossed just 3 times.

8. By Eq. (3), if $P(B) \neq 0$, then $P(A \cap B) = P(B) \cdot P(A|B)$. If $P(B) = 0$, $P(A|B)$ is undefined. But $P(A \cap B) = P(B) \cdot P(A|B)$ is still true in some sense. Why?

9. In a high-school class of 180 students, all of whom took both English and History, 15 failed History, 10 failed English, and 5 failed both. Find the probability that a student chosen at random from this class failed History and passed English. Find the probability that he failed English and passed History.

10. Twenty boys went on a picnic. Five got sunburned, 8 got bitten by mosquitoes, and 10 got home without mishap. What is the probability that a sunburned boy was ignored by the mosquitoes? What is the probability that a bitten boy was also burned?

11. An insurance company finds that about one check in a thousand is drawn on insufficient funds, and that such checks are invariably postdated. The company also finds that about one check in one hundred drawn on sufficient funds is postdated. If a postdated check is received, what is the probability that it comes from a customer having insufficient funds?

12. In the baseball problem, Exercise 11 of Section 4–2, find the theoretical batting average.

13. Suppose 2 bad light bulbs get mixed up with 10 good ones, and that you start testing the bulbs, one by one, until you have found both defectives. What is the probability that you will find the last defective on the 7th testing?

14. (a) If, in the two-dice experiment of Table 3–3, it is known that at least one die has fewer than 3 spots showing, what is the probability that the other die has 3 or more spots? (b) If we are given that $r \leq c + 2$, what is the probability that $r + c = 10$?

15. If a family having 4 children is known to have at least 1 boy, what is the probability that it has exactly 2 boys? (Assume that boys and girls have an equal chance of being born.) What additional unstated assumptions are you making?

16. The integers from 1 through $2n$ are assigned probabilities proportional to their logarithms. (a) Find the probabilities. (b) Show that the conditional probability of the integer 2, given that an even integer occurs, is

$$\frac{\log 2}{n \log 2 + \log (n!)} .$$

17. Prove: If A and B are mutually exclusive and $P(A \cup B)$ is not zero, then

$$P(A|A \cup B) = \frac{P(A)}{P(A) + P(B)} .$$

Which examples in the text illustrate applications of this result?

4–5. USING THE PRODUCT RULE TO ASSIGN PROBABILITIES IN A SAMPLE SPACE

We now illustrate how the rule

$$P(A \cap B) = P(B \cap A) = P(A) \cdot P(B|A) \tag{1}$$

is used in assigning probabilities when A and B are not assumed to be independent.

EXAMPLE 1. Jimmy likes to go shopping with his mother because he can sometimes get her to buy him a toy. The probability that she takes him along on her shopping trip this afternoon is 0.4, and if she does, the probability that he gets a toy is 0.8. What is the probability that she takes him shopping and buys him a toy?

Solution.

$$P \text{ (shopping and toy)} = P \text{ (shopping)} \cdot P \text{ (toy|shopping)}$$
$$= 0.4 \times 0.8 = 0.32.$$

EXAMPLE 2. A magazine advertiser estimates that the probability that his ad will be read by a subscriber is 0.4, and that if it is read, the probability that the reader will buy his product is 0.01. Using these estimates, find the probability that a subscriber will read the ad and buy the product.

Solution.

$$P \text{ (read ad and buy product)} = P \text{ (read ad)} \cdot P \text{ (buy product|read ad)}$$
$$= 0.4 \times 0.01 = 0.004.$$

EXAMPLE 3(a). *Drawing without replacement.* An urn contains 5 black balls and 10 red balls. Two balls are drawn at random, one after the other, without replacement. Set up a sample space for the possible outcomes of the experiment, with appropriate probabilities.

Solution. As a sample space for the experiment, we take

$$S = \{(B, B), \quad (B, R), \quad (R, B), \quad (R, R)\}$$

where, for example, (B, R) means "first ball black, second ball red." Since balls are drawn at random, all balls in the urn at any drawing are equally likely to be drawn. For both balls to be black, the first one drawn must be black ($p_1 = \frac{5}{15}$), and the second one drawn must also be black ($p_2 = \frac{4}{14}$). Therefore

$$P(B, B) = P \text{ (1st ball black)} \cdot P \text{ (2nd ball black|1st ball black)}$$
$$= \tfrac{5}{15} \times \tfrac{4}{14} = \tfrac{2}{21}.$$

Likewise,

$$P(B, R) = P \text{ (1st ball black)} \cdot P \text{ (2nd ball red|1st ball black)}$$
$$= \tfrac{5}{15} \times \tfrac{10}{14} = \tfrac{5}{21},$$

$$P(R, B) = P \text{ (1st ball red)} \cdot P \text{ (2nd ball black|1st ball red)}$$
$$= \tfrac{10}{15} \times \tfrac{5}{14} = \tfrac{5}{21},$$

$$P(R, R) = P \text{ (1st ball red)} \cdot P \text{ (2nd ball red|1st ball red)}$$

$$= \tfrac{10}{15} \times \tfrac{9}{14} = \tfrac{9}{21}.$$

The results are summarized in Table 4–5(a).

TABLE 4–5(a). DRAWINGS WITHOUT REPLACEMENT.

		Second ball		Row totals
		B	R	
First ball	B	$\frac{2}{21}$	$\frac{5}{21}$	$\frac{1}{3}$
	R	$\frac{5}{21}$	$\frac{9}{21}$	$\frac{2}{3}$
Column totals		$\frac{1}{3}$	$\frac{2}{3}$	1

Note that $\tfrac{1}{3} \times \tfrac{1}{3} \neq \tfrac{2}{21}$; the outcome for the second ball is not independent of the outcome for the first ball.

EXAMPLE 3(b). *Drawing with replacement.* If the sampling in Example 3(a) is done with replacement (we put the first ball back before drawing the second ball), then the probability of a black ball on the second drawing is independent of the outcome on the first:

$$P \text{ (2nd ball black)} = P \text{ (1st ball black)} = \tfrac{5}{15} = \tfrac{1}{3}.$$

The probabilities of sample points in this new experiment are shown in Table 4–5(b). Each cell entry is the product of the corresponding row total and column total.

TABLE 4–5(b). DRAWINGS WITH REPLACEMENT.

		Second ball		Row totals
		B	R	
First ball	B	$\frac{1}{9}$	$\frac{2}{9}$	$\frac{1}{3}$
	R	$\frac{2}{9}$	$\frac{4}{9}$	$\frac{2}{3}$
Column totals		$\frac{1}{3}$	$\frac{2}{3}$	1

EXAMPLE 4. *Two urns.* An ordinary die is thrown once. If a 1 or 6 appears, a ball is then drawn from urn I, otherwise a ball is drawn from urn II. Urn I contains 3 red balls, 2 white balls, 1 blue ball. Urn II contains 4 white balls, 2 blue balls, and no red balls. Set up a sample space for the possible outcomes of the experiment and find the probability (a) that a white ball is drawn, and (b) that urn I was used, given that a white ball was drawn.

Solution. The experimental conditions imply the following probabilities:

$$P(\text{I}) = \tfrac{1}{3}, \qquad P(R|\text{I}) = \tfrac{1}{2}, \qquad P(W|\text{I}) = \tfrac{1}{3}, \qquad P(B|\text{I}) = \tfrac{1}{6},$$

$$P(\text{II}) = \tfrac{2}{3}, \qquad P(R|\text{II}) = 0, \qquad P(W|\text{II}) = \tfrac{2}{3}, \qquad P(B|\text{II}) = \tfrac{1}{3}.$$

Using these data, we construct a sample space showing the urn used and the color of ball drawn. Table 4–6 shows probabilities of the possible outcomes of the experiment. Hence, $P(W) = \tfrac{5}{9}$, and

$$P(\text{I}|W) = \frac{P(\text{I} \cap W)}{P(W)} = \frac{1/9}{5/9} = \frac{1}{5}.$$

The chance of urn I, given that a white ball was drawn, is no longer 1 in 3; now it is only 1 in 5.

TABLE 4–6. TWO URNS.

Color of ball

		R	W	B	Row sums
Urn	I	$\tfrac{1}{6}$	$\tfrac{1}{9}$	$\tfrac{1}{18}$	$\tfrac{1}{3}$
	II	0	$\tfrac{4}{9}$	$\tfrac{2}{9}$	$\tfrac{2}{3}$
Column sums		$\tfrac{1}{6}$	$\tfrac{5}{9}$	$\tfrac{5}{18}$	1

EXAMPLE 5. *Bridge and pinochle cards.* In the card room of a men's club, there are 5 ordinary bridge decks and 3 pinochle decks, all having similar construction and designs. One of these 8 decks is chosen at random, and a card is randomly drawn from it. If the card is the jack of hearts, what is the probability that it came from a pinochle deck? From a bridge deck? Pinochle decks contain 48 cards; two each of 9, 10, jack, queen, king, and ace in the four suits clubs, diamonds, hearts, and spades.

Solution. Since the experiment consists of first choosing a deck of cards, and then choosing a card from that deck, the sample space that we think of is a set of ordered pairs (x, y), with

$x =$ bridge, if a bridge deck is drawn,

$x =$ pinochle, if a pinochle deck is drawn,

and $y =$ a designation of a card.

The probability of drawing a jack of hearts from a pinochle deck is $\frac{2}{48}$; from a bridge deck, the probability is $\frac{1}{52}$. Now to answer the question:

$$P(\text{pinochle}|\text{jack of hearts}) = \frac{P(\text{pinochle} \cap \text{jack of hearts})}{P(\text{jack of hearts})}$$

and

$$P(\text{jack of hearts}) = P(\text{pinochle} \cap \text{jack of hearts})$$
$$+ P(\text{bridge} \cap \text{jack of hearts})$$
$$= P(\text{pinochle}) \cdot P(\text{jack of hearts}|\text{pinochle})$$
$$+ P(\text{bridge}) \cdot P(\text{jack of hearts}|\text{bridge})$$
$$= \frac{3}{8} \times \frac{2}{48} + \frac{5}{8} \times \frac{1}{52} = \frac{23}{832} = \frac{23}{8(8)(13)}.$$

Therefore

$$P(\text{pinochle}|\text{jack of hearts}) = \frac{\frac{3}{8} \times \frac{2}{48}}{\frac{23}{8(8)(13)}} = \frac{13}{23}.$$

Similarly,

$$P(\text{bridge}|\text{jack of hearts}) = \frac{\frac{5}{8} \times \frac{1}{52}}{\frac{23}{8(8)(13)}} = \frac{10}{23}.$$

Alternatively, since "bridge deck" and "pinochle deck" are complementary events, we could have computed the $\frac{10}{23}$ from $1 - \frac{13}{23}$. Table 4–7 shows the foregoing computations in another form.

TABLE 4–7. BRIDGE AND PINOCHLE.

	Jack of hearts	Other	Row sums
Bridge	$\frac{5}{8} \times \frac{1}{52}$	$\frac{5}{8} \times \frac{51}{52}$	$\frac{5}{8}$
Pinochle	$\frac{3}{8} \times \frac{2}{48}$	$\frac{3}{8} \times \frac{46}{48}$	$\frac{3}{8}$
Column sums	$\frac{5}{8 \times 52} + \frac{6}{8 \times 48} = \frac{23}{832}$	$\frac{809}{832}$	1

$$P(\text{pinochle}|\text{jack of hearts}) = \frac{\frac{3}{8} \times \frac{2}{48}}{\frac{23}{832}} = \frac{13}{23},$$

$$P(\text{bridge}|\text{jack of hearts}) = 1 - \frac{13}{23} = \frac{10}{23}.$$

We note that the information that the card drawn was the jack of hearts has changed the chances for a pinochle deck from $\frac{3}{8}$, which is less than $\frac{1}{2}$, to $\frac{13}{23}$, which is greater than $\frac{1}{2}$. Naturally, if a 2, 3, 4, 5, 6, 7, or 8 had been drawn, we would know that it came from a bridge deck. *Question:* What is the probability that such a card would be drawn?

EXERCISES FOR SECTION 4-5

1. In the two-urn example, Table 4–6, verify the probabilities of the following events:

    (a) II ∩ W   (b) I ∩ B   (c) I ∩ R   (d) II ∩ B

2. In the two-urn example, Table 4–6, find the following conditional probabilities:

(a) $P(\text{II}|W)$ (b) $P(\text{I}|R)$ (c) $P(\text{II}|R)$ (d) $P(\text{I}|B)$ (e) $P(\text{II}|B)$

3. Suppose that the urn in Example 3, Table 4–5(a), contains b black balls and r red balls. Set up a sample space and assign probabilities to points in it, assuming that two balls are drawn, one after the other, without replacement. Using these probabilities compute:

    (a) P (2nd ball red|1st ball black),   (b) P (2nd ball red),

            (c) P (1st ball red|2nd ball red).

4. Repeat Exercise 3, assuming that the sample is drawn with replacement.

5. (This problem should be worked before going on to Section 4–6.) In a certain factory, machine A produces 30% of the output, machine B produces 25%, and machine C produces the rest. One percent of the output of machine A is defective, as is 1.2% of B's output, and 2% of C's. In a day's run, the three machines produce 10,000 items. What is the probability that one item drawn at random from these 10,000 is defective? If it is defective, what is the probability that it was produced by A? by B? by C?

6. Suppose $P(E) = 0.3$, $P(F) = 0.2$, and $P(E \cup F) = 0.4$. Make a two-by-two table showing probabilities of $E \cap F$, $\overline{E} \cap F$, $E \cap \overline{F}$, $\overline{E} \cap \overline{F}$. What are the following probabilities equal to?

    (a) $P(E \cap F)$ (b) $P(E|F)$ (c) $P(F|E)$ (d) $P(\overline{E}|\overline{F})$

          (e) $P(E \cup \overline{F})$ (f) $P(\overline{E} \cup \overline{F})$

7. In rolling a die repeatedly, what is the probability that a 1 appears for the first time on the 4th roll?

8. In dealing cards from a bridge deck, what is the probability that the first spade occurs at the 5th card?

9. In Example 1, suppose that the probability that Jimmy's mother will buy him a toy when she does not take him with her is 0.3. If the other probabilities are unchanged, what is the probability that she gets him a toy when she goes shopping?

10. In Example 2, make the further assumption that the probability that a nonsubscriber will read the ad is 0.003, and that if a nonsubscriber reads the ad, the probability that he will buy the product is 0.008. What is the probability that a randomly chosen person will read the ad and buy the product? Assume there is one chance in 20 that a person is a subscriber.

11. From twelve tickets numbered from 1 through 12, two tickets are drawn, one after the other, without replacement. What is the probability that (a) both numbers are even? (b) both numbers are odd? (c) the first number is even and the second number is odd? (d) one number is even and the other number is odd?

12. In preparation for an examination, a student has been given two sets of questions to study, with 5 questions in each set. At the time of the examination, he knows the answers to all of the questions in the first set, and to 4 of the 5 questions in the second set. If the examination consists of 3 questions, 2 chosen at random from one set, and 1 chosen at random from the other set, and the examiner tosses a coin to decide which set to take the two problems from, what is the probability that the student will be able to answer all of the questions? That he can answer only 2 of them?

13. Suppose, in Exercise 12, that there are 10 questions in each set and, at the time of the examination, the student knows the answers to 9 questions in the first set and 8 questions in the second set. If the other conditions of Exercise 12 are unchanged, what is the probability that the student can answer all 3 questions on the examination? That he can answer none of the questions?

14. In the bridge-and-pinochle example, suppose that there were equal numbers of bridge decks and pinochle decks in the card room. If a deck is selected at random and a card is chosen at random from that deck, and the card is the 10 of spades, what is the probability that it came from a pinochle deck? From a bridge deck?

15. Answer the questions of Exercise 14 assuming, however, that there are 8 pinochle decks and 4 bridge decks in the card room.

4-6. BAYES' THEOREM

At the start of the experiment in the bridge-and-pinochle example at the end of Section 4–5, the probabilities of drawing a bridge deck or a pinochle deck were $\frac{5}{8}$ and $\frac{3}{8}$, in that order. These probabilities measure the chances that a bridge deck, or a pinochle deck, *will be* used, and are often called *a priori*, or *prior*, probabilities. They are probabilities *prior* to any information that the experiment may yield.

Suppose now that we know the conditions of the experiment, and that we are allowed to see only the card that was drawn. If a prize is offered for correctly guessing the kind of deck the card came from, should we always guess "bridge" on the ground that its prior probability was $\frac{5}{8}$ while that of "pinochle" was only $\frac{3}{8}$? Obviously not, for if a face card is drawn, it is more likely to have come from a pinochle deck. We are therefore interested in the conditional probabilities of "bridge" and "pinochle," given the designation of the card that was drawn. These are called the *a posteriori*, or *posterior*, probabilities because they are the probabilities *after* the result of the experiment is known; or at least after we know the designation of the card that was drawn.

Table 4–8 shows the posterior probabilities of "bridge" and "pinochle" for each possible card drawn. It also shows the prior probabilities, for comparison. We notice here that only the outcome "9 through ace" would change our guess from "bridge" to "pinochle." If 2 through 8 is drawn, the probability is 1 that it came from a bridge deck.

TABLE 4–8. PRIOR AND POSTERIOR PROBABILITIES.

	Prior	Posterior, given card was:	
		2 through 8	9 through ace
Bridge	$\frac{5}{8}$	1	$\frac{10}{23}$
Pinochle	$\frac{3}{8}$	0	$\frac{13}{23}$

EXAMPLE 1. *Two urns.* In the two-urn example, Example 4 of Section 4–5, find the posterior probabilities of urns I and II, given that the first ball drawn is replaced and, after mixing, a second ball is drawn from the same urn as the first ball, and that both balls are white.

Solution. We forego listing the sample space S consisting of sample points like $(I; R, R)$, $(I; R, W)$, and so on to $(II; B, B)$, where $(I; R, W)$ means "urn I is used, the first ball drawn is red, and the second ball drawn is white," and so on. But we have such a sample space in mind, and we assign probabilities to its points in accord with the laws of conditional probability. For example, since the first ball is replaced before the second is drawn,

$$P(I; R, W) = P(I) \cdot P(R|I) \cdot P(W|I)$$

$$= \tfrac{1}{3} \cdot \tfrac{1}{2} \cdot \tfrac{1}{3} = \tfrac{1}{18}.$$

The purpose of this example is to introduce the notation used in the general Bayes' Theorem, so we do not leap at once to the numerical solution.

Let E be the event "two white balls are drawn":

$$E = \{(I; W, W), (II; W, W)\}.$$

Also, let H_1 be the event "urn I was used," and H_2 the event "urn II was used." Note that H_1 and H_2 are mutually exclusive and that their union is S. We want the conditional probabilities

$$P(H_1|E) \qquad \text{and} \qquad P(H_2|E).$$

The formula for conditional probability tells us that

$$P(H_1|E) = \frac{P(H_1 \cap E)}{P(E)}, \tag{1}$$

and we can write a similar equation with H_2 in place of H_1. It is easy to compute $P(H_1 \cap E)$ and $P(H_2 \cap E)$; their values are

$$P(H_1 \cap E) = P(I; W, W) = \tfrac{1}{3} \cdot \tfrac{2}{6} \cdot \tfrac{2}{6} = \tfrac{1}{27}, \tag{2a}$$

$$P(H_2 \cap E) = P(II; W, W) = \tfrac{2}{3} \cdot \tfrac{4}{6} \cdot \tfrac{4}{6} = \tfrac{8}{27}. \tag{2b}$$

Moreover,

$$P(E) = P(H_1 \cap E) + P(H_2 \cap E) = \tfrac{9}{27}, \tag{3}$$

since E must occur either with H_1 or with H_2, and it cannot occur simultaneously with both. If we now substitute from Eqs. (2) and (3) into Eq. (1), we get

$$P(H_1|E) = \frac{P(H_1 \cap E)}{P(H_1 \cap E) + P(H_2 \cap E)} = \frac{1/27}{9/27} = \frac{1}{9} \approx 0.11,$$

$$P(H_2|E) = \frac{P(H_2 \cap E)}{P(H_1 \cap E) + P(H_2 \cap E)} = \frac{8/27}{9/27} = \frac{8}{9} \approx 0.89.$$

Note how the evidence provided by the outcome "both balls white" is reflected in the high posterior probability of urn II, where white balls predominate.

Bayes' Theorem, which generalizes the results of examples like the foregoing, can be used in scientific work in the following way. Suppose there are several mutually exclusive and exhaustive hypotheses $H_1, H_2, \ldots, H_n$ to account for a phenomenon that is subject to test by experiment. Before a particular experiment begins, it may be very hard to assign probabilities, i.e., prior probabilities, to these hypotheses. An experimenter might assign probabilities that are in some way proportional to the "intensity of belief" he has in the various hypotheses. (Another investigator might assign quite different probabilities.)   An experiment is performed, with the aim of discovering evidence to modify these prior probabilities.   Such evidence may even assign such low *posterior* probabilities to some of the hypotheses as to eliminate them from further consideration, just as the drawing of an eight eliminates the pinochle deck.

Each new experiment can begin with *a priori* probabilities of the remaining hypotheses proportional to the *a posteriori* probabilities that resulted from the previous experiments.   In this way, scientific evidence accumulates and modifies our beliefs, weakening our intensity of belief in some hypotheses, strengthening it in others.   And the more evidence that accumulates, the less does it matter what the original *a priori* probabilities were, provided they were all tenable and that no possible hypothesis was assigned prior probability 1 or zero.

4-9 Bayes' theorem.   Let $H_1, H_2, \ldots, H_n$ be mutually exclusive events whose union is the sample space S of an experiment.   Let E be an arbitrary event of S such that $P(E) \neq 0$.   Then

$$P(H_1|E) = \frac{P(H_1 \cap E)}{P(H_1 \cap E) + P(H_2 \cap E) + \cdots + P(H_n \cap E)}, \qquad (4)$$

and similar results hold for H_2, H_3, and so on.

Proof.   The proof will be given for the case $n = 3$.   Figure 4-3 and Tables 4-9 and 4-10 illustrate this case.   The three hypotheses $H_1, H_2,$ and H_3 are mutually exclusive and exhaustive; their union is S.   The part of E that is in H_1 is $H_1 \cap E$, the part in H_2 is $H_2 \cap E$, and the part in

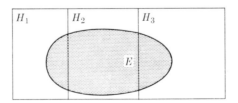

Fig. 4-3.   Partitioning where $n = 3$: $S = H_1 \cup H_2 \cup H_3$, $E = (H_1 \cap E)$ $\cup (H_2 \cap E) \cup (H_3 \cap E)$.

H_3 is $H_3 \cap E$. The entire event E is the union of these three mutually exclusive events—similarly for the complementary event $\overline{E}$, which we include for completeness but which plays no part in the proof.

TABLE 4-9. PARTITION OF SAMPLE SPACE.

Event

Hypothesis	E	$\overline{E}$	Unions of rows
H_1	$H_1 \cap E$	$H_1 \cap \overline{E}$	H_1
H_2	$H_2 \cap E$	$H_2 \cap \overline{E}$	H_2
H_3	$H_3 \cap E$	$H_3 \cap \overline{E}$	H_3
Unions of columns	E	$\overline{E}$	S

Table 4–10 gives the probabilities of the joint events in the cells of Table 4–9.

TABLE 4–10. PROBABILITIES FOR TABLE 4–9.

Event

Hypothesis	E	$\overline{E}$	Row sums
H_1	$P(H_1 \cap E)$	$P(H_1 \cap \overline{E})$	$P(H_1)$
H_2	$P(H_2 \cap E)$	$P(H_2 \cap \overline{E})$	$P(H_2)$
H_3	$P(H_3 \cap E)$	$P(H_3 \cap \overline{E})$	$P(H_3)$
Column sums	$P(E)$	$P(\overline{E})$	1

Since the H's are mutually exclusive and exhaustive, the first column sum is $P(E)$:

$$P(E) = P(H_1 \cap E) + P(H_2 \cap E) + P(H_3 \cap E). \qquad (5)$$

By the law of conditional probability,

$$P(H_1|E) = \frac{P(H_1 \cap E)}{P(E)}$$
$$= \frac{P(H_1 \cap E)}{P(H_1 \cap E) + P(H_2 \cap E) + P(H_3 \cap E)}.$$

This completes the proof for $n = 3$. The proof for $n = 2$, or $n \geq 4$, follows the same pattern and leads to Eq. (4) in each case. $\square$

EXAMPLE 2. (See Exercise 5, Section 4–5.) In a factory, machine A produces 30% of the output, machine B produces 25%, and machine C produces the remaining 45%. One percent of the output of machine A is defective, as is 1.2% of B's output, and 2% of C's. In a day's run, the three machines produce 10,000 items. An item drawn at random from a day's output is defective. What is the probability that it was produced by A? by B? by C?

Solution. You have already applied Bayes' Theorem if you solved this exercise in Section 4–5. The connection is made by taking E, H_1, H_2, and H_3 to be the following events:

$$E: \text{defective item,}$$
$$H_1: \text{item produced by machine } A,$$
$$H_2: \text{item produced by machine } B,$$
$$H_3: \text{item produced by machine } C.$$

Then $P(H_1|E)$ is the probability that the item was produced by A, *given* that it was defective. $P(H_1 \cap E)$ is the probability of the event "produced by A *and* defective," with similar meanings for $P(H_2 \cap E)$ and $P(H_3 \cap E)$. The data give the following probabilities for an item selected at random from the total day's production:

$$P(H_1) = 0.30, \quad P(E|H_1) = 0.010,$$
$$P(H_2) = 0.25, \quad P(E|H_2) = 0.012,$$
$$P(H_3) = 0.45, \quad P(E|H_3) = 0.020.$$

From these data we may compute

$$P(H_1 \cap E) = P(H_1) \cdot P(E|H_1) = 0.003$$
$$P(H_2 \cap E) = P(H_2) \cdot P(E|H_2) = 0.003$$
$$P(H_3 \cap E) = P(H_3) \cdot P(E|H_3) = 0.009.$$
$$\text{Total:} \quad P(E) = 0.015.$$

Before an item is drawn from the population and examined, the probabilities of its having been produced by machines A, B, and C are 0.30, 0.25, and 0.45 in that order. Bayes' Theorem is useful in telling us how these probabilities are modified when we have the additional information that the item drawn was defective. The new probabilities are

$$P(H_1|E) = \frac{P(H_1 \cap E)}{P(E)} = \frac{0.003}{0.015} = 0.20,$$

$$P(H_2|E) = \frac{P(H_2 \cap E)}{P(E)} = \frac{0.003}{0.015} = 0.20,$$

$$P(H_3|E) = \frac{P(H_3 \cap E)}{P(E)} = \frac{0.009}{0.015} = 0.60.$$

We summarize these results:

	Machine		
	A	B	C
A *priori* probability (before information that item is defective)	0.30	0.25	0.45
A *posteriori* probability (after information that item is defective)	0.20	0.20	0.60

This example illustrates one of the chief applications of Bayes' Theorem. We start with a set of prior probabilities associated with the possibilities H_1, H_2, and so on. Next, we perform an experiment and observe that event E has occurred. Then we use this information to modify the set of prior probabilities, replacing

$$P(H_1) \quad \text{by} \quad P(H_1|E),$$

$$P(H_2) \quad \text{by} \quad P(H_2|E),$$

and so on, with the help of Eq. (4).

REMARK 1. In order to compute $P(H_1 \cap E)$ we use the a *priori* probability $P(H_1)$ and the conditional probability of E, given H_1, because

$$P(H_1 \cap E) = P(H_1) \cdot P(E|H_1). \tag{6a}$$

Similarly for the other "hypotheses," H_2 and so on,

$$P(H_i \cap E) = P(H_i) \cdot P(E|H_i). \tag{6b}$$

If we use Eqs. (6a,b) to evaluate the numerator and denominator in Eq. (4), we also have

$$P(H_1|E) = \frac{P(H_1) \cdot P(E|H_1)}{P(H_1) \cdot P(E|H_1) + P(H_2) \cdot P(E|H_2) + \cdots + P(H_n) \cdot P(E|H_n)}.$$

(7)

The left side of Eq. (7) is the *a posteriori* probability of H_1, given E; on the right side appear the *a priori* probabilities of $H_1, H_2, \ldots, H_n$ together with the probabilities of E given H_1, of E given H_2, and so on.

REMARK 2. In the bridge-pinochle example, the *a priori* odds are 5 to 3 in favor of selecting a bridge deck. The *a posteriori* odds, given that a jack of hearts was drawn, are 13 to 10 in favor of a pinochle deck. The result in Bayes' Theorem can always, as here, be expressed in terms of *odds*. The *a priori* odds are proportional to the *a priori* probabilities

$$P(H_1), \qquad P(H_2), \qquad \ldots, \qquad P(H_n).$$

The *a posteriori* odds are proportional to the numerators of Eq. (4) and the other equations like it, since they all have the same denominator. Hence the *a posteriori* odds are proportional to

$$P(H_1 \cap E), \qquad P(H_2 \cap E), \qquad \ldots, \qquad P(H_n \cap E).$$

EXERCISES FOR SECTION 4-6

1. Sixty percent of the students in a school are boys. Eighty percent of the boys and 75% of the girls have activity tickets for all the school activities. A ticket is found and turned in to the school's lost and found department. What is the probability that it belongs to a girl? To a boy?

2. Three girls, Alice, Betty, and Charlotte, wash the family dishes. Since Alice is the oldest, she does the job 40% of the time. Betty and Charlotte share the other 60% equally. The probability that at least one dish will be broken when Alice is washing them is 0.02; for Betty and Charlotte the probabilities are 0.03 and 0.02. The parents don't know who is washing the dishes, but one night they hear one break. What is the probability that Alice was washing? Betty? Charlotte?

3. An experiment consists of throwing a three-sided die and then, depending upon the outcome of the throw, selecting a ball from one of two urns. If the die falls "1 or 2," the ball is drawn from an urn containing 1 red ball and 4 black balls; if the die falls "3" the ball is drawn from an urn with 3 red and 2 black balls. You didn't see the die thrown, but you observed that a red ball was drawn. What is the probability that it came from the first urn? From the second?

4. Suppose, in the two-urn problem of Example 1, the first ball is not replaced, and a second ball is drawn from the same urn as the first. If both balls are white, what is the probability that urn I was used? urn II?

5. (Continuation.) In Exercise 4 above, suppose that 2 blue balls are drawn, without replacement. What are the *a posteriori* probabilities of the two urns?

6. (Continuation.) In Exercise 5, suppose that the first ball is replaced before the second is drawn. Find the *a posteriori* probabilities of the urns if both balls are blue.

7. A fair coin is tossed and if it falls "heads" we draw a ball from urn I; if "tails," from urn II. Urn I contains 3 red balls and 1 white ball. Urn II contains 1 red ball and 3 white balls. What are the *a priori* and *a posteriori* probabilities of the two urns, assuming (a) that a red ball is drawn, (b) that a white ball is drawn?

8. Solve Exercise 7 under the modified assumptions that the *a priori* probabilities are 0.1 for the first urn and 0.9 for the second.

9. In Exercise 8, suppose the experiment continues for n drawings, the ball being replaced and the contents of each urn thoroughly mixed before the next drawing. If all n balls drawn are red, what are the *a posteriori* probabilities of the urns? For what value, or values, of n are these *a posteriori* probabilities approximately equal? What happens to these probabilities if n is very large? What is your interpretation of this result?

10. Assume that 1 coin in 10,000,000 has two heads; the rest are legitimate. If a coin, chosen at random, is tossed 10 times and comes up "heads" every time, what is the probability that it is two-headed?

11. (Continuation.) In Exercise 10, suppose the coin falls "heads" n times in a row. How large must n be to make the odds approximately even that the coin is two-headed?

12. A commuter who works in Boston must either go through the Sumner tunnel or across the Mystic River bridge to get home. He varies his route, choosing the tunnel with probability $\frac{1}{3}$, the bridge with probability $\frac{2}{3}$. If he goes by tunnel, he gets home by 6 o'clock 75% of the time; if he goes by bridge, he gets home by 6 o'clock only 70% of the time, but he likes the scenery better that way. If he gets home after 6 o'clock, what is the probability that he used the bridge?

13. An automobile insurance company classifies drivers as class A (good risks), class B (medium risks), and class C (poor risks). They believe that class A risks constitute 30% of the drivers who apply to them for insurance, class B 50%, and class C 20%. The probability that a class A driver will have one or more accidents in any 12-month period is 0.01, for a class B driver the probability is 0.03, and for a class C driver it is 0.10. The company sells Mr. Jones an insurance policy and within 12 months he has an accident. What is the probability that he is a class A risk? Class B? Class C?

14. (Continuation.) If a policyholder, in Exercise 13, goes n years without an accident, and years are independent, what are the odds that he belongs to class A? Class B? Class C?

15. In a factory, machine A produces 40% of the output and machine B produces 60%. On the average, 9 items in 1000 produced by A are defective

and 1 item in 250 produced by B is defective. An item drawn at random from a day's output is defective. What is the probability that it was produced by A? by B?

16. Friends of yours play two games about equally often. One game is played with one die, the other with two dice. The score in either game is the number of dots on the top face, or faces. You hear the score of a throw announced as 2. What is the chance they are playing the one-die game?

17. Answer the question of Exercise 16 if the announced score is 6. If it is 7. If it is 1.

18. Under hypothesis H_1 a rare event E has the very small probability p of occurring, while under a second hypothesis, H_2, its probability is p^2. (a) If the two hypotheses are equally likely, and are the only ones, and E occurs, find $P(H_1|E)$. Interpret. (b) Suppose that, instead of E, $\overline{E}$ occurs. Find $P(H_1|\overline{E})$, compare it with $P(H_1)$, and comment on the value of one $\overline{E}$ observation.

19. Events $A_1, A_2, \ldots, A_n$ are mutually exclusive, exhaustive, and equally likely *a priori* hypotheses. The conditional probability of E, given A_i, is

$$P(E|A_i) = \frac{i}{n}; \quad i = 1, 2, \ldots, n.$$

If, in two independent trials, EE occurs, find $P(A_i|EE)$. Evaluate for $i = n$, $n = 10$. [You may use the formulas

$$\sum_{i=1}^{n} i = n(n+1)/2, \quad \sum_{i=1}^{n} i^2 = n(n+1)(2n+1)/6.]$$

MISCELLANEOUS EXERCISES FOR CHAPTER 4

For Exercises 1 through 3, use the following data. A box contains 5 books. A boy randomly takes out one book and then replaces it. He does this 5 times.

1. What is the probability that he has had every book out of the box?
2. What is the probability that he has taken exactly 4 different books from the box?
3. What is the probability that the number of different books he takes out of the box is exactly 3? Exactly 2? Exactly 1?

In Exercises 4 through 7, 4 dice are thrown, and we want to know the probability that:

4. All four dice show the same number.
5. No two are alike.
6. Two are alike of one kind and two are alike of another kind.
7. Two are alike and the other two differ from these and from each other.

In Exercises 8 through 15, use the following information about a game played with two regular dice. A player throws two dice, and if he scores 7 or 11, he wins. If he scores 2, 3, or 12, he loses. But if he scores 4, 5, 6, 8, 9, or 10, he throws the dice again, and keeps on throwing until he gets a 7, in which case he loses, or he gets the score that he got on his first throw, in which case he wins. Find the probability that:

8. He loses on the first throw.
9. He wins on the first throw.
10. He scores 4 on the first throw, and goes on to win.
11. He scores 5 on the first throw, and goes on to win. (*Note.* Throws other than 5 and 7 can be ignored, once the 5 is thrown.)
12. He scores 8 on the first throw, and wins.
13. He scores 9 on the first throw, and wins.
14. He scores 10 on the first throw, and wins.
15. He wins.

In Exercises 16 through 19, assume that 4 cards are drawn, without replacement, from an ordinary bridge deck. What is the probability that:

16. All 4 suits are represented.
17. Exactly 3 suits are represented.
18. All cards are from the same suit.
19. Exactly 2 suits are represented.

20. Draw 4 cards from a shuffled pack, then put them back and repeat until 25 hands are drawn. Record the numbers of different suits represented in each hand. Compare the experimental relative frequencies with the theoretical results you got in Exercises 16 through 19.

In Exercises 21 through 26, assume that 5 cards are drawn, without replacement, from a pinochle deck. Find the probability that the number of red cards in the hand is:

21. 5   22. 4   23. 3   24. 2   25. 1   26. 0

27. Use a pinochle deck (or remove the four 2's from a bridge deck), and draw a hand of 5 cards, without replacement. Record the number of red cards. Replace the 5 cards that were drawn, shuffle the pack, and repeat the experiment until 25 hands have been drawn and the results recorded. Compare the observed relative frequencies with the theoretical probabilities of Exercises 21 through 26.

In Exercises 28 through 31, use the following information. Three students A, B, C, have equal claims for an award. They decide that each will toss a coin, and that the man whose coin falls unlike the other two wins. (The "odd man" wins.) If all three coins fall alike, they toss again.

28. Describe a sample space for the result of the first toss of the three coins, and assign probabilities to its elements. What is the probability that A wins

on the first toss? That B does? That C does? That there is no winner on the first toss?

29. Given that there is a winner on the first toss, what is the probability that it is A?

30. What is the probability that no winner is decided in the first 2 tosses? In the first n tosses?

31. Given that no winner is decided in the first n tosses, what is the probability that A wins on the next toss?

5

NUMBERS DETERMINED
BY EXPERIMENTS.
RANDOM VARIABLES

5-1. RANDOM VARIABLES AND THEIR PROBABILITY FUNCTIONS

This chapter introduces two important new concepts: *random variable* and *probability function*. The idea of a sample space is familiar, and we use examples based on this idea to show how random variables and their probability functions arise. The examples point the way to general definitions, and we then go on to study some properties of random variables.

EXAMPLE 1. Three coins are tossed. How many fall "heads"?

Discussion. The answer is a number determined by the outcome of the experiment. The number may be 0, 1, 2, or 3. Although we cannot predict the outcome exactly, we can say what the possibilities and probabilities are. A sample space for the experiment is shown in the first column of Table 5–1. The second column shows the number of heads for each

TABLE 5–1. THREE COINS.

Sample point	Number of heads	Probability
HHH	3	$\frac{1}{8}$
HHT	2	$\frac{1}{8}$
HTH	2	$\frac{1}{8}$
THH	2	$\frac{1}{8}$
HTT	1	$\frac{1}{8}$
THT	1	$\frac{1}{8}$
TTH	1	$\frac{1}{8}$
TTT	0	$\frac{1}{8}$

sample point, and the third column shows the probabilities of the sample points.

The information about the possible numbers of heads, and their probabilities, is collected in Table 5–2. The probability of getting exactly 2 heads is found by adding the probabilities of HHT, HTH, THH, and similarly for other possibilities.

TABLE 5–2. THREE COINS. PROBABILITY FUNCTION FOR
NUMBER OF HEADS.

Probability	$\frac{1}{8}$	$\frac{3}{8}$	$\frac{3}{8}$	$\frac{1}{8}$
No. of heads	0	1	2	3

If we let the variable X represent the number of heads, then Table 5–2 shows the possible values that X can have, and the probability of each value. This set of ordered pairs, each of the form

(number of heads, probability of that number),

is the *probability function* of X. Since the value of X is a number determined by the outcome of an experiment, X is called a *random variable*.

It may seem a bit awkward at first, but we often wish to distinguish between a random variable X and one of its values. To help us make such a distinction we use the capital letter X for the random variable and the small letter x for one of its values. And we use $f(x)$ (read "f at x") for the probability that the random variable X takes on the value x:

$$f(x) = P(X = x).$$

Thus, in the three-coin experiment,

$$f(0) = P(X = 0) = \tfrac{1}{8}, \qquad f(2) = P(X = 2) = \tfrac{3}{8},$$

$$f(1) = P(X = 1) = \tfrac{3}{8}, \qquad f(3) = P(X = 3) = \tfrac{1}{8}.$$

NOTE. In this example, the values of $f(x)$ are

$$1 \times \tfrac{1}{8}, \qquad 3 \times \tfrac{1}{8}, \qquad 3 \times \tfrac{1}{8}, \qquad 1 \times \tfrac{1}{8}.$$

The coefficients 1, 3, 3, 1 are the binomial coefficients $\binom{3}{x}$ for $x = 0, 1, 2, 3$. Consequently all values of $f(x)$ are given by the following formulas:

$$f(x) = P(X = x) = \binom{3}{x}\left(\frac{1}{2}\right)^3$$

$$= \frac{3!}{x!(3 - x)!}\left(\frac{1}{2}\right)^3, \quad x = 0, 1, 2, 3.$$

EXAMPLE 2. *Sums.* A three-sided die is made from an engineer's ruler by painting the numbers 1, 2, and 3 on the three long faces. If such a die is thrown twice, what is the probability function of the random variable X, where X is the sum of the two face-down digits?

Solution. All pairs of faces are equally likely. The sample space of outcomes can be conveniently listed in a square array, as in Table 5–3. In that table $(2, 1)$, for example, indicates that 2 was the outcome of the first throw and that 1 was the outcome of the second throw. We enter the value of X below each outcome pair.

TABLE 5–3. SAMPLE SPACE FOR 2 THROWS OF THREE-SIDED DIE.

Outcome of second throw

		1	2	3
Outcome of first throw	1	(1, 1) 2	(1, 2) 3	(1, 3) 4
	2	(2, 1) 3	(2, 2) 4	(2, 3) 5
	3	(3, 1) 4	(3, 2) 5	(3, 3) 6

Because each cell has probability $\frac{1}{9}$, the probability function of X, the sum of the numbers on the two bottom faces, is obtained by counting the number of ways each sum can happen and dividing by 9. The result is the probability function in the following table:

Probability, $f(x)$	$\frac{1}{9}$	$\frac{2}{9}$	$\frac{3}{9}$	$\frac{2}{9}$	$\frac{1}{9}$
Sum, x	2	3	4	5	6

You may have noticed that in this example X is the sum of two other random variables, the outcome on the first throw and the outcome on the second throw, which might be labeled U and V, respectively. Thus $X = U + V$.

TABLE 5–4. NUMBERS OF DIVISORS OF INTEGERS 1 THROUGH 10.

Integer	1	2	3	4	5	6	7	8	9	10
No. of divisors	1	2	2	3	2	4	2	4	3	4

EXAMPLE 3. We select one of the integers 1 through 10 at random and count its divisors, or factors. What is the probability that it has exactly 2 divisors? Exactly 1 divisor? Exactly 4 divisors? More than 4?

Solution. We first explain the terminology, which is conventional in the theory of numbers. We say that one integer is a *divisor*, or *factor*, of a second integer if the second is a whole number times the first. Thus the divisors of 6 are 1, 2, 3, and 6; and the divisors of 7 are 1 and 7. Here we are interested only in positive divisors.

The first row of Table 5–4 is a sample space for the experiment of selecting an integer from 1 through 10 at random. Let X be the number of divisors of the selected integer. The second row shows the value of the random variable for each sample point. Each integer has probability 0.1 of being drawn because the expression "at random" means that the integers 1 through 10 are equally likely.

Next, we combine cases according to the number of divisors and add their probabilities, 0.1 for each sample point, thus obtaining Table 5–5. We let x stand for any one of the possible numbers of divisors, and $f(x)$ for the probability that X takes the value x. Thus with the value $x = 2$, we associate the probability $f(2) = P(X = 2) = 0.4$.

A graph of the points with coordinates x and $f(x)$ is shown in Fig. 5–1. This graph represents the *probability function* of the random variable X, where X is the "number of divisors of an integer from 1 through 10 chosen at random." In the graph, vertical bars with lengths proportional to the probabilities are added to guide the eye. The actual graph consists of just the four points indicated by the dots at the tops of these bars.

TABLE 5–5. NUMBERS OF DIVISORS AND THEIR PROBABILITIES
(FOR INTEGER SELECTED AT RANDOM FROM 1 THROUGH 10)

Probability, $f(x)$	0.1	0.4	0.2	0.3
No. of divisors, x	1	2	3	4

Using Table 5–5, we can easily answer the four original questions about the number of divisors:

$$P(X = 2) = f(2) = 0.4,$$
$$P(X = 1) = f(1) = 0.1,$$
$$P(X = 4) = f(4) = 0.3,$$

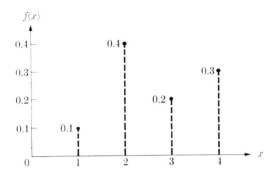

F<small>IG.</small> 5–1. Graph of probability function of number of divisors of integers from 1 through 10.

and, since no integer from 1 through 10 has more than 4 divisors,

$$P(X > 4) = 0.$$

With these examples to guide us, we now formulate the following general definitions.

5–1 Definitions. (1) *Random variable.* A variable whose value is a number determined by the outcome of an experiment is called a *random variable*.

(2) *Probability function.* Let X be a random variable with possible values $x_1, x_2, \ldots, x_t$ and associated probabilities $f(x_1), f(x_2), \ldots, f(x_t)$. Then the set f whose elements are the ordered pairs

$$\big(x_i, f(x_i)\big), \qquad i = 1, 2, \ldots, t,$$

is called the *probability function* of X.

Thus the number of divisors of an integer chosen at random from 1 through 10 is a random variable with $t = 4$ possible values:

$$x_1 = 1, \qquad x_2 = 2, \qquad x_3 = 3, \qquad x_4 = 4.$$

The associated probabilities are those given in Table 5–5. The probability function for this example is the set of ordered pairs of numbers represented by dots in the graph of Fig. 5–1:

$$f = \{(1, 0.1), \ (2, 0.4), \ (3, 0.2), \ (4, 0.3)\}.$$

In this book, we rarely list probability functions as sets of ordered pairs. It is more convenient, and equally valid, to show the probability function by means of a formula for $f(x)$, or by means of a table like Table 5–5.

Probabilities are assigned to events (sets of sample points), and the assignment of a probability to each of the possible events is called the *probability distribution* over the sample space. In finite sample spaces with n elementary events, there are 2^n possible sets; hence if n is large, it is inconvenient to list the probabilities for 2^n sets. Instead, we usually give the *probability function*, which lists a probability for each of the n elementary events. Thus the probability function is one way of summarizing the probability distribution. In discussing probabilities generally, it is common to speak of the probability distribution interchangeably with the probability function.

COMMENT. A random variable is like any other variable except that we may know more about the random variable, namely the probability that it takes any one of its possible values.

EXAMPLE 4. *Matching historical events and dates.* A student is to match three historical events (battle of Lexington and Concord, Columbus's discovery of America, battle of Hastings) with three dates (1775, 1492, 1066). If he guesses, with no knowledge of the correct answers, what is the probability function of the number of answers he gets right?

Solution. A sample space S for the experiment of giving the student this test could be the following six permutations of the three dates:

e_1: 1066, 1492, 1775 e_4: 1492, 1775, 1066

e_2: 1066, 1775, 1492 e_5: 1775, 1066, 1492

e_3: 1492, 1066, 1775 e_6: 1775, 1492, 1066

If he answers strictly by guessing, then each permutation has probability $\frac{1}{6}$.

Next, we associate with each element of S the number of correct answers X that it provides. With no loss of generality, we may assume that the events are listed in the order (1) battle of Hastings, (2) Columbus's discovery of America, and (3) battle of Lexington and Concord. If the student chooses e_1 as his answer, he gets all 3 right. If he chooses e_2, e_3, or e_6, he gets 1 right. If he chooses e_4 or e_5, he gets 0 right. Table 5–6 shows the sample space of permutations $e_1, e_2, \ldots, e_6$ and the number of correct answers in each. Table 5–7 organizes the data in a form that shows the probability function of the random variable X (= "number of correct answers").

TABLE 5–6. MATCHING DATES WITH HISTORICAL EVENTS.

Permutation e_i	Probability of e_i	Number of correct answers, X
e_1	$\frac{1}{6}$	3
e_2	$\frac{1}{6}$	1
e_3	$\frac{1}{6}$	1
e_4	$\frac{1}{6}$	0
e_5	$\frac{1}{6}$	0
e_6	$\frac{1}{6}$	1

TABLE 5–7. PROBABILITY FUNCTION.

Probability, $f(x)$	$\frac{2}{6}$	$\frac{3}{6}$	$\frac{1}{6}$
Number of correct answers, x	0	1	3

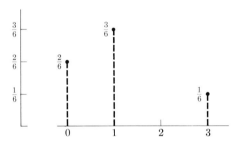

FIG. 5–2. Graph of probability function for matching example.

REMARK. A random variable is often defined to be a *function* that assigns a real number to each sample point. Table 5–6 illustrates this idea; the random variable X may be thought of as a function defined on the domain

$$\{e_1,\ e_2,\ e_3,\ e_4,\ e_5,\ e_6\},$$

with the values (see the third column of Table 5–6):

$$X(e_1) = 3, \quad X(e_2) = 1, \quad X(e_3) = 1,$$
$$X(e_4) = 0, \quad X(e_5) = 0, \quad X(e_6) = 1.$$

From this point of view, the random variable X is the set whose elements are the six ordered pairs

$$(e_1, 3), \quad (e_2, 1), \quad (e_3, 1), \quad (e_4, 0), \quad (e_5, 0), \quad (e_6, 1).$$

The *values* of X are the possible numbers of correct answers: 3, 1, 0. Given a sample point representing the outcome of the experiment, the value of X is determined. Given only the sample space, we know the *possible* values of X and their *probabilities*, the probability function of Table 5–7.

For our present purposes, it is sufficient to consider a random variable as a variable whose value is a number determined by the outcome of an experiment.

Idea of a run. If you toss a coin 9 times and it comes up

$$T\,H\,H\,H\,H\,H\,H\,H\,T,$$

in that order, you may wonder if something in the construction of the coin, or in the way it was tossed, caused so few *runs* (only 3 in this example). Any unbroken sequence of like letters is called a *run*, even though the sequence has only 1 letter (length 1), as at the beginning and end of the foregoing example. The middle run of H's has length 7. Some statistical tests for randomness are based on runs. For instance, in the next example a large number of runs might suggest that people visiting the soda fountain prefer not to sit side by side.

EXAMPLE 5. *Runs of two kinds of elements.* A small soda fountain has 5 seats in a row, 3 of which are occupied. Assuming that all seating arrangements of 3 persons are equally likely, find the probability function of the number of runs of occupied seats (O) and empty seats (E). (Example: $O\ E\ E\ O\ O$ has three runs, as indicated by the underlining.)

Solution. The experiment is to have 3 people come into the soda fountain, when all 5 seats are empty, and sit down. A sample space for this experiment is a list of all possible arrangements of three O's and two E's, corresponding to the three occupied seats and two empty seats. The number of sample points is

$$\binom{5}{3} = \frac{5!}{3!\,2!} = 10,$$

since that is the number of permutations of 5 things, of which three are O's and two are E's. If people choose seats at random, each sample point has probability $\frac{1}{10}$.

The *random variable* of interest to us in this experiment is the number of runs of O's and E's in the sample point that represents the seating arrangement. A list of sample points together with the number of runs in each is given below. We are concerned only with "occupied" or "empty," not with the different persons seated. Thus the seating arrangement designated $O\,O\,O\,E\,E$ means that seats numbered 1 through 3 are occupied, seats 4 and 5 are empty.

Seating	Runs	Seating	Runs
$O\,O\,O\,E\,E$	2	$O\,E\,E\,O\,O$	3
$O\,O\,E\,O\,E$	4	$E\,O\,O\,O\,E$	3
$O\,O\,E\,E\,O$	3	$E\,O\,O\,E\,O$	4
$O\,E\,O\,O\,E$	4	$E\,O\,E\,O\,O$	4
$O\,E\,O\,E\,O$	5	$E\,E\,O\,O\,O$	2

Counting in this list the number of ways to get each possible number of runs, we obtain the probability function of the random variable X, which denotes the number of runs (see Table 5–8).

TABLE 5–8. THE PROBABILITY FUNCTION OF THE
NUMBER OF RUNS OF FIVE ELEMENTS, THREE OF ONE KIND AND
TWO OF ANOTHER.

Probability, $f(x)$	0.2	0.3	0.4	0.1
No. of runs, x	2	3	4	5

Idea of turning points. The next example deals with a topic used in studying economic time series, such as daily stock market averages or weekly production of automobiles. A time series is a set of observations or measurements arranged in the order in which they were made. If there is no trend, these measurements should fluctuate about a mean value, some above and some below. If they continually increase or decrease or follow some cyclical pattern, it may be possible to predict the future behavior of the series.

If among three successive numerical measurements the middle one is the least or the greatest of the three, it is called a *turning point* of the sequence. Thus in the sequence

$$3,\ 5,\ 4,\ 7$$

the numbers 5 and 4 are turning points because 5 is the greatest of 3, 5, 4 and 4 is the least of 5, 4, 7. In random fluctuations there are more likely to be many turning points in the successive measurements than there would be if the measurements were in general increasing or decreasing.

EXAMPLE 6. *Turning points.* If all permutations of four different measurements are equally likely, what is the probability function of the random variable X, where X is the number of turning points?

Solution. For the purpose of counting the number of turning points, there is no loss of generality if we replace the measurements, in order of increasing magnitude, by the numbers 1, 2, 3, and 4. Then any sequence of four different measurements provides some permutation of the four numbers 1, 2, 3, 4. Thus 1 4 2 3 indicates that the smallest measurement is first, the largest second, and so on. And this permutation has two turning points: 4 and 2. We list the 4! permutations, together with the numbers of turning points, in Table 5–9.

TABLE 5–9

PERMUTATIONS OF 1 2 3 4 AND NUMBERS OF TURNING POINTS.

Permu- tation	Turning points	Permu- tation	Turning points	Permu- tation	Turning points	Permu- tation	Turning points
1 2 3 4	0	2 1 3 4	1	3 1 2 4	1	4 1 2 3	1
1 2 4 3	1	2 1 4 3	2	3 1 4 2	2	4 1 3 2	2
1 3 2 4	2	2 3 1 4	2	3 2 1 4	1	4 2 1 3	1
1 3 4 2	1	2 3 4 1	1	3 2 4 1	2	4 2 3 1	2
1 4 2 3	2	2 4 1 3	2	3 4 1 2	2	4 3 1 2	1
1 4 3 2	1	2 4 3 1	1	3 4 2 1	1	4 3 2 1	0

Counting up the frequency of each number of turning points, we get the probability function shown in Table 5–10.

Thus we get no turning points only $\frac{1}{12}$ of the time, one turning point about half the time, and two turning points nearly half the time.

The foregoing examples illustrate the steps in constructing the probability function of a random variable.

---

1. Construct for the given experiment the sample space of possible outcomes, along with their associated probabilities.

2. List the value of the random variable that corresponds to each sample point.

3. List the possible values x_1, x_2, ..., x_t of the random variable, and list the associated probabilities $f(x_1)$, $f(x_2)$, ..., $f(x_t)$. (Compute the probability of x_i by adding together the probabilities of all sample points that correspond to x_i.)

Then the set of ordered pairs

$$(x_i, f(x_i)), \qquad i = 1, 2, \ldots, t$$

is the probability function of the random variable. The probability function is usually displayed either as a table, like Tables 5–2, 5–5, 5–7, 5–8, 5–10, or as a formula for $f(x)$.

TABLE 5–10

Probability, $f(x)$	$\frac{2}{24}$	$\frac{12}{24}$	$\frac{10}{24}$
Number of turning points, x	0	1	2

Further comment on notation. The expression $P(X = x_i)$ denotes the probability that the random variable X takes the value x_i. Usually we shall introduce the probability function and write $f(x_i)$ for the probability $P(X = x_i)$. Sometimes it is convenient to abbreviate $P(X = x_i)$ to $P(x_i)$ when no confusion would develop. If we need to talk about more than one random variable, we may introduce such other letters as Y or Z, having respective values y or z and probability functions g or h. Thus we might have $f(x_i) = P(X = x_i)$, $g(y_j) = P(Y = y_j)$, and $h(z_k) = P(Z = z_k)$.

EXERCISES FOR SECTION 5–1

1. An ordinary six-sided die is thrown once. Find the probability function of the number of dots appearing on the top face. Graph the probability function.

2. Throw an ordinary die 50 times and record the numbers of times it falls with $1, 2, \ldots, 6$ dots up. (Or use your random numbers, Table I, to simulate this experiment.) Divide these numbers by 50 to convert them to relative frequencies and plot the graph of $(x, r(x))$, where $x = 1, 2, \ldots, 6$ and $r(x)$ equals the observed relative frequency. Compare with the graph of the probability function in Exercise 1 above.

3. Suppose a number is selected at random from the integers 1 through 20. Let x be the number of its divisors. Construct the probability function of X and graph it. What is the probability that there will be 4 or more divisors?

4. A coin is tossed 3 times. Let X be the number of runs in the sequence of outcomes: first toss, second toss, third toss. Find the probability function of X and construct its graph. What values of X are most probable?

5. Do a "turning points" example for the case of 3 measurements. What number of turning points has the greatest probability? Least?

6. Two ordinary six-sided dice are thrown (see Table 3–3). Find the probability function for the total score on their top faces and graph it. Do you think the points on the graph lie on any simple curve, or curves? Discuss.

7. (Continuation.) A white die and a red die are thrown at the same time and the difference $R - W$ is observed, where R is the number on top of the red die and W that for the white. Find the probability function of this difference and sketch its graph. What values of $R - W$ are most probable? Least? Compare this probability function and its graph with those obtained in Exercise 6 above. Comment.

8. The three-sided engineer's ruler of Example 2 is thrown 3 times. Find the probability function of the sum of the 3 face-down digits. Sketch and discuss

its graph. [*Hint.* Let X be the sum on the first two throws, Y the score on the third throw, and consider pairs of values of X and Y as constituting the sample space; then form the sum $X + Y$. Use the probability function of X given in Example 2.]

9. Use the table of random numbers at the back of the book and record a sequence of 25 numbers. The results correspond to random sampling, with replacement, from the digits $0, 1, \ldots, 9$. However, interpret "0" as "10," and beside each number record the number of its divisors. Compute the relative frequencies of the various numbers of divisors observed, and plot the graph of relative frequencies against number of divisors. Compare with the probability function of Example 3 and its graph.

10. Throw an ordinary die. Record, in order, the number on top, then the number on the side nearest you (the "front"), next the one on the bottom, and finally the one on the side farthest from you. Repeat this operation 10 times, each time recording a sequence of 4 numbers according to the method described. Next, compute the number of turning points in each sequence and plot their relative frequencies on a graph. Compare with the graph of the probability function of turning points in Example 6 and comment.

11. Graph the probability function of the number of runs in Example 5.

12. Simulate the seating arrangement experiment of Example 5 as follows: shuffle 3 red cards and 2 black cards from a bridge deck, then deal them out one at a time. Record R for red and B for black. Regard reds as "occupied" and blacks as "empty." Repeat the operation 25 times, shuffling the cards well before each deal. Compute the number of runs obtained in each sequence of 5, and the relative frequencies of various numbers of runs obtained in the 25 sequences. Plot, and compare with the graph of the probability function of Example 5.

13. Suppose 4 coins are tossed. If X is the number of tails, find the probability function of X and graph it.

14. Repeat Exercise 13 when X is the number of heads minus the number of tails.

15. From a lot of 10 TV sets containing 4 defectives, a sample of 3 sets is drawn at random without replacement. Let X be the number of defectives in the sample. (a) Describe a sample space for this experiment. (b) How many points are there in your sample space? (c) Tabulate the probability function of X. (d) Graph this probability function.

16. Four people take counts of the number of students in a lecture room, and the results are 51, 52, 52, 53. If all permutations of these counts are equally likely, what is the probability function of the random variable X, where X is the number of turning points?

17. Given the following probability function:

x	0	1	2	3	4	5	6	7
$f(x)$	0	c	$2c$	$2c$	$3c$	c^2	$2c^2$	$7c^2 + c$

(a) Find c. (b) Evaluate $P(X \geq 5)$ and $P(X < 3)$. (c) If $P(X \leq k) > \frac{1}{2}$, find the minimum value of k.

5–2. MATHEMATICAL EXPECTATION OF A RANDOM VARIABLE: POPULATION MEAN

In this section, we introduce the concept of the *mean value* of a random variable. It is closely related to the notion of the arithmetic mean, or average.

EXAMPLE 1. A bowl contains 300 tags; 150 are numbered 1, 100 are numbered 2, and 50 are numbered 3. A tag is drawn at random from the bowl, its number X is recorded, the tag is returned to the bowl, and the tags are thoroughly mixed. This process is repeated 500 times. What is the arithmetic average of the values of the random variable X that are thus recorded?

Solution. Let n_1 of the tags that were drawn have the number 1, n_2 have 2, and n_3 have 3. Then the arithmetic average $\bar{x}$ (read "x bar") is

$$\bar{x} = \frac{1 \times n_1 + 2 \times n_2 + 3 \times n_3}{n_1 + n_2 + n_3}. \tag{1}$$

The numerator of this expression is a "weighted sum" of 1's, 2's, and 3's, each "weighted" by a factor n_1, n_2, or n_3 that is equal to the number of times the given number is drawn. This average (1) can also be expressed in terms of the *proportions* n_1/n, n_2/n, n_3/n, with

$$n = 500 = n_1 + n_2 + n_3,$$

to yield

$$\bar{x} = 1 \times \frac{n_1}{n} + 2 \times \frac{n_2}{n} + 3 \times \frac{n_3}{n}. \tag{2}$$

The expression (2) exhibits the average as another weighted sum of 1's, 2's, and 3's; here the three numbers are weighted by their relative proportions. Of course, we don't know the exact values of these proportions (unless we actually perform the experiment), so we can't say in advance just what the average produced by this particular experiment is. But since the probability of drawing a 1 is $f(1) = \frac{1}{2}$, of drawing a 2 is $f(2) = \frac{1}{3}$, and of drawing a 3 is $f(3) = \frac{1}{6}$, we might suppose that the proportions n_1/n, n_2/n, and n_3/n are approximately equal to $f(1)$, $f(2)$, and $f(3)$, in that order. Thus, for a value of n as large as 500, we might expect an average near

$$1 \times f(1) + 2 \times f(2) + 3 \times f(3) = 1 \times \tfrac{1}{2} + 2 \times \tfrac{1}{3} + 3 \times \tfrac{1}{6} = \tfrac{5}{3}.$$

The arithmetic mean of *all* the tags in the bowl is also $\frac{5}{3}$:

$$\frac{1 \times 150 + 2 \times 100 + 3 \times 50}{150 + 100 + 50} = \frac{500}{300} = \frac{5}{3}.$$

For a *small* sample of tags, we would not expect the sample average necessarily to be near this population mean, but for a large sample most people do expect it, and it usually is near.

EXAMPLE 2. The number of divisors of an integer from 1 through 10, chosen at random, is a random variable X. What is its expected value?

Solution. Table 5–5 provides the probability function for the number of divisors X. We use this probability function to compute the "population mean" in the way indicated in Example 1 above. The result is

$$1 \times 0.1 + 2 \times 0.4 + 3 \times 0.2 + 4 \times 0.3 = 2.7.$$

This is the *average* result that we might expect from a *large number* of performances of the experiment. Of course, no number has 2.7 divisors; moreover, on just *one* performance of the experiment, the most likely number of divisors is 2, since that has the highest probability.

The foregoing examples lead us to the following definitions.

5–2 Definition. *Sample average.* Let X be a random variable whose possible values are x_1, x_2, ..., x_t. Suppose that a sample of n observations produces n_1 values of X that are equal to x_1, n_2 that are equal to x_2, ..., n_t that are equal to x_t:

Frequencies	n_1	n_2	...	n_t	Total: n
Values of X	x_1	x_2	...	x_t	

Then the *average* value of X for this *sample* is

$$\bar{x} = \frac{x_1 n_1 + x_2 n_2 + \cdots + x_t n_t}{n_1 + n_2 + \cdots + n_t} = \frac{\sum x_i n_i}{\sum n_i},$$

or

$$\boxed{\bar{x} = \frac{1}{n} \sum_{i=1}^{t} x_i n_i.} \tag{3}$$

(See Appendix II for a discussion of the summation symbol, $\sum$.)

The set of ordered pairs (x_i, n_i), $i = 1, 2, \ldots, t$, displayed as a table in Definition 5–2 is called the *frequency distribution* of the sample values. In dealing with samples, the frequency distribution plays an important role, just as the probability function does in dealing with populations.

5–3 Definition. *Mathematical expectation: population mean.* Let X be a random variable with probability function as follows:

Probability, $f(x)$	$f(x_1)$	$f(x_2)$	$\ldots$	$f(x_t)$
Value of X, x	x_1	x_2	$\ldots$	x_t

The *mathematical expectation* of X, denoted by $E(X)$, is defined to be

$$E(X) = x_1 f(x_1) + x_2 f(x_2) + \cdots + x_t f(x_t),$$

or

$$E(X) = \sum_{i=1}^{t} x_i f(x_i). \tag{4}$$

$E(X)$ is also called the *mean* of X, or the *population mean.*

REMARK. The mean is also abbreviated μ (read "mew" and spelled "mu"), the Greek letter for "m," the first letter of the word "mean." Sometimes several random variables X, Y, $\ldots$ are being studied together. We may use these letters as subscripts on μ to indicate the means. Thus we would write

$$\mu_X = E(X) \quad \text{and} \quad \mu_Y = E(Y).$$

When only one random variable is being considered, the subscript is usually omitted.

We may express the result of Eq. (4) in words:

To compute the mean of a random variable, multiply each possible value of the variable by its probability and add these products.

Equations (3) and (4) are not identical, but they are similar. In particular, the proportions n_i/n in Eq. (3) vary from one sample to another, and it is only a coincidence if n_i/n is equal to the probability $f(x_i)$. However, it is true that

$$\frac{n_i}{n} \approx f(x_i),$$

and therefore

$$\bar{x} \approx \mu.$$

These approximations are usually better when n is large, and, of course, become equalities if the sample coincides with the entire population.

EXAMPLE 3. One die is thrown. What is the mathematical expectation of the number of dots on the top face?

Solution. Let the random variable X denote the number of dots on the top face of the die. The possible values are 1, 2, . . . , 6, each with probability $\frac{1}{6}$. Hence, by Eq. (4),

$$\mu = E(X)$$
$$= 1 \times \tfrac{1}{6} + 2 \times \tfrac{1}{6} + 3 \times \tfrac{1}{6} + 4 \times \tfrac{1}{6} + 5 \times \tfrac{1}{6} + 6 \times \tfrac{1}{6} = \tfrac{21}{6} = 3.5.$$

EXAMPLE 4. What is the mathematical expectation of the number of runs when 3 things of one kind and 2 things of another kind are arranged at random in a row?

Solution. Here the random variable X is the number of runs whose probability function is given in Table 5–8. Using it, we compute

$$\mu = E(X) = 2 \times 0.2 + 3 \times 0.3 + 4 \times 0.4 + 5 \times 0.1 = 3.4.$$

REMARK. Note that in this example, again, the mathematical expectation of the number of runs is 3.4, not an integer, and not any value that the random variable could actually have. The same is true of the mathematical expectation of the number of dots on the top face of the die in Example 3 and of the number of divisors in Example 2. We mention this because the term "mathematical expectation" is often abbreviated "expectation." The examples show that this *"expectation" is not something we "expect" in the ordinary sense of the word, except that the long-run average over repeated experiments is likely to be close to it.* Again, the term "expected value" is sometimes used as a synonym for "mathematical expectation," but there should be no implication that this value is frequent, highly probable, or even possible. It is merely the weighted mean of the possible values, each weighted by its probability.

EXAMPLE 5. According to an American experience mortality table, the probability that a 25-year-old man will survive one year is 0.992, and that he will die within a year is 0.008. An insurance company offers to sell such a man a $1000 one-year term life insurance policy for a premium of $10. What is the company's expected gain?

Solution. The "gain," X, is a random variable that may take the value $+\$10$ (if the man lives) or $-\$990$ (if he dies). The probability function is as follows:

$f(x)$	0.992	0.008
x	$+10$	-990

and

$$\mu = E(X) = 10 \times 0.992 - 990 \times 0.008 = 2.$$

It is important that the expected gain (before administrative expenses and taxes) be positive in order to enable the insurance company to stay in business and to build up reserves to pay its beneficiaries and policy-holders.

EXAMPLE 6. *One-armed bandit.* A simplified slot machine has 2 dials. Each dial has 3 kinds of pictures on it, identified as "apples," "bells," and "cherries." The machine is rigged so that the 2 dials operate independently, and after they are spun, each comes to rest with 1 of the 3 pictures showing in a window on the front of the machine. The probabilities of the possible outcomes, for each dial, are

Outcomes	Bells	Cherries	Apples
Probabilities	0.4	0.5	0.1

Each play costs five cents. A play consists of pulling a lever that spins the dials, resulting in one of the 9 possible combinations of 2 pictures, 1 on each dial. The machine pays off as follows:

for 2 apples,   50¢   for 2 cherries,   5¢
for 2 bells,   10¢   for anything else it pays nothing

Find the mathematical expectation of net profit (in money) to a person who plays once.

Solution. The random variable X here equals the number of cents won. Table 5–11 shows a sample space of possible outcomes, their probabilities, and the corresponding profit in cents. The three entries in the upper left corner,

$$(a, a): 45$$
$$0.01$$

mean that the outcome "two apples" has an associated profit of 45 cents, and occurs with probability 0.01.

TABLE 5–11. ONE-ARMED BANDIT.

Second dial

	Apples 0.1	Bells 0.4	Cherries 0.5
Apples 0.1	(a, a): 45 0.01	(a, b): −5 0.04	(a, c): −5 0.05
Bells 0.4	(b, a): −5 0.04	(b, b): 5 0.16	(b, c): −5 0.20
Cherries 0.5	(c, a): −5 0.05	(c, b): −5 0.20	(c, c): 0 0.25

First dial (label on left side of rows)

The expected value of the random variable X, the profit on one play, is

$$\mu_X = E(X) = 45 \times 0.01 + 5 \times 0.16 + 0 \times 0.25 - 5 \times 0.58$$
$$= .45 + .80 - 2.90 = -1.65 \text{ (cents)}.$$

In ten plays, the expected loss is 16.5 cents; in 100 plays, \$1.65.

EXERCISES FOR SECTION 5–2

1. In Example 2, Section 5–1, what is the expected sum of the 2 face-down digits in the experiment with the engineer's ruler?

2. In Example 4, Section 5–1, what is the expected number of correct answers?

3. In Example 5, Section 5–1, what is the expected number of runs?

4. From a bag of 7 marbles, 5 red and 2 blue, 3 marbles are drawn at random without replacement. Check that the expected number of blue marbles is $3 \times \frac{2}{7}$.

5. For Exercise 17, Section 5–1, compute the expected value of X.

6. For Exercise 15, Section 5–1, find the expected number of defective TV sets.

7. Refer to Example 6, Section 5–2: one-armed bandit. Find the expected number of cents profit for one play on a two-independent-dial slot machine, given the following data for one dial:

Outcomes	Bells	Cherries	Apples
Probabilities	0.3	0.6	0.1

Payoffs: for 2 apples, 25¢   for 2 cherries, 5¢

for 2 bells, 10¢   for anything else, zero

8. *Problem of points.* To decide who wins a \$4 prize, A and B play the following game. A coin is tossed. If the coin falls heads A gets a point; if it falls tails, B gets a point. The first person to get three points wins. After 3 tosses, A has 2 points and B has 1. Make a sample space for the rest of the game. Let X be A's winnings. What is the expected value of A's winnings when he has 2 points and B has 1?

9. In a lottery, 100 tickets are sold at 25 cents each. There are 4 cash prizes, worth \$10, \$3, \$2, and \$1, respectively. What is the expected net gain for a purchaser of two tickets?

10. Four identical light bulbs are temporarily removed from their sockets and placed in a box. The bulbs are then taken at random from the box and put back in the sockets. What is the expected number of bulbs that will be replaced in their original sockets?

11. Calculate the expected number of "heads" when n coins are tossed together if (a) $n = 1$, (b) $n = 2$, (c) $n = 3$, (d) $n = 4$. What do you predict for the answer for an arbitrary value of n? Can you prove it?

12. Find the expected value of the sum of the numbers of dots on the top faces of two ordinary cubical dice, on one throw.

13. *Roulette.* A roulette wheel has 38 equally spaced openings numbered 00, 0, 1, 2, 3, $\ldots$, 35, 36. A gambler may bet \$1 on any number. The croupier spins the roulette wheel and drops a small ball onto it while it is spinning. If the ball comes to rest on the number the gambler has bet on, he receives \$35 in addition to his bet of \$1, but otherwise he loses his \$1. Find the mathematical expectation of his gain.

14. Find the expected number of turning points in a series of 4 different measurements. (See Table 5–9.)

15. The number of accidents that occur at a particular intersection between 4:30 and 6:30 p.m. on Fridays is 0, 1, 2, or 3, with corresponding probabilities 0.94, 0.03, 0.02, 0.01. Find the expected number of accidents during the period in question. During 100 such periods.

16. Player A pays B \$1, and 3 unbiased dice are rolled fairly. A receives \$2 from B if 1 ace appears, \$4 if 2 aces appear, and \$8 if 3 aces appear; otherwise he gets nothing. Is this a fair game? (That is, do A and B have the same expectation of gain?) If not, how much should A receive from B when 3 aces appear, to make the game fair?

17. In the World Series, suppose one team is stronger than the other and has probability $\frac{2}{3}$ of winning each game, independent of the outcomes of any other games. Under these assumptions, it is possible to show that the probabilities that the series ends in 4, 5, 6 or 7 games respectively are about .21, .30, .27, or .22. Find the expected number of games in the series, under these assumptions.

18. The probability that a man aged 50 will live another year is 0.988. How large a premium should the insurance company charge him for a \$1000 term life insurance policy for one year (not including insurance company charges for administration, profit, etc.)?

19. In one play of the game called "chuck-a-luck," the player wins an amount 15, 10, 5, or -5 cents (-5 means he loses 5 cents), with probabilities $\frac{1}{216}$, $\frac{15}{216}$, $\frac{75}{216}$, and $\frac{125}{216}$, respectively. (Cf. Wallis and Roberts, *Statistics, a new ap-*

proach, The Free Press, 1956, p. 332.) Find the mathematical expectation of the player's gain (a) on one play of the game, (b) on 100 plays.

20. A sample of 4 balls is drawn without replacement from an urn containing 3 red and 5 white balls. If the sample contains 2 or more red balls, the player receives one dollar; otherwise he loses fifty cents. What is the mathematical expectation of his gain? (First set up an appropriate sample space for the experiment.)

21. A fair coin is tossed until the first time a tail comes up or until three heads occur. Write out a sample space for this experiment and assign probabilities to its elements. Find the expected number of tosses in one performance of the experiment.

22. A farmer estimates that during the coming year his hens will produce 10,000 dozen eggs. He further estimates that, after taking into account his various costs and the seasonal price fluctuations, he may gain as much as 6 cents per dozen, or lose as much as 2 cents per dozen, and that the probabilities associated with these possibilities are as follows:

Gain (in cents per doz.)	6	4	2	0	−2
Probability	0.20	0.50	0.20	0.06	0.04

What does he estimate as his expected gain (a) in cents per dozen, and (b) on the 10,000 dozen?

23. The possible values of a random variable X are the integers from n through $n + m$. If these possibilities are equally likely, find $E(X)$.

24. The random variable X has values 0 and n with probabilities $(n - 1)/n$ and $1/n$, in that order. Find $E(X)$. Describe the graph of the probability function of X (a) for $n = 5$, (b) for $n = 20$, (c) for $n = 1000$, (d) for $n \rightarrow$ "infinity." What is the limit of $E(X)$ as $n \rightarrow$ "infinity"?

25. The possible values of a random variable X are the integers 1, 2, 3, ..., n and $P(X = x) = cx$ for some constant c. (The probability function has a triangular shaped graph.) Show that $c = 2/n(n + 1)$. Find $E(X)$. Is $E(X) \approx \frac{2}{3}n$ when n is large? Discuss and interpret the result.

5-3. MEAN OF A FUNCTION OF A RANDOM VARIABLE

Suppose that X is a random variable, a variable whose value is a number determined by the outcome of an experiment. If the value of X is increased by 5, the result is again a number determined by the outcome of that experiment: a number that is a value of the new random variable $X + 5$. Or, if the value of X is squared, the result is a value of the random variable X^2. In this section, we study random variables that are related to X: variables such as aX, $X + c$, $aX + c$, X^2, and $(X - c)^2$, where a and c are constants. Each of these random variables has a probability function, which we can get from the probability function of X, and each has a mean. In the next example, we show how these means are computed directly from the probability function of X without going through the intermediate step of finding the probability function of the related random variable.

EXAMPLE 1.   The random variable X has probability function as follows:

Probability, $f(x)$	0.2	0.3	0.5
Values of X, x	-1	0	1

Compute the following means: $E(X)$, $E(2X)$, $E(X + 1)$, $E(2X + 1)$, $E(X^2)$, and $E[(X - 0.3)^2]$.

Solution. (a) $E(X) = -1 \times 0.2 + 0 \times 0.3 + 1 \times 0.5 = 0.3$. Thus, the mean of X is 0.3.

(b) The possible values of $2X$, and their probabilities, are as follows:

Probabilities	0.2	0.3	0.5
Values of $2X$	-2	0	2

Note that $P(2X = -2)$ is the same as $P(X = -1)$, and so on. If we multiply each possible value of $2X$ by its probability and add these products, we get the mean, or expected value, of $2X$:

$$\mu_{2X} = E(2X) = -2 \times 0.2 + 0 \times 0.3 + 2 \times 0.5$$
$$= 0.6 = 2E(X).$$

Doubling every number doubles the mean.

(c) $\mu_{X+1} = E(X + 1)$
$$= (-1 + 1) \times 0.2 + (0 + 1) \times 0.3 + (1 + 1) \times 0.5$$
$$= 1.3 = E(X) + 1.$$

Obviously, if we add 1 to every number, the mean is increased by 1.

(d) $E(2X + 1) = (-2 + 1) \times 0.2 + (0 + 1) \times 0.3 + (2 + 1) \times 0.5$
$$= 1.6 = 2E(X) + 1.$$

Doubling every number and adding 1 doubles the mean and adds 1 to the result.

(e) $E(X^2) = (-1)^2 \times 0.2 + (0)^2 \times 0.3 + (1)^2 \times 0.5$
$$= 0.7 \neq [E(X)]^2.$$

Note that the mean of the square is not the square of the mean.

(f) $E[(X - 0.3^2)] = (-1.3)^2 \times 0.2 + (-0.3)^2 \times 0.3 + (0.7)^2 \times 0.5$
$$= 0.61 = E(X^2) - [E(X)]^2.$$

There is something special about 0.3 in this example; it is the mean of X.

The common feature in all these examples is this: we have computed the mean of a function of X by substituting in the formula for the function the possible values of X (in these cases -1, 0, 1), multiplying the results by the probabilities of these values of X (here 0.2, 0.3, 0.5), and adding the products. We formalize this procedure in the following definition.

5–4 Definition. *Mean of a function.* Let X be a random variable whose probability function is as follows:

Probability, $f(x)$	$f(x_1)$	$f(x_2)$	$\cdots$	$f(x_t)$
Values of X, x	x_1	x_2	$\cdots$	x_t

Let H be a function of X. Then the mean, or expected value, of the new random variable $H(X)$ is given by

$$E[H(X)] = H(x_1)f(x_1) + H(x_2)f(x_2) + \cdots + H(x_t)f(x_t), \qquad (1)$$

or

$$E[H(X)] = \sum_{i=1}^{t} H(x_i)f(x_i). \qquad (2)$$

REMARK. The mean of the new random variable $Y = H(X)$ can be computed from the probability function of Y by multiplying each possible value of Y by its probability and adding these products. In Example 1(b) above, we have illustrated this for $Y = 2X$. The possible values of Y are

$$y_1 = 2x_1 = 2 \times (-1) = -2,$$
$$y_2 = 2x_2 = 2 \times 0 = 0,$$
$$y_3 = 2x_3 = 2 \times 1 = 2,$$

and their probabilities are

$$P(Y = y_1) = P(Y = -2) = P(X = -1) = f(x_1),$$
$$P(Y = y_2) = P(Y = 0) = P(X = 0) = f(x_2),$$
$$P(Y = y_3) = P(Y = 2) = P(X = 1) = f(x_3).$$

Hence we find, for that example,

$$
\begin{aligned}
E(Y) &= y_1 P(Y = y_1) + y_2 P(Y = y_2) + y_3 P(Y = y_3) \\
&= y_1 f(x_1) \qquad\quad + y_2 f(x_2) \qquad\quad + y_3 f(x_3) \\
&= 2x_1 f(x_1) \qquad\quad + 2x_2 f(x_2) \qquad\quad + 2x_3 f(x_3),
\end{aligned}
$$

which corresponds to the result given by Eq. (1). Note that we do *not* get

$$
2x_1 f(2x_1) + 2x_2 f(2x_2) + 2x_3 f(2x_3),
$$

because the probability that $2X$ takes the value $2x_i$ is the same as the probability that X takes the value x_i, and this is $f(x_i)$, not $f(2x_i)$.

Sometimes two or more values of X yield the same value of the new random variable $H(X)$. For example, both $X = -1$ and $X = +1$ yield the value $X^2 = +1$ in Example 1(e) above. More generally, suppose that $Y = H(X)$ takes the value y_1 for m distinct values of X, say for $X = x_1, x_2, \ldots, x_m$. Then

$$
y_1 = H(x_1) = H(x_2) = \cdots = H(x_m). \tag{3}
$$

The corresponding contribution to the mean of Y is

$$
y_1 \cdot P(Y = y_1).
$$

But

$$
P(Y = y_1) = f(x_1) + f(x_2) + \cdots + f(x_m),
$$

so that

$$
y_1 \cdot P(Y = y_1) = y_1 f(x_1) + y_1 f(x_2) + \cdots + y_1 f(x_m),
$$

and when we take Eq. (3) into account, we see that

$$
y_1 \cdot P(Y = y_1) = H(x_1)f(x_1) + H(x_2)f(x_2) + \cdots + H(x_m)f(x_m). \tag{4}
$$

Similarly, if another set of values of X corresponds to y_2, a third set to y_3, and so on, we can group the terms on the right side of Eq. (1) into terms corresponding to

$$
y_1 P(Y = y_1) + y_2 P(Y = y_2) + \cdots = E(Y).
$$

Thus Eq. (1) allows us to use the probability function of X to get the same result that we would get by computing the mean of $Y = H(X)$ from the probability function of Y.

Example 1 has illustrated some results that we now state as theorems, since they are true in general. We also provide algebraic proofs.

5–5 Theorem. Let X be a random variable. Then

$$\boxed{E(aX + b) = aE(X) + b,}$$ (5)

for any numerical constants a and b.

Proof. Suppose the probability function of X is

$$\{(x_i, f(x_i)): i = 1, 2, \ldots, t\}.$$

Then, by Definition 5–4,

$$E(aX + b) = (ax_1 + b)f(x_1) + (ax_2 + b)f(x_2) + \cdots + (ax_t + b)f(x_t).$$

We expand the right side of this equation, factor out a and b, and get

$$E(aX + b) = a[x_1f(x_1) + x_2f(x_2) + \cdots + x_tf(x_t)]$$
$$+ b[f(x_1) + f(x_2) + \cdots + f(x_t)].$$

The first of the bracketed expressions is $E(X) = \sum x_i f(x_i)$, and the second is 1, since $\sum f(x_i) = 1$. Therefore we have the desired result

$$E(aX + b) = aE(X) + b. \ \square$$

5–6 Corollary. Let X be a random variable with mean $E(X) = \mu$. Then $E(X - \mu) = 0$.

Proof. Take $a = 1$, $b = -\mu$ in Theorem 5–5:

$$E(X - \mu) = E(X) - \mu = \mu - \mu = 0. \ \square$$ (6)

REMARK. The expected value of $X - c$ is often called the *first moment* of X, taken about c. The reason for this terminology is that $E(X - c)$ is, by Definition 5–4,

$$(x_1 - c)f(x_1) + (x_2 - c)f(x_2) + \cdots + (x_t - c)f(x_t),$$ (7)

and this has the following physical interpretation. If we imagine a light but rigid bar with weights (in some system of units) equal to $f(x_1)$ at

x_1, $f(x_2)$ at x_2, and so on, $f(x_t)$ at x_t, then formula (7) represents the sum of products of these weights each multiplied by the length of the "lever arm" from c to that weight. (See Fig. 5–3.)

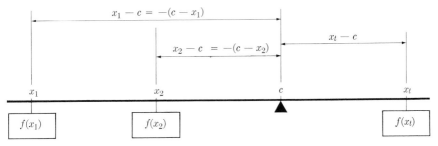

FIG. 5–3. Moment, about c, of weights $f(x_1)$, $f(x_2)$, ..., $f(x_t)$.

In physics, expression (7) is called the first moment of the system of weights about c. If c is at the center of mass of the system the first moment is zero, and there is no tendency for the system to rotate about a support placed at that point. Thus children on a seesaw can balance by placing the support directly under the center of mass. Equation (6) tells us that if we place the fulcrum at the mean $\mu = E(X)$, the first moment about μ is zero. Conversely, if $E(X - c) = 0$, then $c = E(X)$; the mean is the only point about which the first moment is zero. This is one sense in which the mean is used to represent the "location," or the "middle," of the domain of the probability function. It isn't always at an equal distance from the ends of the domain—just as the point of balance of a seesaw isn't always halfway between the two children. If one child is much heavier than the other, the support must be nearer that child. Likewise, if lots of the probability is piled up near one end of the domain of a random variable, the mean is usually near that end.

EXERCISES FOR SECTION 5–3

For Exercises 1 through 4, use the following data:

Probability, $f(x)$	0.2	0.1	0.3	0.3	0.1
Values of X, x	−2	−1	0	1	2

1. Compute $E(X)$.

2. Find the probability table for the function $3X - 1$ and then compute $E(3X - 1)$. Compare your answer with $3E(X) - 1$.

3. Find the probability table for the function $2X + 3$. Compute $E(2X + 3)$ and compare your answer with $2E(X) + 3$.

4. Find the probability function for X^2 and compute $E(X^2)$.

5. Find the probability function for $X^2 + 1$, and compute $E(X^2 + 1)$.

For Exercises 6 through 9, use the following data:

Probability, $f(x)$	0.2	0.3	0.2	0.2	0.1
Values of X, x	1	2	3	4	5

6. Find $E(X)$.

7. Compute, as easily as possible, (a) $E(3X - 7)$, (b) $E(X - 2.7)$, and (c) $E(10X)$.

8. Compute $E(X^2)$.

9. Compute $E(X - 2.7)^2$ and then show that your answer is equal to $E(X^2) - [E(X)]^2$.

ST. PETERSBURG PARADOX EXERCISES

Description of play. A player tosses a coin until it falls tails, or until he has tossed n times without a tail. Let X be the number of heads in one play of the game.

1. Find the probability function of X for $n = 2$.

2. Repeat Exercise 1 for $n = 3$.

3. Repeat Exercise 1 for $n = 4$.

4. Repeat Exercise 1 for a general value of n.

Description of payoff. In the game described above, the number of dollars the player receives is the random variable $Y = 2^X$.

5. For Exercise 1 find $E(Y)$.

6. For Exercise 2 find $E(Y)$.

7. For Exercise 3 find $E(Y)$.

8. For Exercise 4 find $E(Y)$. [*Hint.* Recall that $p + p^2 + \cdots + p^{n-1}$ is the sum of a geometric progression.]

9. Discuss the behavior of $E(Y)$ as n grows large.

10. Lift the restriction to n trials, and consider the expected payoff when the player tosses until he gets a tail. (This is the original St. Petersburg problem, and it is satisfactory to say that the expectation is infinite.)

Fair game. Recall that a game between two persons is said to be fair if the expected value to both persons is zero. Our player plays against a bank (or gambling house), tossing until he gets a tail, with payoff $Y = 2^X$ dollars, as before.

11. If the game is to be fair, and if the bank has unlimited resources, how much should the player pay the bank for one play of the game?

12. Suppose the bank has only 2^{20} dollars ($\$1,048,476$), what should the player pay the bank to make it a fair game?

13. Do Exercise 12 if the bank has 4×10^{11} dollars, about the size of the national debt of the United States of America in 1960.

NOTE. Although it is amusing to see the modest payments required to play a fair game against a bank with astronomical resources, the result in Exercise 11 is somewhat shocking. The importance of that result is not its literal interpretation, i.e., that no one can pay an infinite amount. Rather, consideration of this and similar problems led people to realize that expected dollar value is not the only measure of worth, because a man will not invest a large amount of money in an enterprise with an even larger expected value if the probability that he gets his money back is tiny. Most of us would not care to risk $10,000 for a 1/10,000 chance at a tax-free billion, even though the expected value of the proposition is $90,000. Economists introduced the notion of utility to explain such behavior.

5–4. VARIABILITY

We recall that the probability function of a random variable X tells us the possible values that X can have and the probabilities of those values. For many practical purposes, it is convenient to have a quick summary of the information that the probability function furnishes. The *mean*, or expected value $E(X)$, is one such summary; *it tells where the center of mass of the probability function is located.* Thus the mean number of dots on the top face of a die is 3.5, the mean number of divisors of an integer from 1 through 10 is 2.7, the mean number of heads when two coins are tossed is 1. *The mean is useful in giving us a quick picture of the long-run average result when an experiment is performed over and over.* But it tells us nothing about how outcomes spread out from one performance of the experiment to another. We shall now consider various alternative ways of measuring such variability, or spread, and then introduce the two most commonly used measures of spread, the *standard deviation* and the *variance*. (Either of these measures determines the other because the variance is the square of the standard deviation.)

Idea of spread, or variability. To gain some experience with the idea of variability, we consider six random variables X_A, X_B, ..., X_F whose probability graphs are shown in order A, B, ..., F in Fig. 5–4. These probability functions are symmetrical about the value $x = 0$; their means are all equal to zero. We consider various ways of measuring their spreads about this common mean.

The first measure of variability, or spread, that suggests itself is the *range*, defined as follows. Consider those values of X that have probabilities greater than zero. Then the range of X is the largest of these values minus the smallest. In examples A, B, C the range is 2; in examples D and E the range is 4; and in example F the range is 6. We might prefer a measure of variability that distinguishes among A, B, and C; particularly so since we wish to measure variability around the mean, and X_A has $\frac{6}{8}$ of its probability concentrated at the mean, while X_C has none.

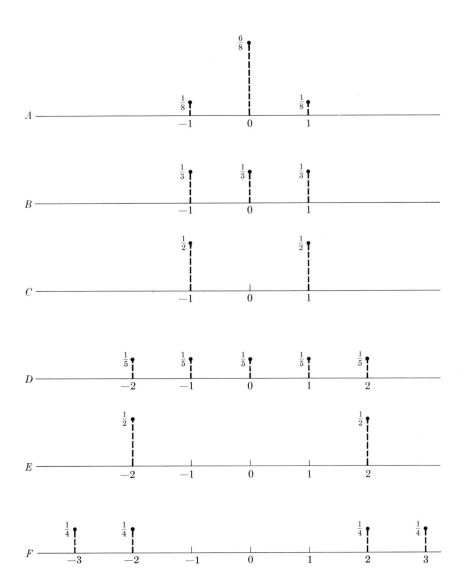

FIG. 5-4. Graphs of six probability functions, illustrating variability.

How would we compare the spread about the mean of the random variables X_A and X_B? First let us consider X_A, the outcome on an experiment A. In 1200 performances of the experiment, we expect 0 as the outcome about 900 times, $+1$ about 150 times, and -1 about 150 times. By contrast, experiment B would yield about 400 zeros, 400 plus ones, and 400 minus ones; results that seem to jump around more than the results of experiment A. Thus it seems reasonable that any measure of variability that is proposed should say that B is more variable than A.

The comparison between B and C is less obvious. However, since we use the *mean* as a measure of *location* of the probability distribution, we shall measure *variability about the mean*. Now B gives a result equal to the mean, 0, about $\frac{1}{3}$ of the time, and a result 1 unit away from the mean about $\frac{2}{3}$ of the time. By contrast, C always gives a result that is 1 unit away from the mean. Hence C seems more variable than B, when variability is measured about the mean.

Clearly, E seems more variable than C, and F more variable than E, but D and C are harder to compare.

Let us try to compare C and D. In C, the outcome is always either $+1$ or -1, and hence is 1 unit away from the mean, 0. In D, on the other hand, the outcome is at the mean about $\frac{1}{5}$ of the time, is 1 unit away from the mean about $\frac{2}{5}$ of the time, and is 2 units away from the mean the remaining $\frac{2}{5}$ of the time. Hence the mathematical expectation of these "distances away from the mean" is

$$0 \times \tfrac{1}{5} + 1 \times \tfrac{2}{5} + 2 \times \tfrac{2}{5} = \tfrac{6}{5},$$

which is slightly greater than the corresponding value for C. Thus, by this line of reasoning, D is more variable than C.

The line of reasoning applied to D in the previous paragraph introduces the mathematical expectation of the absolute distance of X from its mean as a measure of variability. Thus, applying Eq. (1) of Definition 5–4 to the function

$$H(X) = |X_D - \mu|,$$

we have

$$E(|X_D - \mu|) = |-2 - 0| \cdot \tfrac{1}{5} + |-1 - 0| \cdot \tfrac{1}{5} + |0 - 0| \cdot \tfrac{1}{5}$$

$$+ |1 - 0| \cdot \tfrac{1}{5} + |2 - 0| \cdot \tfrac{1}{5}$$

$$= 2(\tfrac{1}{5}) + 1(\tfrac{1}{5}) + 0(\tfrac{1}{5}) + 1(\tfrac{1}{5}) + 2(\tfrac{1}{5}) = \tfrac{6}{5}.$$

The *mean absolute deviation* is defined as follows:

5–7 Definition. *Mean absolute deviation.* Let X be a random variable with mean μ,

$$E(X) = \mu.$$

Then the *mean absolute deviation* of X, about μ, is the expected value of $|X - \mu|$:

$$\text{mean absolute deviation of } X = E(|X - \mu|). \tag{1}$$

In the third column of Table 5–12 we exhibit the mean absolute deviations for the examples shown in Fig. 5–4.

Although the mean absolute deviation gives a sensible measure of variability, it is not mathematically tractable. The absolute values are hard to combine algebraically, so the first thing that suggests itself is to remove them. But the ordinary mean deviation is zero, by Corollary 5–6.

The big advantage of the absolute values of the deviations is that they all count in the same direction; since none is negative, they can't cancel each other. Another function that has this useful feature is the *squared deviation*, $(X - \mu)^2$. And this turns out to be much more tractable mathematically. As we become acquainted with properties of the *variance*, which uses the squares of deviations from the mean to measure variability, we shall see that there are two fundamental reasons for using it rather than some other measure:

(1) *Additivity.* The variance of the sum of two independent random variables is the sum of their variances, and even when the two variables are dependent the variability of their sum has a simple formula.

(2) *Central limit theorem.* The limiting behavior of a random variable that is the sum of a large number of independent random variables depends upon the *variances* of these random variables.

Of course, it isn't just the biggest squared deviation that counts, but rather the weighted mean of all the squared deviations, each weighted according to its probability. Statisticians call this *mean squared deviation*, $E[(X - \mu)^2]$, the "variance," and sometimes denote it by Var (X).

For example D, the computation of the variance goes as follows, since $\mu = 0$:

Probability, $f(x)$	$\frac{1}{5}$	$\frac{1}{5}$	$\frac{1}{5}$	$\frac{1}{5}$	$\frac{1}{5}$
Values of X, x	-2	-1	0	1	2
Values of $X - \mu$, $x - 0$	-2	-1	0	1	2
Values of $(X - \mu)^2$, x^2	4	1	0	1	4
Values of $x^2 f(x)$	$\frac{4}{5}$	$\frac{1}{5}$	0	$\frac{1}{5}$	$\frac{4}{5}$

$$\text{Var }(X) = \quad \tfrac{4}{5} + \tfrac{1}{5} + 0 + \tfrac{1}{5} + \tfrac{4}{5} = 2$$

Hence, for D, the variance is 2. A similar computation for distribution C, which you are asked to perform in Exercise 2, shows that its variance is 1.

5–8 Definition. *Variance.* Let X be a random variable with mean $E(X) = \mu$. The variance of X, denoted by Var (X), is defined by

$$\text{Var }(X) = E[(X - \mu)^2] = \sum_{i=1}^{t} (x_i - \mu)^2 f(x_i). \qquad (2)$$

In words, the variance of X is the mean squared deviation of X from its mean.

One final adjustment is necessary to get from the variance of X to a measure of variability expressed in the original X-units. The units of Var (X) are squares of the units of X, so we recover the original units by taking the positive square root of the variance. The number so obtained is called the *standard deviation* of X. The standard deviation of X is denoted by σ_X (read: "sigma sub-X"), or by the small Greek letter σ (read: "sigma") without a subscript, if it is clear from the context what the random variable is.

5–9 Definition. *Standard deviation.* Let X be a random variable with mean μ. The *standard deviation* of X is the positive square root of the variance, and is given by

$$\sigma_X = \sqrt{\text{Var }(X)} = \sqrt{E[(X - \mu)^2]}. \qquad (3)$$

REMARK. Obviously, the variance of X is the square of the standard deviation:

$$\text{Var }(X) = \sigma_X^2. \qquad (4)$$

TABLE 5–12. MEASURES OF VARIABILITY FOR THE
EXAMPLES OF FIG. 5–4.

Example	Probability function	Mean absolute deviation	Variance	Standard deviation
A	$f(x):$ $\frac{1}{8}$ $\frac{6}{8}$ $\frac{1}{8}$ $x:-1$ 0 1	$\frac{1}{4}$	$\frac{1}{4}$	0.500
B	$f(x):$ $\frac{1}{3}$ $\frac{1}{3}$ $\frac{1}{3}$ $x:-1$ 0 1	$\frac{2}{3}$		0.816
C	$f(x):$ $\frac{1}{2}$ $\frac{1}{2}$ $x:-1$ 1	1		1.000
D	$f(x):$ $\frac{1}{5}$ $\frac{1}{5}$ $\frac{1}{5}$ $\frac{1}{5}$ $\frac{1}{5}$ $x:-2$ -1 0 1 2	$\frac{6}{5}$	2	1.414
E	$f(x):$ $\frac{1}{2}$ $\frac{1}{2}$ $x:-2$ 2	2		2.000
F	$f(x):$ $\frac{1}{4}$ $\frac{1}{4}$ $\frac{1}{4}$ $\frac{1}{4}$ $x:-3$ -2 2 3	$\frac{5}{2}$		2.550

EXAMPLE 1. The fifth column of Table 5–12 shows the standard deviations of the examples A through F of Fig. 5–4. Note that both the mean absolute deviation in column 3 and the standard deviation in column 5 assign measures of variability that increase as we read down the table.

EXAMPLE 2. If X represents the number of heads that appear when one coin is tossed and Y the number of heads that appear when two coins are tossed, compare the variances of the random variables X and Y. The probability functions of X and Y are:

Probability, $f(x)$	$\frac{1}{2}$	$\frac{1}{2}$
Values of X, x	0	1

Probability, $f(y)$	$\frac{1}{4}$	$\frac{1}{2}$	$\frac{1}{4}$
Values of Y, y	0	1	2

Solution. We first compute the means:

$$\mu_X = E(X) = 0 \times \tfrac{1}{2} + 1 \times \tfrac{1}{2} = \tfrac{1}{2},$$

$$\mu_Y = E(Y) = 0 \times \tfrac{1}{4} + 1 \times \tfrac{1}{2} + 2 \times \tfrac{1}{4} = 1.$$

Then the variances are

$$\text{Var}\,(X) = \sigma_X^2 = E[(X - \mu_X)^2]$$

$$= (0 - \tfrac{1}{2})^2 \times \tfrac{1}{2} + (1 - \tfrac{1}{2})^2 \times \tfrac{1}{2} = \tfrac{1}{8} + \tfrac{1}{8} = \tfrac{1}{4},$$

$$\text{Var}\,(Y) = \sigma_Y^2 = E[(Y - \mu_Y)^2]$$

$$= (0 - 1)^2 \times \tfrac{1}{4} + (1 - 1)^2 \times \tfrac{1}{2} + (2 - 1)^2 \times \tfrac{1}{4}$$

$$= \tfrac{1}{4} + \tfrac{1}{4} = \tfrac{1}{2} = 2\sigma_X^2.$$

The variance of the number of heads for two coins is double the variance of the number of heads for one coin.

EXAMPLE 3. A single 6-sided die is tossed. Find the mean and variance of the number of dots on the top face.

Solution. Let X represent the number of dots on the top face. The probability function of X is:

Probability, $f(x)$	$\tfrac{1}{6}$	$\tfrac{1}{6}$	$\tfrac{1}{6}$	$\tfrac{1}{6}$	$\tfrac{1}{6}$	$\tfrac{1}{6}$
Values, x	1	2	3	4	5	6

The mean, as we have found before, is

$$\mu_X = E(X) = 1 \times \tfrac{1}{6} + 2 \times \tfrac{1}{6} + 3 \times \tfrac{1}{6} + 4 \times \tfrac{1}{6} + 5 \times \tfrac{1}{6} + 6 \times \tfrac{1}{6}$$

$$= 21 \times \tfrac{1}{6} = \tfrac{7}{2}.$$

The variance is

$$\sigma_X^2 = E[(X - \mu_X)^2]$$

$$= (1 - \tfrac{7}{2})^2 \times \tfrac{1}{6} + (2 - \tfrac{7}{2})^2 \times \tfrac{1}{6} + (3 - \tfrac{7}{2})^2 \times \tfrac{1}{6}$$

$$+ (4 - \tfrac{7}{2})^2 \times \tfrac{1}{6} + (5 - \tfrac{7}{2})^2 \times \tfrac{1}{6} + (6 - \tfrac{7}{2})^2 \times \tfrac{1}{6} = \tfrac{35}{12}.$$

We shall soon prove a general formula that is usually simpler for computing the variances. The formula is

$$\sigma_X^2 = E(X^2) - [E(X)]^2. \tag{5}$$

We check that Eq. (5) gives the correct result for the variance of the score on the die:

$$E(X^2) = 1^2 \times \tfrac{1}{6} + 2^2 \times \tfrac{1}{6} + 3^2 \times \tfrac{1}{6} + 4^2 \times \tfrac{1}{6} + 5^2 \times \tfrac{1}{6} + 6^2 \times \tfrac{1}{6} = \tfrac{91}{6},$$

$$[E(X)]^2 = (\tfrac{7}{2})^2 = \tfrac{49}{4},$$

so that

$$E(X)^2 - [E(X)]^2 = \frac{91}{6} - \frac{49}{4} = \frac{182 - 147}{12} = \frac{35}{12}.$$

The result agrees with our previous calculation of the variance.

Equation (5) says that *the variance of X is the mean of the square of X minus the square of the mean of X.* We state this important result as a theorem, give a proof for any random variable that takes only three distinct values, and then indicate the proof in general.

5–10 Theorem.   *Variance.*   Let X be a random variable with mean $E(X) = \mu$ and variance Var $(X) = \sigma^2$. Then

$$\boxed{\sigma^2 = E(X^2) - [E(X)]^2 = E(X^2) - \mu^2.} \tag{6}$$

Proof. Suppose the probability function of X is as follows:

Probability, $f(x)$	$f(x_1)$	$f(x_2)$	$\ldots$	$f(x_t)$
Values of X, x	x_1	x_2	$\ldots$	x_t

We temporarily assume that the number of values of X is $t = 3$. The proof for smaller or larger values of t is similar.

By definition,

$$\text{Var } (X) = \sigma^2 = E[(X - \mu)^2]$$

$$= (x_1 - \mu)^2 f(x_1) + (x_2 - \mu)^2 f(x_2) + (x_3 - \mu)^2 f(x_3). \tag{7}$$

We expand the squares, and get

$$(x_1 - \mu)^2 f(x_1) = x_1^2 f(x_1) - 2\mu x_1 f(x_1) + \mu^2 f(x_1),$$

$$(x_2 - \mu)^2 f(x_2) = x_2^2 f(x_2) - 2\mu x_2 f(x_2) + \mu^2 f(x_2),$$

$$(x_3 - \mu)^2 f(x_3) = x_3^2 f(x_3) - 2\mu x_3 f(x_3) + \mu^2 f(x_3).$$

Summing both sides of these equations, and collecting terms on the right according to the powers of μ, we get

$$\sum (x_i - \mu)^2 f(x_i) = [x_1^2 f(x_1) + x_2^2 f(x_2) + x_3^2 f(x_3)]$$

$$- 2\mu [x_1 f(x_1) + x_2 f(x_2) + x_3 f(x_3)]$$

$$+ \mu^2 [f(x_1) + f(x_2) + f(x_3)]$$

$$= \sum x_i^2 f(x_i) - 2\mu \sum x_i f(x_i) + \mu^2 \sum f(x_i). \qquad (8)$$

By definition of mathematical expectation, we have

$$\sum x_i^2 f(x_i) = E(X^2), \qquad (9a)$$

$$\sum x_i f(x_i) = E(X), \qquad (9b)$$

and, since the sum of the probabilities is 1,

$$\sum f(x_i) = 1. \qquad (9c)$$

If we introduce the right-hand terms from Eqs. (9a, b, c) into the right-hand side of the last line of Eq. (8), and recall that $E(X) = \mu$, we get

$$\sum (x_i - \mu)^2 f(x_i) = E(X^2) - 2\mu E(X) + \mu^2$$

$$= E(X^2) - 2E(X) \cdot E(X) + [E(X)]^2$$

$$= E(X^2) - [E(X)]^2 = E(X^2) - \mu^2. \qquad (10)$$

If $t = 3$, the index i in the sums in Eqs. (8), (9), (10) goes from 1 to 3; more generally, it goes from 1 to t. Since, by definition, the left-hand side of Eq. (10) is $E[(X - \mu)^2] = \sigma^2$, the proof of the theorem is thus completed. □

EXAMPLE 4. Find the mean and variance of the number of divisors X in an integer from 1 through 10 chosen at random.

Solution. The random variable X has probability function

Probability, $f(x)$	0.1	0.4	0.2	0.3
Values, x	1	2	3	4

As we found earlier, the mean, or expected value, of X, is

$$\mu = E(X) = \sum x_i f(x_i) = 2.7.$$

It is not convenient to compute $E[(X - 2.7)^2]$ directly. But it is easy to apply Eq. (5):

$$\sigma_X^2 = E(X^2) - \mu^2$$

$$= 1^2 \times 0.1 + 2^2 \times 0.4 + 3^2 \times 0.2 + 4^2 \times 0.3 - (2.7)^2$$

$$= 8.3 - 7.29 = 1.01.$$

Sometimes another way to cut down the labor involved in computing a variance is to shift the origin of the domain of values of the variable, or to change the scale. The addition of a constant to each value of a random variable shifts the mean by that same constant, but does not change the variance. But the multiplication of each value of the variable by a positive constant is equivalent to a change in units (for example, from tons to pounds, or from feet to miles). Such a change in units multiplies both the mean and the standard deviation by the same factor; however, it multiplies the variance by the square of that factor, since variance is measured in *squares* of the units of the variable.

The following theorem states how the variance and standard deviation are affected by such transformations of the random variable. A proof of the theorem is called for in Exercise 9.

5–11 Theorem. Let X be a random variable with variance σ^2. Let c be a number. Then

$$\boxed{\sigma_{cX}^2 = c^2\sigma_X^2; \qquad \sigma_{cX} = |c|\sigma_X} \tag{11}$$

and

$$\boxed{\sigma_{X+c}^2 = \sigma_X^2; \qquad \sigma_{X+c} = \sigma_X.} \tag{12}$$

EXAMPLE 5. Let the probability function of X be as fóllows:

Probability, $f(x)$	0.3	0.2	0.5
Values, x	2025	2050	2075

Find σ_X^2.

Solution. Subtract 2050 from each value of X, and divide the results by 25. The new random variable is

$$Y = \frac{X - 2050}{25}, \qquad (13)$$

and its probability function is

Probability, $g(y)$	0.3	0.2	0.5
Values, y	−1	0	1

We compute the mean of Y and of Y^2:

$$\mu_Y = E(Y) = -1 \times 0.3 + 0 \times 0.2 + 1 \times 0.5 = 0.2,$$

$$E(Y^2) = (-1)^2 \times 0.3 + 0^2 \times 0.2 + 1^2 \times 0.5 = 0.8.$$

Therefore, the variance of Y is

$$\sigma_Y^2 = E(Y^2) - \mu_Y^2$$
$$= 0.8 - 0.04 = 0.76.$$

From Eq. (13), we see that

$$X = 25Y + 2050.$$

Hence

$$\sigma_X^2 = \sigma_{(25Y+2050)}^2$$
$$= \sigma_{25Y}^2 \qquad \text{[by Eq. (12)]}$$
$$= 625\sigma_Y^2 \qquad \text{[by Eq. (11)]}$$
$$= 625 \times 0.76$$
$$= 475.$$

The following corollary can be proved by the method used in the foregoing example.

5-12 Corollary. Let X be a random variable with variance σ_X^2. Let a and b be numbers. Then the variance of $aX + b$ is $a^2\sigma_X^2$:

$$\text{Var}\,(aX + b) = a^2\,\text{Var}\,(X), \qquad (14a)$$

or

$$\sigma_{aX+b}^2 = a^2\sigma_X^2. \qquad (14b)$$

EXERCISES FOR SECTION 5-4

1. (a) Compute the variance and standard deviation for example B of Table 5-12. (b) Compute the mean absolute deviation and compare your answer with that given in the table.

2. (a) Compute the variance and standard deviation for example C of Table 5-12. (b) Compute the mean absolute deviation and compare your answer with that given in the table.

3. (a) Compute the variance and standard deviation for example E of Table 5-12, and compare them with the corresponding results for example C. Comment. (b) Compute the mean absolute deviation for example E of Table 5-12. Compare your answer with that given in the table. Also compare with example C, and comment.

4. The random variable X takes the values -1, 0, and 1 with probabilities 0.3, 0.2, and 0.5, in that order. Find (a) the mean, μ, (b) the mean absolute deviation of X about μ, (c) the variance σ^2, (d) the standard deviation σ.

5. In the medical experiment, Example 2, Section 3-3, Table 3-5 (selections of 3 from 5 treatments), let X be the number of times that treatment a appears in the listing of the 3 chosen. That is, $X = 0$ if a is not among those chosen, and $X = 1$ if a is chosen. Compute $E(X)$ and Var (X).

6. In Example 5, Section 5-1, for runs of 2 E's and 3 O's, let X be the number of runs in the sample point representing the outcome of the experiment. Compute $E(X)$ and σ_X^2.

7. In Example 5, Section 5-1, Table 5-10, on turning points for 4 different measurements, compute $E(X)$ and Var (X), if X represents the number of turning points in a sample point. Let $\sigma = \sqrt{\text{Var}\,(X)}$. What is the probability that $X \geq \mu + \sigma$? That $\mu - 2\sigma \leq X \leq \mu + 2\sigma$?

8. Using Eq. (5) of the text and the formulas

$$1 + 2 + 3 + \cdots + n = \frac{n(n+1)}{2},$$

$$1^2 + 2^2 + 3^2 + \cdots + n^2 = \frac{n(n+1)(2n+1)}{6},$$

show that the mean and variance of a random variable that takes the values 1, 2, 3, . . . , n, each with probability $1/n$, are

$$\mu = \frac{n+1}{2}, \qquad \sigma^2 = \frac{n^2-1}{12}.$$

9. (a) Prove that Var $(cX) = c^2$ Var (X). (b) Prove that Var $(X + c) =$ Var (X).

10. Use Theorem 5–11 to prove Corollary 5–12.

In each of the following exercises, 11 through 14, the probability function of a random variable is given. Find the mean, the variance, and the standard deviation.

11.

Probability, $f(x)$	0.1	0.2	0.3	0.4
Values, x	9998	9999	10,000	10,001

12.

Probability, $f(x)$	0.6	0.3	0.1
Values, x	0.0016	0.0032	0.0064

13.

Probability, $f(x)$	0.25	0.35	0.15	0.25
Values, x	−300	−200	−100	0

14.

Probability, $f(x)$	0.3	0.3	0.3	0.1
Values, x	2.75	3.00	3.25	4.00

For each of the following probability functions of X, calculate the mean, variance, and standard deviation:

15.

Probability, $f(x)$	0.4	0.2	0.4
Values of X, x	−1	0	1

16.

Probability, $f(x)$	0.1	0.3	0.4	0.2
Values of X, x	1	2	3	4

17.

Probability, $f(x)$	0.1	0.2	0.4	0.2	0.1
Values of X, x	−2	−4	6	4	2

18.

Probability, $f(x)$	0.1	0.4	0.5
Values of X, x	650	700	750

19. An engineer's ruler with triangular cross section has the numbers 1, 2, and 3 printed one on each of its three faces. Imagine rolling the ruler on the floor, and let X be the number of the face on the bottom when the ruler comes to rest. Use the result given in Exercise 8 to find the mean, the variance, and the standard deviation of X.

20. Consider the experiment of Exercise 19 with two such rulers. Let Y be the sum of the number on the bottom faces of the rulers when they come to rest. Find the mean and the variance of Y.

21. A regular tetrahedron is a symmetrical solid with four faces. The faces are numbered 1, 2, 3, 4, and the tetrahedron is rolled on the floor. Let the random variable X be the number on the bottom face after the tetrahedron is rolled. Use the result of Exercise 8 to find the mean, variance, and standard deviation of X.

22. Consider rolling two tetrahedrons like the one described in Exercise 21. Let the random variable Y be the maximum face-down number when the two tetrahedrons come to rest. Find the mean, variance, and standard deviation of Y.

23. (Continuation.) In the experiment of Exercise 22, let the random variable Z be the minimum number on a bottom face when the tetrahedrons come to rest. Find the mean, variance, and standard deviation of Z.

24. If the variance of a random variable X is 0.76, what is the variance of the random variable $10X$? Of $2X$? Of $X/2$?

25. If the variance of the random variable Y is 15, what is the variance of $Y + 7$? $Y - 3$?

5–5. AVERAGE AND VARIANCE IN A SAMPLE

In the first four sections of this chapter, we have learned about random variables, probability functions, means, and variances. These ideas apply to *theoretical* outcomes of experiments. They help us to predict what is *likely to happen* as the result of an experiment, provided we know the probability function, but rarely can they tell us exactly what will happen.

In this section, we study the results that actually did happen in some experiments. There are two main reasons for such a study:

(1) A comparison of observed results with predicted theoretical results gives us a better understanding of the theory and of its reliability when used for making predictions.

(2) In many experiments, we don't know the probability distribution of the random variable under study. For instance, in the school bond-issue example, the proportion of people in the district who own property and favor the bond issue is unknown at the time the survey is planned. So we can't use that proportion to predict the outcome of the survey. In fact, we do just the opposite; we use the outcome of the survey to estimate the proportions of people in the four categories of interest. Or, we might

wish to estimate the probability distribution of heights of American men of age 20. It would be costly in time and money to make a complete analysis of heights of all American men of age 20, so a sample is studied; and inferences about the average height and the variability of heights in the population are based on the average height and variability of heights in the sample.

EXAMPLE 1. From an ordinary bridge deck of 52 cards, a hand of 5 cards is dealt without replacement. The number of red cards is tallied. The cards are reshuffled and the experiment is repeated 29 more times, giving a total of 30 hands. The results are shown in Table 5–13. What is the average number of red cards per hand? What is the standard deviation?

TABLE 5–13.   RED CARDS IN HANDS OF FIVE.

No. of red cards	No. of hands
0	1
1	6
2	10
3	7
4	5
5	1
Total	30

Solution. The average number of red cards per hand is found as follows:

$$\text{average} = \frac{\text{total number of red cards in 30 hands}}{\text{total number of hands in 30 hands}}$$

$$= \frac{0 \times 1 + 1 \times 6 + 2 \times 10 + 3 \times 7 + 4 \times 5 + 5 \times 1}{30}$$

$$= \frac{72}{30} = 2.4.$$

We denote this sample average by $\bar{x}$ (read: "x bar"). Thus $\bar{x} = 2.4$.

Next we compute the sample variance, i.e., the average squared deviation from $\bar{x}$, for this sample. In Table 5–13, the first column gives the possible values $x_i = 0, 1, 2, 3, 4, 5$ for the number of red cards per hand; the second column shows the frequency n_i with which the value x_i occurred. The squared deviations $(x_i - \bar{x})^2$ occur with these same frequencies, as shown in Table 5–14.

TABLE 5–14

CALCULATION OF VARIANCE FOR DATA OF TABLE 5–13 ($\bar{x} = 2.4$).

No. of red cards, x_i	No. of hands, n_i	Deviation, $x_i - \bar{x}$	Squared deviation, $(x_i - \bar{x})^2$	Product, $(x_i - \bar{x})^2 n_i$
0	1	−2.4	5.76	5.76
1	6	−1.4	1.96	11.76
2	10	−0.4	0.16	1.60
3	7	+0.6	0.36	2.52
4	5	+1.6	2.56	12.80
5	1	+2.6	6.76	6.76
Totals	30			41.20

Multiplying each squared deviation by the number of times it occurs, and adding, we get 41.20, the *sum of the squared deviations* for all 30 hands. The *average* squared deviation is called the *sample variance*, and is denoted by s^2. Thus, for this example,

$$s^2 = \frac{41.20}{30} \approx 1.37.$$

The *sample standard deviation s* is the positive square root of the variance:

$$s \approx \sqrt{1.37} \approx 1.17.$$

Thus, for the data of Table 5–13, we have found

average number of red cards per hand $= \bar{x} = 2.4$,

standard deviation of numbers of red cards per hand $= s \approx 1.17$.

The sample average and standard deviation together provide a useful, quick summary of the frequency distribution in the sample. The average is a measure of *location*: it tells where the "center" of the sample is located. The standard deviation measures the dispersion, or spread, around the average. In the present example, $\bar{x} = 2.4$ is almost exactly halfway between the extreme values 0 and 5. And those extreme values, in turn, are at distances 2.4 and 2.6 from $\bar{x}$. If we measure these distances in standard deviation units, we find $2.4/1.17 \approx 2.05$ and $2.6/1.17 \approx 2.22$. Thus all of the values of x, in this example, are within 2.22 standard deviations of the sample average. It is usually true that all, or nearly all, of the observations in a sample lie within 3 standard deviations of the sample average.

We now make the following formal definitions:

5–13 Definitions. *Sample variance and standard deviation.* Given a set of n observations or measurements in which the value x_1 occurs n_1 times, x_2 occurs n_2 times, and so on, x_t occurs n_t times:

Frequencies, n_i	n_1	n_2	$\ldots$	n_t	Total: n
Values, x_i	x_1	x_2	$\ldots$	x_t	

Let $\bar{x}$ be the average of the measurements:

$$\bar{x} = \frac{1}{n} \sum x_i n_i. \tag{1}$$

The *variance* s_x^2 is defined by

$$s_x^2 = \frac{(x_1 - \bar{x})^2 n_1 + (x_2 - \bar{x})^2 n_2 + \cdots + (x_t - \bar{x})^2 n_t}{n_1 + n_2 + \cdots + n_t},$$

or

$$s_x^2 = \frac{1}{n} \sum (x_i - \bar{x})^2 n_i. \tag{2}$$

The *standard deviation* s_x is the positive square root of the variance.

Computational formula. The sample variance, Eq. (2), is the average of the squares of the deviations of the observations from their average: briefly, the *average squared deviation.* For computations it is often easier to use the following formula, which is analagous to formula (5) of Section 5–4:

$$s_x^2 = \frac{1}{n} \sum x_i^2 n_i - \bar{x}^2 \tag{3a}$$

or

$$s_x^2 = \text{Ave} \, (x^2) - \bar{x}^2. \tag{3b}$$

In Eq. (3a), we have omitted the limits of summation. [As in Eqs. (1) and (2), i goes from 1 through t. See Appendix II–1, following Eq. (4), for a discussion of omission of limits of summation.] In Eq. (3b), we have used the notation Ave (x^2) to denote the average value of x^2:

$$\text{Ave } (x^2) = \frac{1}{n} \sum x_i^2 n_i.$$

A proof of Eq. (3a) is asked for in Exercise 1 at the end of this section.

REMARK. If random samples of size n are drawn from a population with variance σ^2, the sample variance s^2 varies from sample to sample. Its long-run average can be shown to be $(n-1)\sigma^2/n$. Some authors define the sample variance by dividing by $n-1$ in Eq. (2) rather than by n. Then their sample variance across many samples averages to σ^2. However, $(n-1)/n$ is close to 1 when n is large, so the two definitions are practically identical for large samples.

The numbers $\bar{x}$, s_x^2, and s_x are also called *sample average, sample variance,* and *sample standard deviation,* respectively, to distinguish them from the corresponding features of the *population*. The *sample* values are computed from the observed measurements. Any set of measurements can be thought of as a "sample" from the "population" of all possible sets of measurements obtainable or imaginable under comparable experimental conditions. In the example of 30 hands of 5 cards each (Section 5–5, Example 1), the 30 hands are a "sample" drawn with replacement from the "population" of $\binom{52}{5}$ possible hands. For each hand the cards are dealt without replacement. A different sample would usually have a different average and a different variance. Also, the *sample* average and variance are usually different from the theoretical mean and variance of the *population*.

EXAMPLE 2. Compare the sample mean and variance with the population mean and variance for the problem in Example 1.

Solution. For Example 1, the sample characteristic is the number of red cards in a hand of 5 cards. This is a random variable X whose possible values are 0, 1, 2, 3, 4, 5. There are 52 cards in the deck, composed of 26 red cards and 26 black cards. A hand of 5 cards can be chosen in $\binom{52}{5}$ ways. A hand of 5 cards containing x red cards and $5-x$ black cards can be selected in $\binom{26}{x}\binom{26}{5-x}$ different ways. Hence

$$P(X = x) = \frac{\binom{26}{x} \binom{26}{5-x}}{\binom{52}{5}}. \tag{4}$$

The values of the right-hand side of Eq. (4), for $x = 0, 1, \ldots, 5$, are shown in the following table (probabilities accurate to 3 decimal places):

Probability, $f(x)$	0.025	0.150	0.325	0.325	0.150	0.025
Values, x	0	1	2	3	4	5

The theoretical mean number of red cards in a hand of 5 is

$$\mu \approx 0(.025) + 1(.150) + 2(.325) + 3(.325) + 4(.150) + 5(.025) = 2.5.$$

This result can also be obtained at once by noticing that the probability function is symmetric about $x = 2.5$.

We compute the variance from the formula

$$\sigma^2 = E(X^2) - \mu^2.$$

To compute $E(X^2)$, we square each possible value of X, multiply the result by the probability of that value, and add, to get

$$E(X^2) \approx 7.400.$$

Therefore, to three decimals, the theoretical (population) variance is

$$\sigma^2 \approx 7.400 - 6.250 = 1.150.$$

Recall that the sample average and variance for the sample of 30 hands were

$$\bar{x} = 2.4 \qquad \text{and} \qquad s^2 \approx 1.37,$$

while

$$\mu = 2.5 \qquad \text{and} \qquad \sigma^2 \approx 1.15.$$

We see that the sample average and variance serve as reasonable *estimates* of the theoretical mean and variance of the population.

It is well at this point to summarize and compare some relevant characteristics of populations and samples.

Population	*Sample*
Possible values: $x_1, x_2, \ldots, x_t$	Observed values: $x_1, x_2, \ldots, x_t$
Probability: $f(x_1), f(x_2), \ldots, f(x_t)$	Relative frequency: $\dfrac{n_1}{n}, \dfrac{n_2}{n}, \ldots, \dfrac{n_t}{n}$
Mean: $\mu = \sum x_i f(x_i)$	Average: $\bar{x} = \dfrac{1}{n} \sum x_i n_i$
Variance: $\sigma^2 = \sum (x_i - \mu)^2 f(x_i)$	Variance: $s_x^2 = \dfrac{1}{n} \sum (x_i - \bar{x})^2 n_i$

REMARK. When we group the data, as we have in the frequency tallies, the x_i's in the sample go from x_1 through x_t, just as in the population. But often we don't group the observed data, but list them as

$$x_1, x_2, \ldots, x_n.$$

Then the x_i's in the sample are the values observed, in the order of their occurrence if there is an order. We then think of x_i as an observed value of a random variable X_i, for each i from 1 through n. Thus one full sample, $(x_1, x_2, \ldots, x_n)$, produces values for all of the random variables $(X_1, X_2, \ldots, X_n)$. The sample average

$$\bar{x} = \frac{1}{n} \Sigma x_i$$

is an observed value of the random variable

$$\bar{X} = \frac{1}{n} \Sigma X_i.$$

Usually, in a sample, all of the n random variables X_i have the same probability function: that of the random variable in the population being sampled.

EXERCISES FOR SECTION 5-5

Compute $\bar{x}$, s^2, and s for each of the following sets of measurements:

1. 1, 1.   2. 1, 2, 3.   3. -1, 0, 1.

4. $+2$, -2.   5. 4, -5, -6.   6. .1, .3, .6.

7. Five measurements are 1's, 3 measurements are 2's, and 1 measurement is 3. Find $\bar{x}$, s^2, s.

8. If half the measurements have value 1 and half have value 3, find the variance and standard deviation.

In each of the following problems 9 through 13, values are given for n (the number of observations in a sample), Σx_i, and Σx_i^2. Using these data, find the sample average, variance, and standard deviation. If you think that the given data are inconsistent, state your reason for thinking so.

	n	Σx_i	Σx_i^2
9.	10	35	140
10.	8	-56	408
11.	25	100	400
12.	12	30	65
13.	100	3	.90

In Exercises 14 through 17, we use the following notation: $x_1, x_2, \ldots, x_n$ and $y_1, y_2, \ldots, y_n$ are sets of measurements whose means are $\bar{x}$ and $\bar{y}$ and whose standard deviations are s_x and s_y, respectively; c and k are constants.

14. If $y_i = x_i + k$, show that $\bar{y} = \bar{x} + k$, $s_y = s_x$ and $s_y^2 = s_x^2$.

15. If $y_i = cx_i$, show that $\bar{y} = c\bar{x}$, and $s_y = |c|s_x$ and $s_y^2 = c^2 s_x^2$.

16. If $y_i = cx_i + k$, show that $\bar{y} = c\bar{x} + k$, and $s_y = |c|s_x$ and $s_y^2 = c^2 s_y^2$.

17. If $z_i = x_i + y_i$, then $\bar{z} = \bar{x} + \bar{y}$.

18. Without calculation, explain why the numbers 100, 101, 200 have the same variance as the numbers 1000, 1001, 1100.

19. Without calculation, explain why the standard deviation of the numbers 1, 2, 3, and 4 is half the standard deviation of the numbers 2, 4, 6, and 8.

20. In a certain neighborhood, 3 families have no car, 20 families have 1 car, 15 families have 2 cars, and 2 families have 3 cars. Find the mean and standard deviation of the number of cars per family.

21. The following frequency distribution was obtained in a breeding experiment with mice:

number in litter:	1	2	3	4	5	6	7	8	9
frequency:	7	11	16	17	26	31	11	1	1

Find the mean, variance, and standard deviation of the distribution.

22. The following frequency distribution gives the lengths of 800 ears of corn in inches, to the nearest half inch.

lengths of ears:	4.0	4.5	5.0	5.5	6.0	6.5	7.0	7.5	8.0	8.5	9.0	9.5	10.0
frequencies:	1	1	8	33	70	110	176	172	124	61	32	10	2

(a) Compute the mean and standard deviation of the distribution. (b) What percent of the measurements are within s of $\bar{x}$? Within $2s$? Within $3s$?

23. Ernest Thompson Seton gives, in *The Arctic Prairies*, the numbers of antelopes in 26 bands seen along the Canadian Pacific Railroad in Alberta, within a stretch of 70 miles, as follows:

$$8,\ 4,\ 7,\ 18,\ 3,\ 9,\ 14,\ 1,\ 6,\ 12,\ 2,\ 8,\ 10,$$

$$1,\ 3,\ 4,\ 6,\ 18,\ 4,\ 25,\ 4,\ 34,\ 6,\ 5,\ 16,\ 4.$$

Find the average number in a band, the standard deviation, and the percent of bands within s of $\bar{x}$ and the percent within $2s$ of $\bar{x}$.

24. Show that Eqs. (3a, b) in the text are valid. Compare with Eq. (5), Section 5–4.

5–6. CHEBYSHEV'S THEOREM FOR A PROBABILITY DISTRIBUTION

Up to this point, we have discussed the mean, the variance, and the standard deviation for *probability distributions*, and the sample average, variance, and standard deviation for *observed sets of measurements*. But we have not shown how the standard deviation can be used to provide information about the way probability accumulates in intervals centered on the mean as their widths grow. We have an intuitive feeling that when the standard deviation is small the probability piles up near the mean, and when the standard deviation is large the probability spreads out more. With the aid of a remarkable theorem due to Chebyshev, which we study in this section, we shall be able to answer questions like the following:

What percent of the total probability lies in a given interval centered at the mean?

How wide an interval about the mean is needed to guarantee that, for example, three-quarters of the total probability of the random variable is included in that interval?

Before stating the theorem, however, we look at a simple example.

EXAMPLE 1. Consider the random variable X having the following probability function:

Probability, $f(x)$	$\frac{27}{64}$	$\frac{27}{64}$	$\frac{9}{64}$	$\frac{1}{64}$
Values of X, x	0	1	2	3

Find the probability that is associated with values of X:

(a) at or within 1 standard deviation from the mean,

(b) at or within 2 standard deviations from the mean,

(c) at or within 3 standard deviations from the mean.

Solution. For the mean and standard deviation, calculations give

$$\mu = E(X) = \tfrac{3}{4}, \qquad \sigma = \tfrac{3}{4}.$$

Figure 5–5 shows a graph of the probability function. The mean, $\mu = \tfrac{3}{4}$, is marked with a small wedge, ▲, to suggest a fulcrum. Intervals extending 1σ, 2σ, and 3σ to the left and right of the mean are also shown, along with the corresponding probabilities.

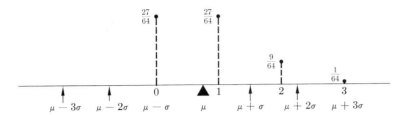

FIG. 5–5. Intervals of width 2σ, 4σ, 6σ around the mean.

(a) The probability at or within $\pm 1\sigma$ from μ is

$$\tfrac{27}{64} + \tfrac{27}{64} = \tfrac{27}{32} \approx 0.84.$$

(b) The probability at or within $\pm 2\sigma$ from μ is

$$\tfrac{27}{64} + \tfrac{27}{64} + \tfrac{9}{64} = \tfrac{63}{64} \approx 0.984.$$

(c) The probability at or within $\pm 3\sigma$ from μ is

$$\tfrac{27}{64} + \tfrac{27}{64} + \tfrac{9}{64} + \tfrac{1}{64} = 1.$$

5–14 Theorem. *Chebyshev's theorem.* At least the fraction $1 - (1/h^2)$ of the total probability of a random variable lies within h standard deviations of the mean.

Discussion. The theorem says, for example, that at least $1 - \tfrac{1}{4}$, or $\tfrac{3}{4}$, of the total probability is within $\pm 2\sigma$ from μ, for any random variable. In the example above, we found that the actual probability in the band from $\mu - 2\sigma$ to $\mu + 2\sigma$ was $\tfrac{63}{64}$, which is much greater than $\tfrac{3}{4}$. The theorem also says that at least $\tfrac{8}{9}$ of the total probability is within 3σ from the mean, and, in the example, we found that the band from $\mu - 3\sigma$ to $\mu + 3\sigma$ contained the total probability of 1.

The theorem can be used to show that sample proportions of sufficiently large random samples from a population are likely to be close to the true proportion of the population. It forms a mathematical foundation for the use of samples to estimate characteristics of a population.

Proof of Chebyshev's theorem. Suppose the random variable X has a mean μ and standard deviation σ. Figure 5–6 represents the domain of its

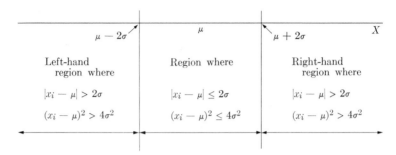

FIG. 5-6. Regions for Chebyshev theorem, $h = 2$.

probability function. We shall first prove the theorem for the case $h = 2$, and to this end we have separated the possible values of X into two sets:

(a) those in the interval $\mu - 2\sigma$ to $\mu + 2\sigma$, including any lying at the boundaries, and

(b) the remainder, those lying beyond the boundaries of the interval.

We want to prove that the probability associated with values of X in the set (a) is at least $\frac{3}{4}$. For convenience, we refer to the set (a) as the values of X *within the interval* and to set (b) as the values *outside the interval*. And the values outside the interval consist of those to the left of $\mu - 2\sigma$, which we shall call the *left-hand outer set;* and those to the right of $\mu + 2\sigma$, which we shall call the *right-hand outer set.*

It is clear from Fig. 5–6 that any point on the x-axis and outside the indicated middle interval is more than 2σ from the mean μ. Therefore the square of its distance from the mean is more than $4\sigma^2$.

Recall the definition of the variance:

$$\sigma^2 = E[(X - \mu)^2] = \sum_{i=1}^{t} (x_i - \mu)^2 f(x_i), \tag{1}$$

where $x_1, x_2, \ldots, x_t$ are the possible values of X, and $f(x_1), f(x_2), \ldots, f(x_t)$ are their associated probabilities. Now the numbering of the x's (the subscripts) is completely arbitrary, so, for convenience, let $x_1, x_2, \ldots, x_r$ denote those that are *outside* the interval, if there are any outside.

Case 1. If there are no values of x_i outside the interval, all values are within 2σ of the mean, so the probability of set (a) is 1, and hence is at least $\frac{3}{4}$.

Case 2. If the number outside the interval is $r \geq 1$, we break up the sum in Eq. (1) into two parts:

$$\sigma^2 = [(x_1 - \mu)^2 f(x_1) + (x_2 - \mu)^2 f(x_2) + \cdots + (x_r - \mu)^2 f(x_r)]$$
$$+ [(x_{r+1} - \mu)^2 f(x_{r+1}) + \cdots + (x_t - \mu)^2 f(x_t)]. \tag{2}$$

Every squared deviation $(x_i - \mu)^2$ is positive or zero, and $f(x_i)$ is also positive. If any squared deviation is replaced by a smaller number, then the right-hand side of Eq. (2) is reduced. We shall make such reductions and get an inequality that yields the proof.

We reduce the first r squared deviations (arising from values of x_i outside the interval) by replacing each of them by the smaller value $4\sigma^2$. Then we reduce the rest of the squared deviations (arising from values of x_i inside the interval) by replacing each of them by the smaller or possibly equal value 0. When we have made these replacements, we get the inequality

$$\sigma^2 \geq 4\sigma^2 [f(x_1) + f(x_2) + \cdots + f(x_r)]. \tag{3}$$

If $\sigma^2 = 0$, all the probability is concentrated at the mean, and therefore within 2σ of the mean. Why?

If $\sigma^2 > 0$, then we may divide both sides of the inequality (3) by $4\sigma^2$, and get

$$\tfrac{1}{4} \geq [f(x_1) + f(x_2) + \cdots + f(x_r)] = P(|X - \mu| > 2\sigma). \tag{4}$$

The last equality in (4) follows from the definition of $P(|X - \mu| > 2\sigma)$: it is the probability that X is more than 2σ from the mean μ, and this probability is the sum of the probabilities assigned to the points x_1, $x_2, \ldots, x_r$ that are outside the interval. Therefore, from the inequality (4), we see that at most $\tfrac{1}{4}$ of the total probability is assigned to points lying outside the interval. Hence the probability assigned to points lying within a distance 2σ from the mean is *at least* $1 - \tfrac{1}{4} = \tfrac{3}{4}$. This completes the proof of Chebyshev's theorem for $h = 2$.

The demonstration just given can be generalized to intervals $\mu - h\sigma$ to $\mu + h\sigma$ for any $h > 0$. We replace 2σ by $h\sigma$ and $4\sigma^2$ by $h^2\sigma^2$ throughout the argument. When these replacements are made, the inequality that replaces (4) is

$$\boxed{\frac{1}{h^2} \geq P(|X - \mu| > h\sigma).} \tag{5}$$

This says that the probability assigned to values of X outside the interval $\mu - h\sigma$ to $\mu + h\sigma$ is at most $1/h^2$. Hence the probability assigned to values of X within a distance $h\sigma$ of the mean is at least $1 - (1/h^2)$. $\square$

EXERCISES FOR SECTION 5-6

Answer Exercises 1 through 4, assuming that $\mu_X = 0$ and $\sigma_X = 1$.

1. At least how much of the probability of X lies within 2 units of the mean?
2. What is the minimum value of $P(-3 \leq X \leq 3)$?
3. What is the maximum value of $P(|X| \geq 3)$?
4. What value of k guarantees $P(|X| \leq k) \geq 0.96$?

Answer Exercises 5 through 8, assuming that $\mu_X = 7$ and $\sigma_X = 2$.

5. What is the least value of $P(3 < X < 11)$? Of $P(1 \leq X \leq 13)$?
6. What is the greatest value of $P(|X - 7| > 2)$? Of $P(|X - 7| > 3)$?
7. What is the least value of $P(|X - 7| \leq 5)$?
8. What value of k guarantees that $P(|X - 7| \leq k) \geq 0.99$?

9. When $h \leq 1$, Chebyshev's theorem is useless. Why?

10. Make the required substitutions and generalize the proof of Theorem 5–14 from intervals

$$|X - \mu| < 2\sigma \quad \text{to} \quad |X - \mu| < h\sigma.$$

11. Using Chebyshev's theorem, what value of h guarantees that at least 90% of the probability is within $h\sigma$ of the mean? What value of h guarantees 99%?

12. What is the maximum probability lying at least 2σ away from the mean? 3σ? 5σ?

13. Under what conditions on X is its variance zero? How much probability then lies more than 0.01σ away from the mean?

In Exercises 14 through 22, the random variable X takes the values $-c$, 0, and $+c$, with probabilities p, $1 - 2p$, and p, in that order.

14. Find μ and σ^2.
15. Find a relation between σ and c if $P(|X - \mu| \geq \sigma) = 1$.
16. Show that $c = \sigma$ when $p = \frac{1}{2}$.
17. If $c = 2\sigma$, what does p equal?
18. If $c = 3\sigma$, what does p equal?
19. In Exercise 16, what is the probability of an absolute deviation $|X - \mu|$ at least as great as one standard deviation? As great as 2σ?
20. In Exercise 17, what is the probability of an absolute deviation at least as great as 2σ? As great as 3σ?
21. In Exercise 18, what is the probability of an absolute deviation at least as great as 3σ? As 4σ?
22. By proper choice of p, can you make $c = h\sigma$, for any positive h? If so, what is the proper choice of p, in terms of h, and what is the probability of an absolute deviation at least as great as $h\sigma$?

REMARK. Exercise 22 shows that if h is given, then we can find a random variable X such that the probability that X takes values at least $h\sigma$ away from its mean is $1/h^2$, the maximum allowed by the Chebyshev theorem.

In this sense, the conclusion in Chebyshev's theorem is the best possible. But a probability distribution that has the maximum allowable probability at least $h\sigma$ away from μ for one particular value of h may not do so for a different value of h. Part of the charm of the Chebyshev theorem is that it works for all probability distributions with finite means and variances.

5-7. CHEBYSHEV'S THEOREM FOR A FREQUENCY DISTRIBUTION OF MEASUREMENTS

We have seen how the standard deviation σ provides a yardstick for measuring distances from the mean of a random variable X. Chebyshev's theorem tells us that the worst that can happen is that the fraction $1/h^2$ of the probability will be assigned to points more than h standard deviations away from the mean, for any positive h. We may well wonder if an analogous theorem holds for measurements or observations in a *sample*. The answer is "yes." We state the result formally as a theorem, but we do not give the proof, since it is almost identical with the proof given in Section 5-6.

5-15 Theorem. *Chebyshev's theorem for measurements.* At least the fraction $1 - (1/h^2)$ of the measurements in any sample lie within h standard deviations of the average of the measurements.

EXAMPLE 1. Suppose the measurements are -8, -1, -1, 0, 0, 0, 0, 1, 1, 8. Verify that at least $\frac{3}{4}$ of the measurements are within 2 standard deviations of $\bar{x}$, and at least $\frac{8}{9}$ are within 3 standard deviations of $\bar{x}$.

Solution. The sum of the 10 measurements is 0, hence $\bar{x} = 0$. The sum of the squares of the measurements is 132. Hence the average of the squared deviations is $s^2 = \text{Ave}(x^2) - \bar{x}^2 = 13.2 - 0 = 13.2$, and the standard deviation is $s \approx 3.6$. The interval containing all measurements within two standard deviations from the mean extends from -7.2 to $+7.2$, and contains 80% of the measurements (hence at least $\frac{3}{4}$ of them). The interval extending three standard deviations from the mean in both directions goes from -10.8 to $+10.8$ and contains 100% of the measurements (hence at least $\frac{8}{9}$ of them).

REMARK. For work with large numbers of measurements, stronger results than those given by Chebyshev's theorem usually hold. Table 5-15 gives a rough rule for the percentage of measurements usually found in intervals about the mean. The numbers given for the empirical rule agree exactly with those for the *normal probability distribution*, which we shall study in more detail in Section 6-4 and in Chapter 7.

The results of Chebyshev's theorem *guarantee* lower bounds on the percentage of measurements within h standard deviations of the average.

TABLE 5-15

PERCENTAGES OF MEASUREMENTS CONTAINED IN INTERVALS ABOUT THE MEAN.

	Empirical rule	Chebyshev's theorem
Interval	Contains about this percentage of the measurements	Contains at least this percentage of the measurements
$\bar{x} - s$ to $\bar{x} + s$	68%	0%
$\bar{x} - 2s$ to $\bar{x} + 2s$	95%	75%
$\bar{x} - 3s$ to $\bar{x} + 3s$	99.7% (nearly all)	89%

They may help us (a) discover an error in calculation, or (b) interpret and use the standard deviation. The middle column of Table 5-15 is even more valuable in helping to interpret a set of measurements. The figures 68%, 95%, and 99.7% are not to be taken literally. If you found 64% or 73% of the measurements within one standard deviation of the mean, you should not be startled. Indeed, it is possible to find 100% of the measurements within one standard deviation of the average.

EXERCISES FOR SECTION 5-7

Given that $\bar{x} = 0$ and $s_x = 1$ for a set of n measurements, use Chebyshev's theorem to answer the following:

1. At least how many measurements lie within 3 units of the mean?
2. At least how many measurements will lie between -2 and 2, inclusive?
3. At most how many measurements will be greater than 2 or less than -2?
4. What value of $k > 0$ will guarantee that 96% of the measurements lie between $-k$ and k, inclusive?

If $\bar{x} = 5$ and $s_x = 2$, use the empirical rule of Table 5-15 to answer the following:

5. About what percent of the measurements lie between 3 and 7, inclusive? Between 1 and 9, inclusive?
6. About what percent of the measurements are greater than 9 or less than 1?

If $\bar{x} = 1$ and $s_x = 3$, use Chebyshev's theorem to answer the following:

7. What is the least number of measurements that lie between -5 and 7, inclusive? Between -8 and 10, inclusive?
8. What is the greatest number of measurements that are greater than 7 or less than -5? Greater than 10 or less than -8?

6

REPEATED TRIALS WITH TWO
TYPES OF OUTCOMES: THE
BINOMIAL DISTRIBUTION

6–1. EXAMPLES OF BINOMIAL EXPERIMENTS

Some experiments are composed of repetitions of independent trials, each with *two* possible outcomes. The binomial probability distribution may describe the variation that occurs from one set of trials of such a *binomial* experiment to another. We devote a chapter to the binomial distribution not only because it is a mathematical model for an enormous variety of real life phenomena, but also because it has important properties that recur in many other probability models. We begin with a few examples of binomial experiments.

Marksmanship example. A trained marksman shooting five rounds at a target, all under practically the same conditions, may hit the bull's-eye from 0 to 5 times. In repeated sets of five shots his numbers of bull's-eyes vary. What can we say of the probabilities of the different possible numbers of bull's-eyes?

Inheritance in mice. In litters of eight mice from similar parents, the number of mice with straight instead of wavy hair is an integer from 0 to 8. What probabilities should be attached to these possible outcomes?

Aces (ones) with three dice. When three dice are tossed repeatedly, what is the probability that the number of aces is 0 (or 1, or 2, or 3)?

General binomial problem. More generally, suppose that an experiment consists of a number of independent trials, that each trial results in either a "success" or a "non-success" ("failure"), and that the probability of success remains constant from trial to trial. In the examples above, the occurrence of a bull's-eye, a straight-haired mouse, or an ace could be called a "success." In general, any outcome we choose may be labeled "success."

The major question in this chapter is: What is the probability of exactly x successes in n trials?

In Chapters 3 and 4 we answered questions like those in the examples, usually by counting points in a sample space. Fortunately, a general formula of wide applicability solves all problems of this kind. Before deriving this formula, we explain what we mean by "problems of this kind."

Experiments are often composed of several identical trials, and sometimes experiments themselves are repeated. In the marksmanship example, a trial consists of "one round shot at a target" with outcome either one bull's-eye (success) or none (failure). Further, an experiment might consist of five rounds, and several sets of five rounds might be regarded as a super-experiment composed of several repetitions of the five-round experiment. If three dice are tossed, a trial is one toss of one die and the experiment is composed of three trials. Or, what amounts to the same thing, if one die is tossed three times, each toss is a trial, and the three tosses form the experiment. Mathematically, we shall not distinguish the experiment of three dice tossed once from that of one die tossed three times. These examples are illustrative of the use of the words "trial" and "experiment" as they are used in this chapter, but they are quite flexible words and it is well not to restrict them too narrowly.

EXAMPLE 1. *Student football managers.* Ten students act as managers for a high-school football team, and of these managers a proportion p are licensed drivers. Each Friday one manager is chosen by lot to stay late and load the equipment on a truck. On three Fridays the coach has needed a driver. Considering only these Fridays, what is the probability that the coach had drivers all 3 times? Exactly 2 times? 1 time? 0 time?

Discussion. Note that there are 3 trials of interest. Each trial consists of choosing a student manager at random. The 2 possible outcomes on each trial are "driver" or "nondriver." Since the choice is by lot each week, the outcomes of different trials are independent. The managers stay the same, so that $p = P$ (driver) is the same for all weeks. We now generalize these ideas for general binomial experiments.

For an experiment to qualify as a *binomial experiment*, it must have four properties:

(1) there must be a fixed number of trials,

(2) each trial must result in a "success" or a "failure" (a binomial trial),

(3) all trials must have identical probabilities of success,

(4) the trials must be independent of each other.

Below we use our earlier examples to describe and illustrate these four properties. We also give, for each property, an example where the property is absent. The language and notation introduced are standard throughout the chapter.

1. *There must be a fixed number n of repeated trials.* For the marksman, we study sets of five shots ($n = 5$); for the mice, we restrict attention to litters of eight ($n = 8$); and for the aces, we toss three dice ($n = 3$).

Experiment without a fixed number of trials. Toss a die until an ace appears. Here the number of trials is a random variable, not a fixed number.

2. *Binomial trials.* Each of the n trials is either a success or a failure. "Success" and "failure" are just convenient labels for the two categories of outcomes when we talk about binomial trials in general. These words are more expressive than labels like "A" and "not-A." It is natural from the marksman's viewpoint to call a bull's-eye a success, but in the mice example it is arbitrary which category corresponds to straight hair in a mouse. The word "binomial" means "of two names" or "of two terms," and both usages apply in our work: the first to the names of the two outcomes of a binomial trial, and the second to the terms p and $(1 - p)$ that represent the probabilities of "success" and "failure." Sometimes when there are many outcomes for a single trial, we group these outcomes into two classes, as in the example of the die, where we have arbitrarily constructed the classes "ace" and "not-ace."

Experiment without the two-class property. We classify mice as "straight-haired" or "wavy-haired," but a hairless mouse appears. We can escape from such a difficulty by ruling out the animal as not constituting a trial, but such a solution is not always satisfactory.

3. *All trials have identical probabilities of success.* Each die has probability $p = \frac{1}{6}$ of producing an ace; the marksman has some probability p, perhaps 0.1, of making a bull's-eye. Note that we need not know the value of p, for the experiment to be binomial.

Experiment where p is not constant. During a round of target practice the sun comes from behind a cloud and dazzles the marksman, lowering his chance of a bull's-eye.

4. *The trials are independent.* Strictly speaking, this means that the probability for each possible outcome of the experiment can be computed by multiplying together the probabilities of the possible outcomes of the single binomial trials. Thus in the three-dice example P (ace) $= p = \frac{1}{6}$, P (not-ace) $= 1 - p = \frac{5}{6}$, and the independence assumption implies that the probability that the three dice fall ace, not-ace, ace in that order is $(\frac{1}{6})(\frac{5}{6})(\frac{1}{6})$. Experimentally, we expect independence when the trials have nothing to do with one another.

Examples where independence fails. A family of five plans to go together either to the beach or to the mountains, and a coin is tossed to decide.

We want to know the number of people going to the mountains. When this experiment is viewed as composed of five binomial trials, one for each member of the family, the outcomes of the trials are obviously not independent. Indeed, the experiment is better viewed as consisting of one binomial trial for the entire family. The following is a less extreme example of dependence. Consider couples visiting an art museum. Each person votes for one of a pair of pictures to receive a popular prize. Voting for one picture may be called "success," for the other "failure." An experiment consists of the voting of one couple, or two trials. In repetitions of the experiment from couple to couple, the votes of the two persons in a couple probably agree more often than independence would imply, because couples who visit the museum together are more likely to have similar tastes than are a random pair of people drawn from the entire population of visitors. Table 6–1 illustrates the point. The table shows that 0.6 of the boys and 0.6 of the girls vote for picture A. Therefore, under independent voting, 0.6×0.6 or 0.36 of the couples would cast two votes for picture A, and 0.4×0.4 or 0.16 would cast two votes for picture B. Thus in independent voting, $0.36 + 0.16$ or 0.52 of the couples would agree. But Table 6–1 shows that $0.45 + 0.25$ or 0.70 agree, too many for independent voting.

TABLE 6–1. COUPLES VOTING FOR PICTURES A AND B.

Girls' votes

		A	B	
Boys' votes	A	0.45	0.15	0.6
	B	0.15	0.25	0.4
		0.6	0.4	1

Each performance of an n-trial binomial experiment results in some whole number from 0 through n as the value of the random variable X, where

X = total number of successes in n binomial trials.

We want to study the *probability function* of this random variable. For example, we are interested in the number of bull's-eyes, not which shots were bull's-eyes. A binomial experiment can produce random variables other than the number of successes. For example, the marksman gets 5 shots, but we take his score to be the number of shots *before* his first bull's-eye, that is, 0, 1, 2, 3, 4 (or 5, if he gets no bull's-eye). Thus we do not score the number of bull's-eyes, and the random variable is not the number of successes.

The constancy of p and the independence are the conditions most likely to give trouble in practice. Obviously, very slight changes in p do not change the probabilities much, and a slight lack of independence may not make an appreciable difference. (For instance, see Example 2 of Section 5–5, on red cards in hands of 5.) On the other hand, even when the binomial model does not describe well the physical phenomenon being studied, the binomial model may still be used as a baseline for comparative purposes; that is, we may discuss the phenomenon in terms of its departures from the binomial model.

> *To summarize:* A *binomial experiment* consists of n (≥ 1) independent binomial trials, all with the same probability p ($0 \leq p \leq 1$) of yielding a success. The outcome of the experiment is X successes. The random variable X takes the values $x = 0, 1, \ldots, n$ with probabilities $P(X = x)$ or, more briefly $P(x)$.

We shall find a formula for the probability of exactly x successes for given values of p and n. When each number of successes x is paired with its probability of occurrence $P(x)$, the set of pairs $(x, P(x))$, $x = 0$, $1, \ldots, n$, is a probability function called a *binomial distribution*. The choice of p and n determines the binomial distribution uniquely, and different choices always produce different distributions (except when $p = 0$; then the number of successes is always 0). The set of all binomial distributions is called *the family of binomial distributions*, but in general discussions this expression is often shortened to "the binomial distribution," or even "the binomial" when the context is clear. Binomial distributions were treated by James Bernoulli about 1700, and for this reason binomial trials are sometimes called *Bernoulli trials*.

Random variables. Each binomial trial of a binomial experiment produces either 0 or 1 success. Therefore each binomial trial can be thought of as producing a value of a random variable associated with that trial and taking the values 0 or 1, with probabilities q and p respectively. The several trials of a binomial experiment produce a new random variable X, the total number of successes, which is just the sum of the random variables associated with the single trials.

EXAMPLE 2. The marksman gets two bull's-eyes, one on his third shot and one on his fifth. The numbers of successes on the five individual shots are, then, 0, 0, 1, 0, 1. The number of successes on each shot is a value of a random variable that has values 0 or 1, and there are 5 such random variables here. Their sum is X, the total number of successes, which in this experiment has the value $x = 2$.

We turn now to another simple example that illustrates the features of a binomial experiment and its associated binomial distribution.

EXAMPLE 3.   *Binomial experiment with three thumbtacks.*   When a thumbtack is tossed it can land point up (U), or point down (D). Suppose three thumbtacks: 1 red, 1 white, 1 blue, but otherwise alike, are tossed. We want the probability function for the random variable X, the number of tacks landing U. The sample space of possible outcomes for the three thumbtacks contains 8 sample points, with associated values of X, and probabilities as shown in Table 6–2. The first, second, and third letters of any sample point indicate in order the outcomes for the red, white, and blue tacks. Thus UDD means that the red tack landed point up, and the other two landed point down.

TABLE 6–2

Sample point	X, number of U's	Probability
DDD	0	q^3
DDU	1	pq^2
DUD	1	pq^2
UDD	1	pq^2
DUU	2	p^2q
UDU	2	p^2q
UUD	2	p^2q
UUU	3	p^3

Let the probabilities of U and D be p and q, respectively, where $p + q = 1$. Then we have

$$P(U) = p, \qquad P(D) = q. \tag{1}$$

We assume that outcomes on the three tacks are independent. Hence the probability assigned to any one of the sample points is obtained by multiplying three probabilities. For instance,

$$P(UDU) = P(U) \cdot P(D) \cdot P(U) = pqp = p^2q.$$

We let $b(x; 3, p)$ denote the probability of getting x U's when there are three tacks each with probability p of landing U. [For $b(x; 3, p)$ read "b of x when $n = 3$ and probability of success is p."] We can summarize the preceding results by writing the binomial distribution we have just obtained in the form of a *probability table:*

Probability, $b(x; 3, p)$	q^3	$3pq^2$	$3p^2q$	p^3
Value of X, x	0	1	2	3

$$(2)$$

Since the coefficients 1, 3, 3, 1 in the top line of table (2) are binomial coefficients, we can write a formula for $b(x; 3, p)$, as follows:

$$b(x; 3, p) = \binom{3}{x} p^x q^{3-x}, \qquad x = 0, 1, 2, 3, \tag{3}$$

where $\binom{3}{x} = 3!/[x!(3 - x)!]$ is the number of permutations of x U's and $(3 - x)$ D's (Corollary 2–13).

Although we derived Eq. (3) for the thumbtack problem, the formula is more general. The set of four probabilities arising from formula (3), together with the associated values of x, form the binomial distribution for 3 independent trials, each having p as the probability of success. The probability table (2) also displays this binomial distribution.

Note that the right-hand side of formula (3) is composed of two parts:

(1) the binomial coefficient $\binom{3}{x}$, which counts the number of different arrangements of exactly x successes and $3 - x$ failures in 3 trials;

(2) the factor $p^x q^{3-x}$, which gives the probability for any one of the different ways of getting x successes and $3 - x$ failures.

When we derive the generalization of formula (3) in the next section, we exploit the fact that binomial probabilities are always products of two such parts.

Adding all of the probabilities given in formula (3) for $x = 0, 1, 2, 3$, we get

$$q^3 + 3q^2p + 3qp^2 + p^3.$$

This sum is the binomial expansion of $(q + p)^3$, since

$$(q + p)^3 = q^3 + 3q^2p + 3qp^2 + p^3. \tag{4}$$

This is another reason for calling the set of probabilities obtained from formula (3) a "binomial" distribution. And because $q + p = 1$ and $1^3 = 1$, Eq. (4) shows that the sum of the four probabilities is 1.

We recall from Chapter 5 that another way to represent the probabilities in a binomial distribution is to make a graph. Thus, if we erect the ordinates q^3, $3q^2p$, $3qp^2$, p^3 at $x = 0, 1, 2, 3$, respectively, we obtain the *probability graph*.

Because the four probabilities q^3, $3q^2p$, $3qp^2$, p^3 add up to 1, the ordinates also add up to 1. In Fig. 6–1, $p = 0.3$, $q = 0.7$.

Numerical values. Suppose $P(U) = p = 0.3$, as in Fig. 6–1. Compute the probabilities of getting 0, 1, 2, 3 U's when the three tacks are tossed.

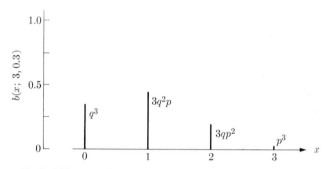

Fig. 6–1.   Probability graph for the binomial distribution $n = 3$, $p = 0.3$, $q = 0.7$.

We use formula (3), with $p = 0.3$, $q = 1 - p = 0.7$, and substitute in succession $x = 0, 1, 2, 3$. From these calculations we get the following probability table for this binomial distribution:

$b(x; 3, 0.3)$	0.343	0.441	0.189	0.027
x	0	1	2	3

(5)

In this same example, we can calculate still other probabilities. For instance, the probability of getting *at least* 2 U's is

$$P(X \geq 2) = 3qp^2 + p^3$$
$$= b(2; 3, 0.3) + b(3; 3, 0.3) = 0.189 + 0.027 = 0.216.$$

The probability of getting not more than one U is

$$P(X \leq 1) = q^3 + 3pq^2$$
$$= b(0; 3, 0.3) + b(1; 3, 0.3) = 0.343 + 0.441 = 0.784.$$

REMARK. In examples like that of the marksman hitting the bull's-eye or that of the thumbtacks, the value of p cannot be readily guessed.

However, a good estimate of p in such problems can be made if we record the results of several hundred shots, or tosses, and take as the estimate the ratio of the number of bull's-eyes, or U's, to the total number of trials.

EXERCISES FOR SECTION 6-1

1. Verify that the probability table (5) for the thumbtack example is correct, and check by addition that the sum of the probabilities is 1.

2. Verify that formula (3) is correct by substituting $x = 0, 1, 2, 3$ in succession, and thus check the entries in probability table (2).

3. A bag contains 1 red and 2 white balls, identical except for color. If 3 balls are randomly drawn one at a time with replacement after each draw, find the exact binomial distribution of the number of white balls in the sample of 3.

4. Three candidates run for different offices in different states. Each has 1 chance in 3 of being elected in his state. What is the chance that at least one of them is elected?

5. If $n = 3$ in a binomial experiment, what *values* can p have if $P(0)$ is to equal $P(1)$? Determine p if $P(0) = P(3)$.

6. Three dice were thrown 648 times and the number of times a "5 or 6" appeared was tabulated as follows:

Number of "5 or 6"'s	Observed frequency
0	179
1	298
2	141
3	30
Total	648

Obtain the theoretical probability for each outcome for perfect dice, multiply by 648, and compare the resulting theoretical frequencies with the observed ones.

7. Toss 3 coins 24 times and compare the observed numbers of heads with their theoretical frequencies. (Be sure each coin is flipped separately.)

8. In a binomial experiment with $n = 3$ show that $P(X = 1 \text{ or } 2) = 3pq$.

9. (For students without calculus.) Make a graph of $b(2; 3, p)$ as p varies from 0 to 1 and estimate the value of p that maximizes it.

   (For students with some calculus.) Find the value of p that makes $b(2; 3, p)$ a maximum and evaluate the maximum. [*Hint.* Replace q by $1 - p$ before differentiating.]

10. A thumbtack that can fall point up, U, or point down, D, with $P(U) = p$ and $P(D) = q = 1 - p$, is independently tossed 4 times. List a sample space for the possible outcomes of this experiment. Assign probabilities to its points. Show that the sum of these probabilities is 1. Find the probability distribution of the number that fall point up.

11. *Puzzle.* In seeking the probability of either 3 heads or 3 tails in a single throw of 3 coins, it has been reasoned that of 3 coins at least 2 must show like faces, and the probability that the third coin is the same as the other 2 is $\frac{1}{2}$, the desired probability. What is the correct probability? Try to find the flaw in the reasoning.

6–2. EXTENSION OF THE BINOMIAL EXPERIMENT TO n TRIALS

In the thumbtack example, if n thumbtacks are tossed, there are two different outcomes for each toss, U or D. Therefore, by the multiplication rule, there are $2 \times 2 \times \cdots \times 2$ (n factors), or 2^n, different outcomes for the experiment (Section 2–1). Hence the sample space S for this experiment has 2^n distinct points. Each point determines a value of the random variable X, where X is the number of U's in the sample point. What is the probability of x U's, where x is any one of the numbers $0, 1, 2, \ldots, n$? That is, what is $b(x; n, p)$?

In Section 6–1 we found that the binomial probabilities for 3 binomial trials had two parts: a coefficient $\binom{3}{x}$ and a factor $p^x q^{3-x}$. We proceed to find the two parts of $b(x; n, p)$ in general, using the language of trials, successes, and failures instead of tosses, U's and D's.

First, in how many ways can we get exactly x successes in n trials? From the theory of permutations of two kinds of objects (Section 2–4) the number of ways is $\binom{n}{x}$; that is, the sample space S has exactly $\binom{n}{x}$ points representing outcomes with x successes and $n - x$ failures.

Second, what is the probability of x successes and $n - x$ failures in a given order? If we assume that the outcomes for the n trials are independent, then the probability for x successes and $n - x$ failures *in any given order* is the product of x p's and $(n - x)$ q's. We had the identical pattern in the set of probabilities in the thumbtack example of Section 6–1 [calculations following Eq. (1) of that section]. The reason we get the same probability for each arrangement of the x successes and $n - x$ failures is that independence implies multiplication, and multiplication is commutative. Thus the desired probability for any given order of x successes and $n - x$ failures is

$$p^x q^{n-x}. \tag{1}$$

This is true when x is any one of the numbers $0, 1, 2, \ldots, n$.

Among the 2^n points in S, there are $\binom{n}{x}$ points with x successes, each point having the probability $p^x q^{n-x}$ assigned to it. Therefore

$$b(x; n, p) = \binom{n}{x} p^x q^{n-x}, \qquad x = 0, 1, 2, \ldots, n. \tag{2}$$

Note that the probability $b(x; 3, p)$ [Section 6–1, Eq. (3)] is a special case of formula (2) with $n = 3$.

We observe that $\binom{n}{x} p^x q^{n-x}$ is the $(x + 1)$st term in the binomial expansion of $(q + p)^n$, because the binomial expansion (Section 2–5) can be displayed as follows:

$$(q + p)^n = q^n + \binom{n}{1} pq^{n-1} + \cdots + \binom{n}{x} p^x q^{n-x} + \cdots + p^n. \quad (3)$$

Since $q + p = 1$, $(q + p)^n = 1$. This result is reassuring, because it shows that our derivation has accounted for all the probability in the sample space. The set of ordered pairs

$$\left(x, \binom{n}{x} p^x q^{n-x} \right), \qquad x = 0, 1, \ldots, n,$$

is the general *binomial distribution*, or binomial probability function. We have proved the following general theorem about binomial experiments:

6–1 Theorem. *Binomial distribution.* If an experiment consists of n independent binomial trials, each with probability p of success and probability q ($=1 - p$) of failure, then the probability that the experiment results in exactly x successes and $n - x$ failures is

$$\boxed{b(x; n, p) = \binom{n}{x} p^x q^{n-x}, \qquad x = 0, 1, 2, \ldots, n.} \quad (4)$$

EXAMPLE 1. *Five coin tosses.* In tossing a coin, the probability of a head is assumed to be $\frac{1}{2}$. If the coin is tossed 5 times, what is the probability (a) of exactly two heads? (b) of more than one head?

Solution. Let X be the number of heads on the 5 tosses.

(a) By Eq. (2),

$$P(X = 2) = b\left(2; 5, \frac{1}{2}\right) = \binom{5}{2}\left(\frac{1}{2}\right)^2\left(\frac{1}{2}\right)^3 = 10 \cdot \frac{1}{4} \cdot \frac{1}{8} = \frac{10}{32} = \frac{5}{16}.$$

(b) $P(X > 1)$ is found most easily by using complementary events. The various mutually exclusive events are 0, 1, 2, 3, 4, or 5 heads. Therefore

$$P(X > 1) = 1 - P(X \leq 1)$$

$$= 1 - b(0; 5, \tfrac{1}{2}) - b(1; 5, \tfrac{1}{2})$$

$$= 1 - (\tfrac{1}{2})^5 - 5(\tfrac{1}{2})^5 = \tfrac{26}{32} = \tfrac{13}{16}.$$

EXAMPLE 2. *Batter's problem.* Suppose the probability that a batter gets a hit is $\frac{1}{4}$. At first glance, some people interpret this figure to mean that the batter is sure to get a hit if he bats four times. What is the probability?

Solution. In 4 times at bat, the probability of *at least one hit* is

$$P(X \geq 1) = 1 - b(0; 4, \tfrac{1}{4})$$
$$= 1 - (\tfrac{1}{4})^0(\tfrac{3}{4})^4 = \tfrac{175}{256}.$$

The answer is about 0.68, which is far from a certainty. The confusion arises from the fact that the mean number of hits is one, a confusion between a mean and a probability. We discuss the matter further in Section 6–3.

EXAMPLE 3. *Two- and four-engine planes.* Suppose that, in flight, airplane engines fail with probability q, independently from engine to engine, and that a plane makes a successful flight if at least half of its engines run. For what values of q is a two-engine plane to be preferred to a four-engine one? The probability an engine does not fail is $p = 1 - q$.

Solution. We begin by computing the probabilities of successful flights for the two types of planes. Let X be the number of engines that do not fail.

Two-engine plane

P (successful flight) $=$

$$P(X \geq 1) = 1 - P(0)$$
$$= 1 - b(0; 2, p)$$
$$= 1 - q^2$$

Four-engine plane

P (successful flight) $=$

$$P(X \geq 2) = 1 - P(0) - P(1)$$
$$= 1 - b(0; 4, p) - b(1; 4, p)$$
$$= 1 - q^4 - 4pq^3$$
$$= 1 - q^4 - 4(1 - q)q^3$$
$$= 1 - 4q^3 + 3q^4$$

Graphical approach. In Fig. 6–2, a graph is given of the probabilities of successful flights for the two kinds of planes as a function of q, the probability that a single engine fails. The crossing point of the two curves cannot be read precisely (but it is near $q = \frac{1}{3}$), and so the following algebraic approach may be preferred.

Algebraic approach. The inequality that implies that the probability of successful flight for the two-engine plane is greater than or equal to the corresponding probability for the four-engine plane is

$$1 - q^2 \geq 1 - 4q^3 + 3q^4.$$

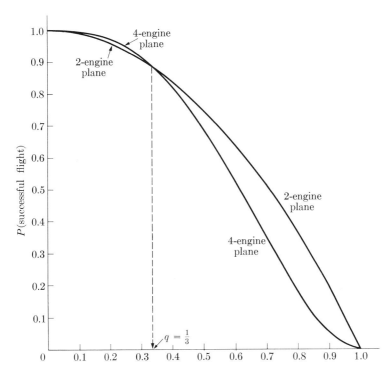

Fig. 6-2.   Probabilities of successful flights plotted against q, the probability of failure for a single engine.

Subtracting $1 - q^2$ from both sides of this inequality, we have the following equivalent relation:

$$0 \geq q^2 - 4q^3 + 3q^4.$$

Factoring q^2 from the expression on the right yields

$$0 \geq q^2(1 - 4q + 3q^2).$$

Finally, we factor the right-hand side further and obtain

$$0 \geq q^2(1 - q)(1 - 3q). \tag{5}$$

If $q = 0$, $q = 1$, or $q = \frac{1}{3}$, the right-hand member is zero and the two kinds of planes have equal chances of successful flights.

Figure 6–3 graphs the right-hand side of inequality (5) against q. The graph also shows that equal chances of successful flights for the two

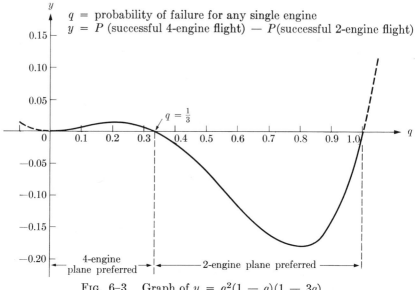

FIG. 6–3.   Graph of $y = q^2(1 - q)(1 - 3q)$.

types of plane occur when $q = 0$, $q = 1$, or $q = \frac{1}{3}$. The graph further shows that if $\frac{1}{3} < q < 1$, then the right side of inequality (5) is less than zero because the curve falls below the q-axis. Similar reasoning shows that for $0 < q < \frac{1}{3}$ the curve is above the q-axis and the four-engine plane is to be preferred. The foregoing facts can also be obtained by studying the signs of the factors of the right-hand member of inequality (5) for various values of q. Needless to say, the practical situation is that q, the probability that any one engine fails, is very much less than $\frac{1}{3}$.

EXERCISES FOR SECTION 6–2

1. A baseball player's batting average is .300. What is the probability that he gets exactly 2 hits in 4 times at bat? Are there considerations that make you doubt that the number of hits in 4 times at bat is binomially distributed?

2. A thumbtack falls point up 40% of the time. Compute the probability function for the number of times it falls point up in 5 tosses. Display the results in a probability table and in a graph.

3. Why do you think the number of baseball games won by the home team in a double-header may fail to be binomially distributed?

4. If n coins are independently tossed, show that the probability that all or all but one will fall with the same face up is $(n + 1)/2^{n-1}$, if $n > 2$. What is the correct answer when $n = 2$?

5. Suppose an amateur rifleman has a probability of 0.05 of hitting a bull's-eye on a single shot. What is the probability that in 20 shots he never hits the bull's-

eye? (Use logarithms.) Also set up, but do not evaluate, the probability calculation for hitting it 4 or more times in 20 shots. (The setup of this latter
problem is straightforward, but the numerical computations are excessively
long. In the next section we show how such problems can be solved easily by
the use of tables.)

6. Compare the performance of a one-engine plane with that of a two-engine
plane, using the same assumptions as those of Example 3.

7. In a binomial experiment consisting of 3 trials, the probability of exactly
2 successes is 12 times as great as that for 3 successes. Find p.

8. One-third of the male freshmen entering a college are at least 6 feet tall.
If roommates are assigned randomly for freshmen, 4 to a room, what is the
probability that at least 3 of the 4 in one room are under 6 feet? (Ignore the
fact that the actual sampling is without replacement.)

9. Two-thirds of the secretaries in a large stenographic pool are licensed motor-
vehicle operators. If 4 secretaries are drawn at random to go on a trip, what
is the probability that at least 2 are licensed drivers?

10. A quiz has 6 multiple-choice questions, each with 3 alternatives. Sheer
guesswork yields what probability of 5 or more right?

11. A risky operation used for patients with no other hope of survival has
a survival rate of 80%. What is the probability that exactly 80% of the next 5
patients operated upon survive?

12. (For students with some calculus.) For given values of x and n, consider
$b(x; n, p)$ as a function of p and show that it is maximized when $p = x/n$.
[*Hint*. First solve the problem assuming that x is neither 0 nor n, then handle
those two cases separately.] *Remark*. This is one reason for using the observed
number of successes divided by the total number of trials as an estimate of p.
That estimate, x/n, $x = 0, 1, \ldots, n$, is called the *maximum likelihood estimate*
of p because of the maximizing property you are to prove.

13. Consider two binomial experiments each with $p = \frac{1}{2}$, one of size $n = 2m$
trials, the other of size $n = 2m - 1$ trials, where m is a positive integer. Show
that $P(m)$ is the same for both experiments.

14. For what values of q is a one-engine plane to be preferred to a three-
engine plane? Use the assumptions of Example 3.

15. For what values of q is a two-engine plane to be preferred to a three-
engine plane? Use the assumptions of Example 3.

16. Suppose three- and five-engine planes fly if more than half their engines
work. If q is the probability of failure for a single engine and engines perform
independently, find the values of q for which the three-engine plane is to be
preferred.

17. Two independent binomial experiments, one of n and the other of m trials,
both have probability p of success on each trial. Show that the probability of a
total of exactly x successes in the two experiments combined is

$$\binom{n+m}{x} p^x (1 - p)^{n+m-x},$$

and interpret this result.

6–3 EXPECTED VALUE OF A BINOMIAL RANDOM VARIABLE

In this chapter we have dealt entirely with probabilities for the binomial distribution, not at all with the mean or expected outcome $E(X) = \mu$. In Example 2 of Section 6–2 we computed the probability that a batter with $P(\text{hit}) = \frac{1}{4}$ gets at least 1 hit in 4 times at bat. To obtain the mean number of hits μ, we multiply each possible number of hits by its probability of occurrence and add as follows:

$$\mu = 0P(0) + 1P(1) + 2P(2) + 3P(3) + 4P(4)$$

$$= 0 \cdot 1(\tfrac{3}{4})^4 + 1 \cdot 4(\tfrac{3}{4})^3(\tfrac{1}{4}) + 2 \cdot 6(\tfrac{3}{4})^2(\tfrac{1}{4})^2$$

$$+ 3 \cdot 4(\tfrac{3}{4})(\tfrac{1}{4})^3 + 4 \cdot 1(\tfrac{1}{4})^4$$

$$= 0 + \tfrac{27}{64} + \tfrac{27}{64} + \tfrac{9}{64} + \tfrac{1}{64} = 1.$$

Thus, in the long run, the batter gets 1 hit in 4 tries. The misinterpretation mentioned in Example 2, Section 6–2, stems from a confusion between a mean and a probability. In his work, Cardan, one of the first writers on probability, had a similar confusion, which contributed to the neglect of Cardan's findings in the theory of probability until 1953,[*] when Oystein Ore sorted out Cardan's mistakes from his discoveries. This is the same Cardan who worked on the solution of the cubic equation.[†]

In the batter example, the random variable X, whose value is determined by the experiment of batting four times, is the number of hits, and its possible values are $x = 0, 1, 2, 3, 4$. The *mean* number of hits μ is the mean of the distribution of the random variable X. If the batter repeats the batting experiment, then each repetition yields a value of X. In six repetitions the values might be 0, 2, 0, 3, 1, 1. If we compute the ordinary average $\overline{X}$ for these several values of X, we have $\frac{7}{6}$ as an estimated value for μ, instead of 1, the true value. If the outcomes of many experiments are used in computing the average of the observed values, the estimated value is likely to be very close to μ, the mean of the distribution of X.

More generally, we want to obtain the expected number of successes in n binomial trials. Recall that X is the sum of n random variables, each of which takes the value 1 with probability p and the value 0 with probability $(1 - p)$. The mean of any one of these random variables is

$$1 \times p + 0 \times (1 - p) = p.$$

---

[*] Oystein Ore, *Cardano*, Princeton University Press, 1953.
[†] D. E. Smith, *History of Mathematics*, Vol. 1, Ginn & Co., 1923, pp. 295–297.

In order to obtain the desired result, we shall make use of the following theorem, which we state without proof: "The mean of the sum of any finite collection of random variables is the sum of their means." Since X is the sum of n random variables each having mean p,

$$E(X) = \underbrace{p + p + \cdots + p}_{n \text{ terms}} = np.$$

6–2 Theorem. *Binomial mean.* Let p be the probability of success at each trial of a binomial experiment. Then the mean number of successes in n trials is

$$\boxed{\mu = E(X) = np.} \tag{1}$$

EXAMPLE 1. We apply formula (1) to the problem of the batter with $p = P(\text{hit}) = \frac{1}{4}$, $n = 4$. What is the mean number of hits in 4 times at bat?

Solution. $\mu = 4(\frac{1}{4}) = 1$, as before.

EXAMPLE 2. Fifteen dice are thrown, what is the expected number of aces?

Solution. $\mu = 15(\frac{1}{6}) = 2.5$.

EXERCISES FOR SECTION 6-3

1. The probability of a thumbtack landing point up is 0.3. If 15 thumbtacks are tossed, find the expected number that land with points up.

2. How many dice must be tossed if the expected number of aces is to be 5?

3. Two binomial experiments are performed: 13 cards are randomly drawn from a bridge deck, with replacement after each draw, and twelve dice are rolled. Find the expected total number of aces (ones) and deuces (twos) in the two experiments combined.

4. In a binomial experiment, if μ must be at least a distance $3\sqrt{npq}$ from both 0 and n, show that $n \geq 9$ times the larger of p/q and q/p.

5. In a binomial experiment with $n = 2$, $p = \frac{1}{200}$, find the probability of 1 or more successes, and compare the result with $\mu = np$. Make a similar comparison for $n = 3$, $p = \frac{1}{300}$; for $n = 3$, $p = 0.1$. Comment on these results.

6. (Continuation.) For a binomial experiment, show that if μ is near zero $P(X \geq 1) \approx \mu$. [*Hint.* Recall the approximation of $(1 + x)^n$, Section 2–5, Example 4.]

7. (Continuation.) Use the results of Exercise 6 to find, approximately, $P(X \geq 1)$, in a binomial experiment with $n = 50$, $p = \frac{1}{2000}$.

*8. Prove Theorem 6–2 directly from the definition

$$E(X) = \sum_{x=0}^{n} x \binom{n}{x} p^x q^{n-x}$$

by first showing that, for $1 \leq x \leq n$,

$$x \binom{n}{x} p^x q^{n-x} = np \binom{n-1}{x-1} p^{x-1} q^{(n-1)-(x-1)}.$$

Then, since the term in the summation with $x = 0$ is zero,

$$E(X) = \sum_{x=1}^{n} np \binom{n-1}{x-1} p^{x-1} q^{(n-1)-(x-1)}$$

$$= np (q + p)^{n-1}$$

$$= np.$$

6–4. BINOMIAL PROBABILITY TABLES

It is a dreary task to compute the probability of every outcome for a large set of binomial trials. Extensive tables are available for the binomial distribution, and we present a small one (Table IV) for your use.

This table, at the end of the book, is in two parts. Part A gives $b(x; n, p)$, the probability of observing exactly x successes in a binomial experiment composed of n trials. Values are given for all x for $n = 2$ to 25 and for $p = .01, .05, .10, .20, .30, .40, .50, .60, .70, .80, .90, .95, .99$.

Part B of the table gives, for the same binomial distributions, the probability of observing r or more successes. Thus this part of the table gives the "cumulative" probability from r through n, rather than the probability of a single number of successes. Many applications require sums rather than single probabilities. Symbolically, this part of the table gives

$$P(X \geq r) = b(r; n, p) + b(r + 1; n, p) + \cdots + b(n; n, p)$$

$$= \sum_{x=r}^{n} b(x; n, p).$$

Each 3-digit entry in the table should be read with a decimal preceding it. The symbol $1-$ means a probability larger than 0.9995, but less than 1. The symbol $0+$ means a probability less than 0.0005, but greater than 0.

Let us check a value in the table. To find the probability of 4 or more successes in 5 trials when $p = 0.8$, we compute

$$b(4; 5, 0.8) + b(5; 5, 0.8)$$

and get

$$\binom{5}{4}(.8)^4(.2) + \binom{5}{5}(.8)^5(.2)^0 = .40960 + .32768 = .73728.$$

We read in Table IV–A that $b(4; 5, 0.8) \approx 0.410$ and that $b(5; 5, 0.8) \approx 0.328$, and in the cumulative Table IV–B for $n = 5$, $r = 4$, $p = 0.8$, we read 0.737. All three tabled probabilities agree to three decimal places with our calculated values.

EXAMPLE 1. For $n = 10$, $p = 0.4$, find the probability of 3 or more successes.

Solution: Reading directly from Table IV–B, we find that the probability to three decimal places is 0.833.

EXAMPLE 2. *Interpolation in the tables.* With $n = 25$, find the value of p that makes $P(X \geq 8) = 0.4$.

Solution: A tabular array assists with such a problem.

	$P(X \geq 8)$, $n = 25$
$p = 0.20$	0.109
$p = ?$	0.400
$p = 0.30$	0.488

By ordinary interpolation, we have

$$\frac{p - 0.2}{0.3 - 0.2} \approx \frac{0.400 - 0.109}{0.488 - 0.109},$$

whence

$$p \approx 0.2 + \frac{0.400 - 0.109}{0.488 - 0.109}(0.3 - 0.2) \approx 0.28.$$

This result agrees, to two decimal places, with the value obtained from a bigger table than ours.

EXAMPLE 3. If $n = 15$, $p = 0.05$, find the probability of 2 or fewer successes.

Solution 1.

$$P(X \leq 2) = 1 - P(X \geq 3)$$
$$\approx 1 - 0.036 = 0.964.$$

Solution 2. We could, instead, focus on the number of failures. Two or fewer successes is equivalent to 13 or more failures. We would then enter the table with p appropriate to failures, 0.95. Then we read directly

$$P(X \geq 13) \approx 0.964.$$

Other tables. A brief list of more extensive tables of the binomial distribution follows. The notation $n = 1[1]10[5]100$ means that n goes from 1 to 10 in steps of 1 and from 10 to 100 in steps of 5.

1. Harvard Computation Laboratory, *Tables of the Cumulative Binomial Probability Distribution*, Harvard University Press (1955). Cumulatives only for $n = 1[1]50[2]100[10]200[20]500[50]1000$, $p = 0.00[0.01]0.50$ and $\frac{1}{3}, \frac{1}{6}, \frac{1}{8}, \frac{3}{8}, \frac{1}{12}, \frac{5}{12}, \frac{1}{16}, \frac{3}{16}, \frac{5}{16}, \frac{7}{16}$.

2. National Bureau of Standards, *Tables of the Binomial Probability Distribution*, Applied Mathematics Series 6 (1950). Gives both cumulative and single terms for $n = 1[1]49$, $p = 0.00[0.01]0.50$.

3. Harry G. Romig, 50–100 *Binomial Tables*, New York: John Wiley & Sons, Inc. (1953). Gives both cumulative and single terms for $n = 50[5]100$, $p = 0.00[0.01]0.50$.

4. Ordnance Corps, *Tables of the Cumulative Binomial Probabilities*, Ordnance Corps Pamphlet ORDP 20–1, U. S. Government Printing Office (September, 1952). Gives cumulative only for $n = 1[1]150$, $p = 0.00[0.01]0.50$.

EXERCISES FOR SECTION 6–4

In the following exercises 1 through 9, let X denote the number of successes in n binomial trials, with probability p of success on each trial.

1. For $n = 15$ and $p = 0.6$, find (a) $P(X \geq 7)$, (b) $P(X = 7)$.
2. For $n = 25$ and $p = 0.8$, find (a) $P(X > 19)$, (b) $P(X = 19)$.
3. For $n = 20$ and $p = 0.3$, find (a) $P(X \geq 6)$, (b) $P(X = 6)$.
4. For $n = 25$ and $p = 0.65$, find (a) $P(X \geq 11)$, (b) $P(11$ or more failures), (c) $P(X = 11)$.
5. With $n = 22$, find the value of p that makes $P(X \geq 8) = 0.4$.
6. With $n = 20$, find the value of p that makes $P(X \geq 7) = 0.5$.
7. With $n = 15$, find the value of p that makes $P(X \geq 10) = 0.8$.
8. Given that $n = 12$ and $p = 0.8$, find (a) $P(X = 8)$, (b) $P(X \leq 8)$, (c) $P(X \geq 8)$.
9. For $n = 6$ and $p = 0.2$, find the value of $P(X = 2)$.

10. In shooting a rifle the probability that John hits the target is 0.95, the probability that he gets a bull's-eye is 0.20. He shoots 25 times. What is the

probability that he hits the target more than 20 times? That he gets exactly 5 bull's-eyes? That he gets 5 or more bull's-eyes?

11. (Continuation.) Suppose John shoots only 22 times. What is the probability of exactly 10 bull's-eyes? Fewer than 10? More than 10? Check that the three results add to 1.

12. A die is tossed 12 times. What is the probability of more than 4 aces?

13. If the probability of seven or more successes in 25 trials in a binomial experiment is 0.5, what is the probability of success on each trial? (Give answer to two decimal places.)

14. Twenty-five coins are poured from a sack onto a table. What is the probability that the number of heads is between 8 and 17, inclusive?

15. If 40% of the voters in a large town favor candidate A, what is the probability that in a random sample of 25 voters, the majority in the sample will favor him?

16. A census of a United States town of 25,000 showed that 75% of the families owned refrigerators. Twenty families were randomly selected for intensive sociological and economic investigation. Approximately what is the probability that 10 or fewer of these families have refrigerators? (A binomial calculation here is approximate because we ignore the fact that the sampling is done without, instead of with, replacement. Since the sample size is small compared with the population size, the approximation is a good one.)

17. What is the probability of exactly 8 successes in a binomial experiment of 11 trials if the probability of success on each trial is 0.8?

18. Use Table IV to work Exercise 5 of Section 6–2.

19. For $n = 25$, use binomial tables to find the two values of p that satisfy $P(X = 8) = 0.075$.

20. Five balls were drawn, one at a time, with replacement, from a bag containing an equal number of black and white balls. The number of black balls was then tabulated for 819 sets of consecutive drawings to give the following observed frequency distribution:

Number of black balls	Observed frequency
0	30
1	125
2	277
3	224
4	136
5	27
Total	819

Obtain the theoretical frequencies from the binomial and compare them with the observed values.

21. Assume that you serve on the school committee for your community, and that you know that the population of 4th-grade school children has 95% right-handed and 5% left-handed children. You observe that the 4th-grade classroom has 20 tablet armchairs, all with the tablet on the right arm. Assume that the 20 students assigned to this room are a random sample of the 4th-grade school population.

(a) What is the probability of one or more left-handed students in a class of 20?

(b) Suppose that you influence the school committee to exchange one of the chairs for a left-armed one. What is the probability that the chairs just come out even with the students: 1 left-armed chair, 1 left-handed student; 19 right-armed chairs, 19 right-handed students?

(c) How much have you improved the probability that everyone's handedness is provided for?

(d) The chairs are permanently installed. You could arrange that there be 21 chairs, one left-armed, for 20 students. Now what is the probability that everyone's handedness is provided for?

22. (a) Compare $b(1; 4, .30)$ with $b(3; 4, .70)$.   (b) Compare $b(6; 18, .40)$ with $b(12; 18, .60)$.

23. (Continuation.) Prove $b(r; n, p) = b(n - r; n, q)$ if $q = 1 - p$. This shows that tables like Table IV–A need not tabulate for values of p in excess of 0.5.

24. (a) Use Table IV–B, $n = 23$, to compare $P(X \geq 11)$ for $p = 0.6$ with $1 - P(X \geq 13)$ for $p = 0.4$.   (b) Use Table IV–B, $n = 5$, to compare $P(X \geq 2)$, $p = 0.2$ with $1 - P(X \geq 4)$ with $p = 0.8$.

25. (Continuation.) Prove

$$\sum_{x=r}^{n} b(x; n, p) = 1 - \sum_{x=n-r+1}^{n} b(x; n, q).$$

This shows that cumulative binomial tables need not have values of p in excess of 0.5. However, such values are a convenience.

26. Suppose 5 cards are drawn from an ordinary bridge deck, with replacement and reshuffling after each card is drawn. Find the probability function of the number of red cards in the sample of 5 cards. Compare the results with those of the table following Eq. (4), Section 5–5, for sampling without replacement.

6–5. PROPERTIES OF THE BINOMIAL DISTRIBUTION

In this section we study the shapes of graphs of binomial distributions produced under two conditions: (1) for a fixed number of trials n, but different values of p; and (2) for a fixed value of p, but different values of n. We study especially how the graphs change shape as n grows large. Such a study helps us understand the family of binomial distributions, and it also helps us understand other sequences of probability distribution functions, because the changes within the binomial family resemble the changes within many other families of distributions.

Some properties are merely stated and illustrated without proof. The binomial tables at the back of the book can provide further numerical illustrations. In the discussion of figures, we sometimes abbreviate the notation for the binomial ordinate at x, which is $b(x; n, p)$, to $b(x)$.

(1) *Fixed n, varying p.* As p varies, the shape of the graph of the binomial distribution changes. Figures 6–4(a) through (i) illustrate this for $n = 5$. For p near zero or near one (Fig. 6–4a, b), the probability spikes up at $x = 0$ and $x = n$, respectively. The abscissa corresponding to the largest ordinate is called *the mode*. For p more centrally located, $b(x)$ increases with each successive x until the largest $b(x)$ is achieved (Fig. 6–4c, d, g, h) and then, except possibly for a tie at $x + 1$ (Fig. 6–4e, f, i), $b(x)$ decreases as x continues to increase. Thus, unless two adjacent ordinates are tied in value, there is just one largest ordinate, and the ordinates decrease steadily as we move to the right or to the left from the mode. The proof would divert us, but it is an exercise in the manipulation of inequalities that is within the range of an enthusiastic student.

When $p = \frac{1}{2}$ (Fig. 6–4i), the distribution is symmetric about $n/2$; if n is odd two central values of x have equal ordinates (Fig. 6–4i); if n is even the ordinate at the middle value of x is the largest (Fig. 6–5). If $p \neq \frac{1}{2}$ the distribution is asymmetric.

In Figs. 6–4 and 6–5 the fulcrum ▲ on the horizontal axis shows the mean, μ, for each distribution. You can see that the means of these binomial distributions are within one unit of the abscissa with largest probability (the mode). In binomial distributions, the mean and mode are *always* within one unit of each other. Furthermore, if np is an integer, the mode and mean are identical. We shall not prove these facts.

(2) *Fixed p, increasing n.* As n increases, the successive binomial distributions (a) "walk" to the right, (b) flatten, and (c) "spread." We discuss these features in turn.

(a) *"Walking."* As n increases, the mean μ moves to the right a distance p for each unit increase in n because $\mu = np$. The mode and the other large ordinates are near the mean, so the central mass of the distribution also "walks" to the right as n increases.

(b) *Flattening.* Consider further the unadjusted random variable X. As the means walk, the distributions flatten (Fig. 6–5a through e). We wish to study the rate of flattening. It can be proved that, for large n, the sizes of the central ordinates are inversely proportional to $\sqrt{n}$. We shall illustrate this fact graphically. To do this, let us first recall that $y = mx$ is an equation of a straight line through the origin with slope m.

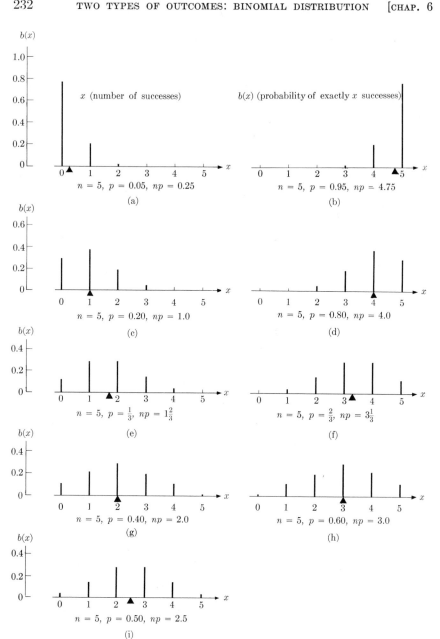

FIG. 6–4.   Binomial distributions for $n = 5$, displaying the change in form as p varies.

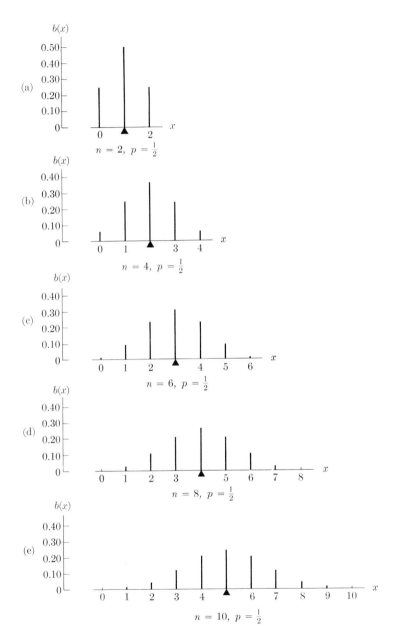

FIG. 6-5. Walking, flattening, and spreading as n increases.

When y is a constant times x, y varies directly as x. If $x = 1/\sqrt{n}$, then we usually say that y varies inversely as $\sqrt{n}$. But we can also say that y varies directly as $1/\sqrt{n}$; and when we plot y against $1/\sqrt{n}$, we get a straight line through the origin. The point is that we have a linear relation if we regard $1/\sqrt{n}$ as an independent variable. In other words, one way to show that y is inversely proportional to $\sqrt{n}$ is to show that y is directly proportional to $1/\sqrt{n}$. We use this idea in Fig. 6–6.

Mode proportional to $1/\sqrt{n}$. To return to the main discussion, Fig. 6–6 shows how the middle ordinates of symmetric binomial distributions ($p = \frac{1}{2}$) decrease as n grows. The relation is smooth when n is taken as even. (A similar smooth relation holds for n odd.) The modal value of x is $n/2$. When we choose the horizontal axis as the axis of $1/\sqrt{n}$, we see that, as n grows, $P(\text{mode})$ decreases, following a curve that is almost a straight line through the origin. (A scale of values of n is marked below the axis.) The points on the curve for $p = \frac{1}{2}$ have coordinates $(1/\sqrt{n}, b(\frac{1}{2}n))$, n even. Our binomial table IV–A can be used to check a point on the curve. For $n = 24$, $b(12) \approx 0.161$ and $1/\sqrt{24} \approx 0.204$.

Similarly, the relation between $P(\text{mode})$ and $1/\sqrt{n}$ is approximated by a straight line through the origin for binomial distributions with $p = \frac{1}{5}$ (for smoothness, we have chosen values of n that are multiples of 5, and

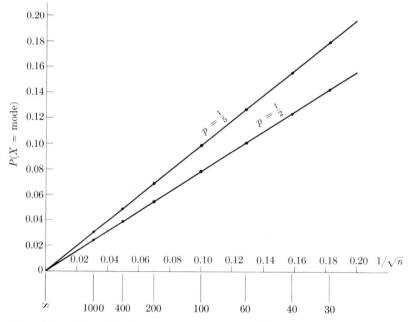

FIG. 6–6. Plot of $P(X = \text{mode})$ against $1/\sqrt{n}$ to show the nearly straight-line relationship for $p = \frac{1}{2}$ and $p = \frac{1}{5}$.

then the mode is $n/5$). Our binomial table IV–A can be used to check a point for $n = 25$. Then $1/\sqrt{n} = 0.20$, and $b(5) \approx 0.196$. This graph is adequate to illustrate the approximation: *the modal ordinate and its neighbors decrease inversely as* $\sqrt{n}$.

(c) *Spreading.* We recall that the sum of the ordinates is always 1. Naturally, if the distributions flatten as n increases, and the total probability must remain constant, successive distributions must spread out.

In order to find the rate of spread, we need to know the variance and standard deviation for the binomial distribution. To get this information, we assume without proof the following theorem:

> The variance of the sum of n independent random variables is the sum of the variances.

The rest follows readily. For if the random variable X denotes the number of successes in a binomial experiment of n trials, then

$$X = X_1 + X_2 + X_3 + \cdots + X_n,$$

where X_i is a random variable denoting the number of successes in the ith trial. The values of X_i are 0 and 1, with probabilities $1 - p$ and p, respectively:

$P(X_i = x)$	$1 - p$	p
x	0	1

Since the mean of X_i is p (Section 6–3), we have

$$\begin{aligned}
\text{Var}\,(X_i) &= E(X_i^2) - \mu^2 \\
&= 0^2(1 - p) + 1^2(p) - p^2 \\
&= p - p^2 \\
&= p(1 - p) \\
&= pq.
\end{aligned}$$

And, since the X_i's are independent,

$$\begin{aligned}
\sigma_X^2 &= \text{Var}\,(\textstyle\sum X_i) \\
&= \textstyle\sum (\text{Var}\, X_i) \\
&= \underbrace{pq + pq + pq + \cdots + pq}_{n \text{ terms}} = npq.
\end{aligned}$$

Thus, the standard deviation for the binomial distribution is

$$\sigma_X = \sqrt{npq}.$$

Since the standard deviation is a measure of spread and since its value is proportional to $\sqrt{n}$ when p is constant, we conclude that as n increases the binomial distribution has a spread proportional to $\sqrt{n}$.

The *total* range of the binomial is from 0 to n, and thus the range is proportional to n. But we know from Chebyshev's theorem that there is very little probability near the ends of the distribution compared with the amount within a few standard deviations of the mean. The standard deviation is sensitive to the rate at which the central mass of the binomial distribution spreads (the 75% or the 99% near the mean), and it is this central mass whose behavior we have studied.

To summarize: as n grows, (a) successive binomial distributions walk to the right at a rate proportional to n; (b) the modal ordinates flatten at a rate proportional to $1/\sqrt{n}$; and (c) the distributions spread out—their standard deviations increase in proportion to $\sqrt{n}$.

EXERCISES FOR SECTION 6–5

All problems in this set refer to binomial distributions.

1. Find the mean and standard deviation of the binomial distribution with (a) $n = 4$, $p = \frac{1}{2}$, (b) $n = 10$, $p = \frac{1}{5}$.

2. If $\mu = 45$, $\sigma = \sqrt{npq} = 6$, find n and p.

3. If $\mu = 10$, $\sigma = \sqrt{npq} = 3$, find n and p.

4. Show that if $p = \frac{1}{2}$ and $n = 2m - 1$, then $b(m - 1) = t'(m)$.

5. Show that if $p = \frac{1}{2}$ and $n = 2m$, then $b(m)$ is larger than $b(m - 1)$ or $b(m + 1)$.

6. (Continuation.) If $p = \frac{1}{2}$, $n = 2m$, and $m \geq 2$, show that $b(r - 1) \leq b(r)$ for $1 \leq r \leq m$.

7. If $p = \frac{1}{3}$, how fast does the sequence of means of binomial distributions walk to the right, per unit increase in n?

8. Make a graph like that of Fig. 6–6 for $p = 0.4$, using your binomial tables. Choose n's that are multiples of 5 to smooth the plotting. Do not forget to label the axes. Assume that the curve through the points passes through the origin.

9. It is desired to show that points like those in Fig. 6–6 do not lie along a straight line. It is convenient to choose values of n that are perfect squares, say 1, 9, 25. If $p = \frac{1}{2}$, the modal ordinates are $b(0; 1, \frac{1}{2})$, $b(4; 9, \frac{1}{2})$, $b(12; 25, \frac{1}{2})$ at $1/\sqrt{1}$, $1/\sqrt{9}$, $1/\sqrt{25}$, respectively. Show that the slopes of the chords connecting the points are not equal. Use tables.

10. For $n = 2$, find the values of p for which the three points with ordinates $b(x; 2, p)$ lie on a straight line when a graph like Fig. 6–4 is made.

11. For $n = 4$, $p = 0.2$, use your binomial tables to assist in plotting the graph of the probability function, as in Fig. 6–4. Be sure to indicate the mean.

12. For $n = 25$, $p = \frac{1}{2}$, use your tables to find the probabilities contained within σ of the mean μ, within 2σ of the mean, and within 3σ of the mean. Compare these results with those given by the Chebyshev inequality and with those given by the empirical rule of Table 5–15, Section 5–7.

13. Assuming that Fig. 6–6 is correct and that the curve for any p passes through the origin, show that for a fixed p ($\neq 0$ or 1), as n approaches infinity $b(x; n, p)$ approaches zero, and therefore that in the limit, the sequence of binomial distributions does collapse onto the x-axis. (*Puzzle.* The total probability had to add to 1; where did it go?)

*14. Let X be a random variable with $P(X = x) = b(x; n, p)$. Prove that $\sigma_X^2 = npq$ as follows:

(a) By Eq. (6), Section 5–4, $\sigma_X^2 = E(X^2) - [E(X)]^2$.

(b) By Exercise 8, Section 6–3, $E(X) = np$.

(c) By definition, $E(X^2) = \sum_{x=0}^{n} x^2 \binom{n}{x} p^x q^{n-x}$.

Show that this can also be expressed as

$$E(X^2) = \sum_{x=1}^{n} npx \binom{n-1}{x-1} p^{x-1} q^{(n-1)-(x-1)}.$$

Then, since $x = (x - 1) + 1$, we can write

$$E(X^2) = np \sum_{x=1}^{n} (x - 1) \binom{n-1}{x-1} p^{x-1} q^{(n-1)-(x-1)}$$

$$+ np \sum_{x=1}^{n} \binom{n-1}{x-1} p^{x-1} q^{(n-1)-(x-1)}$$

$$= np \cdot (n - 1)p \cdot (q + p)^{n-2} + np \cdot (q + p)^{n-1}.$$

Since $(q + p) = 1$, $E(X^2) = (n^2 - n)p^2 + np$. Therefore

$$\sigma_X^2 = (n^2 - n)p^2 + np - (np)^2$$

$$= n(p - p^2) = npq.$$

7

SOME STATISTICAL APPLICATIONS OF PROBABILITY

7–1. ESTIMATION AND THE TESTING OF HYPOTHESES

Our work in the general theory of probability and our detailed study of the family of binomial distributions are applied in this chapter to a few problems in statistical inference. We focus attention on two related problems—*estimation* and *hypothesis testing*. Each is studied first without the use of prior information, as it would ordinarily be treated by probabilists of the objective school, and then with the use of prior information, in the manner of the personalistic school.

Starting with our experiments in Chapter 1, we have used observed averages to estimate population means and observed proportions to estimate p, the binomial probability of a success. These estimates are familiar and natural, but we have not established their variability or reliability. If a professional basketball player sinks 65 foul shots out of 100, we estimate the value of p, the probability that he sinks a foul, to be $\frac{65}{100} = 0.65$. Assuming that the outcomes of successive shots are independent (not too safe an assumption in this example), how sure are we that $0.6 \leq p \leq 0.7$? The method of *confidence limits* presented in this chapter gives one way of making probability statements about such an *interval estimate*.

Suppose that the basketball player has a long history of foul-shooting, with an average success of 0.54. Is there good reason to suppose that his new performance of 0.65 represents a change in his probability of making a successful foul shot? This kind of question is treated in the statistical testing of hypotheses, discussed later in this chapter. Similar problems arise when a new medication for relief from headaches is proposed. Does the new medication relieve more headaches than the usual remedy? Does a new dust for the disease *Botrytis* reduce the number of affected plants, as compared with no treatment?

If prior information is available, both the theory of estimation and that of hypothesis testing can be extended by the use of Bayes' Theorem. In Sections 7–3 and 7–5 we discuss examples of such extensions within the limitation of discrete probability distributions.

7–2. ESTIMATING p, THE BINOMIAL PROBABILITY OF SUCCESS

An estimate of p. To establish our notation, recall the usual way of obtaining a numerical estimate of p, the probability of success for a single trial of a binomial experiment. We execute n trials, count the number of successes x, and compute $x/n = \bar{p}$ to obtain a value for the estimate of p.

If team A beats team B 4 times in 20, we estimate A's probability of beating team B as $\frac{4}{20} = 0.2$. Now we wish to discuss the properties of the estimate $\bar{p}$, giving special attention to its variability. What is its mean and what is its standard deviation? Answers to these questions follow easily from our work in Chapter 6.

The usual estimate of p is

$$\bar{p} = \frac{X}{n},$$

where X is the number of successes. Since X is a random variable, so is $\bar{p}$. Thus the value of $\bar{p}$ may vary from one binomial experiment of size n to another. The possible values of X are $x = 0, 1, \ldots, n$, and so the possible values of $\bar{p}$ are $x/n = 0, 1/n, 2/n, \ldots, (n-1)/n, 1$.

Mean of $\bar{p}$. What is the mean value of $\bar{p}$? Since X is the random variable denoting the number of successes, $E(X) = np$. To get the mean of the random variable $\bar{p} = X/n$, we have, from the definition of $\bar{p}$,

$$E(\bar{p}) = E\left(\frac{X}{n}\right). \tag{1}$$

Recall that $E(cX) = cE(X)$, where c is a constant. Because $1/n$ is a constant, we apply this theorem to Eq. (1) and get

$$E(\bar{p}) = \frac{1}{n} E(X) = \frac{1}{n} (np) = p. \tag{2}$$

Thus "on the average" we get the correct value of p, which is the result most people expect. This feature has a name: we say that $\bar{p}$ is an *unbiased estimate* of p. Lack of bias gives some backing for the use of $\bar{p}$ as an estimate of p.

Closeness. That an estimate has a long-run mean with value p is not an adequate basis for its use. We ought at least to know that $\bar{p}$ is often close to p. To illustrate this need, consider the outcome of a binomial experiment of size $n = 100$. Let us deliberately throw away the results of the last 99 trials and estimate the probability of success to be 1 if the first trial resulted in success, and 0 otherwise. This method of estimating is also unbiased because it corresponds to B/n, with $n = 1$ and B the number of successes on the *first* trial, and here again

$$E\left(\frac{B}{n}\right) = \frac{1}{n} E(B) = p.$$

Yet we do not like this estimate very well. Indeed we could easily be persuaded to use, instead, $X/99$ or $X/101$, with X the number of successes on the 100 trials, even though these estimates are not unbiased, since

$$E\left(\frac{X}{99}\right) = \frac{100}{99}\, p, \qquad E\left(\frac{X}{101}\right) = \frac{100}{101}\, p.$$

What is missing from our discussion is some notion of closeness. We want an estimate that is more likely than other estimates to be close, in some sense, to the true value of p.

As just stated, the notion of closeness is rather vague, and we shall not pursue it. But we can find from binomial tables how often $\bar{p}$ is within a given distance of p.

Distribution of $\bar{p}$ for small n. For given values of p, and $n \leq 25$, we can obtain the probability function for $\bar{p}$ from our binomial tables. The only difference from our work in Chapter 6 is that we change the horizontal scale from x to $\bar{p}$. Figure 7–1 illustrates this for $n = 10$, $p = 0.2$. The ordinates for $x = 0, 1, \ldots, 10$ are found in the binomial tables. But instead of plotting $b(x; 10, 0.2)$ against x, we plot it against x/n, or $x/10$. The bulk of the probability in the binomial distribution with $n = 10$,

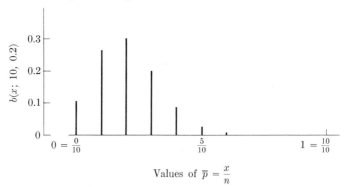

Values of $\bar{p} = \dfrac{x}{n}$

FIG. 7–1.   Probability function for $\bar{p}$, $n = 10$, $p = 0.2$.

$p = 0.2$, is between 0 and $\frac{1}{2}$ $(= \frac{5}{10})$, inclusive. Thus we can be practically certain that $\bar{p}$ is within 0.3 of p if $n = 10$, $p = 0.2$. Furthermore, from Table IV, A or B, we can compute for $n = 10$, $p = 0.2$, the probabilities

$$P(p - 0.1 \leq \bar{p} \leq p + 0.1) \approx 0.77,$$

$$P(p - 0.2 \leq \bar{p} \leq p + 0.2) \approx 0.97.$$

The first is the probability that $\bar{p}$ falls within 0.1 of p; the second, the probability that it falls within 0.2 of p. Alternatively, we use the absolute value symbol, $|\bar{p} - p|$, to denote the distance from p to $\bar{p}$. (See Appendix I, Section I-2.) Then

$$P(|\bar{p} - p| \leq 0.1) \approx 0.77,$$

and

$$P(|\bar{p} - p| \leq 0.2) \approx 0.97.$$

In this example, values of $\bar{p}$ are whole numbers of tenths. Consequently, the probability that $\bar{p}$ is within 0.1 of $p = 0.2$ is also the probability that $\bar{p}$ is within 0.12, 0.15, or 0.1999 of $p = 0.2$. Thus when we speak of $\bar{p}$ as within 0.1 of p, we are choosing the shortest possible distance with probability 0.77, and if we speak of $\bar{p}$ as within 0.199 . . ., we are choosing the longest distance with probability 0.77. Perhaps, for a fairer picture, we should regard the typical distance here as 0.15.

By similar computations for many different values of p, we could make a graph of the probability that $\bar{p}$ is within, say, 0.15 of p. Figure 7–2 shows such a graph for $n = 10$. (Extensive binomial tables were used in its construction.) Observe that for $p = 0.2$, $P(|\bar{p} - p| \leq 0.15) \approx 0.77$, as computed above.

Figure 7–2 is a good example of a discontinuous curve. The value at exactly $p = 0.05$ is indicated by the dot on the upper branch. The value at $p = 0.15$ is indicated by the isolated dot at the top of the broken vertical line. An example will explain how the discontinuities at 0.05, 0.15, 0.25, and so on, come about. For $\bar{p}$ to be within 0.15 of $p = 0.14$, say, $\bar{p}$ must lie in the interval from $p - 0.15 = -0.01$ to $p + 0.15 = 0.29$, and $\bar{p} = 0.0$, 0.1, and 0.2 are the only values in this interval because values of $\bar{p}$ are whole numbers of tenths when $n = 10$. Similarly, for $p = 0.16$ the interval for $\bar{p}$ runs from $p - 0.15 = 0.01$ to $p + 0.15 = 0.31$ and $\bar{p} = 0.1$, 0.2, and 0.3 are in the interval. Even though $p = 0.14$ and $p = 0.16$ are close, the fact that different sets of $\bar{p}$'s fall in their intervals makes the graph jump. Exactly at $p = 0.15$, $\bar{p} = 0.0$, 0.1, 0.2, and 0.3 are in the interval $p \pm 0.15$, and since this interval has 4 values of $\bar{p}$ instead of 3, there is a high dot at $p = 0.15$. The figure illustrates that for some purposes we need a table with a finer grid for p than our Table IV has.

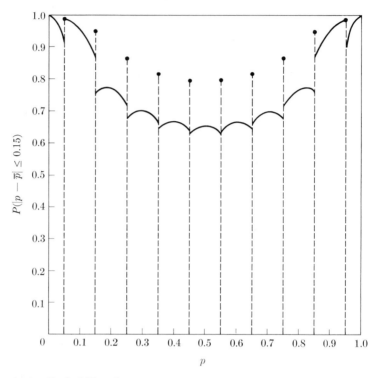

FIG. 7-2. Probability that $\bar{p}$ is within 0.15 of p, for $0 \leq p \leq 1$; $n = 10$.

In spite of its complexity, Fig. 7–2 has a fairly simple message. With $n = 10$, the probability is at least 0.64 that $\bar{p}$ is within 0.15 of p for all values of p. We also see that when p is near 0 or 1, we are more likely to find $\bar{p}$ in the interval $p \pm 0.15$ than when p is near $\frac{1}{2}$. Similar curves could be drawn for other values of the distance and for other values of n. Fortunately, for large values of n we can forego the tiresome task of drawing the graphs, for reasons that we now investigate.

Large samples. If we know the variance of $\bar{p}$, or X/n, we can take further steps to answer questions about closeness. We need the fact that $\sigma_X^2 = npq$. (See Section 6–5, text or Exercise 14.)

In Section 5–4 we noted that Var $(cX) = c^2\sigma_X^2$, for c a constant. We now find $\sigma_{\bar{p}}^2$ where $\bar{p} = X/n$. The number $1/n$ is a constant, therefore

$$\sigma_{\bar{p}}^2 = \text{Var}\left(\frac{X}{n}\right) = \text{Var}\left(\frac{1}{n}X\right)$$

$$= \frac{1}{n^2}\sigma_X^2 = \frac{1}{n^2}(npq) = \frac{pq}{n}, \tag{3}$$

or

$$\boxed{\sigma_{\bar{p}} = \sqrt{\frac{pq}{n}}.}$$

(4)

This result is encouraging, and rather as we expected. Although σ_X increases as n increases for fixed p, $\sigma_{\bar{p}}$ decreases as n increases.

Recall from Chapter 6 that $\bar{p}$ is the *average* of the values of n random variables, each of which has value 0 or 1, while X is the *sum* of these same n random variables. The results for σ_X and $\sigma_{\bar{p}}$ are symptomatic of a more general fact: *sums of independent random variables ordinarily vary more than their component random variables, while averages vary less.*

EXAMPLE 1. In a biological study, 1000 fruit flies are to be counted for the presence or absence of a certain characteristic. If $\bar{p}$ is used to estimate p, the probability that a fruit fly has the characteristic, how near p will the value of $\bar{p}$ be?

Solution. Conservative Chebyshev approach. We apply Chebyshev's Theorem to the random variable $\bar{p}$, with mean $\mu_{\bar{p}} = p$ and standard deviation $\sigma_{\bar{p}} = \sqrt{pq/n}$. Thus the probability that $\bar{p}$ is within $h\sigma_{\bar{p}}$ of p is at least $1 - 1/h^2$. One difficulty is that we don't know $\sigma_{\bar{p}}$ because we don't know the value of p. However, we can find the value of p that maximizes $\sigma_{\bar{p}}^2 = pq/n$. Since the graph of $pq = p(1 - p)$ is a parabola that is symmetrical about the line $p = \frac{1}{2}$, the maximum value of pq is attained when $p = q = \frac{1}{2}$. Therefore the maximum value of pq is $\frac{1}{2} \cdot \frac{1}{2} = \frac{1}{4}$, and

$$\sigma_{\bar{p}} = \sqrt{\frac{pq}{n}} \leq \sqrt{\frac{1}{4n}} = \frac{1}{\sqrt{4n}}.$$

As before, we write the distance from $\bar{p}$ to p as $|\bar{p} - p|$. Since p is the mean of $\bar{p}$, we can say, from Chebyshev's theorem with $h = 2$, that the probability is at least 0.75 that the distance of $\bar{p}$ from its mean, p, is no more than $2\sigma_{\bar{p}}$:

$$|\bar{p} - p| \leq \frac{2}{\sqrt{4n}}.$$

Similarly, with $h = 3$ the probability is at least 0.88 that the distance

$$|\bar{p} - p| \leq \frac{3}{\sqrt{4n}};$$

and, in general, the probability is at least $1 - 1/h^2$ that the distance

$$|\bar{p} - p| \leq \frac{h}{\sqrt{4n}}.$$

(5)

For our example, if $n = 1000$ and if we choose $h = 2$, the probability is at least 0.75 that

$$|\overline{p} - p| \leq \frac{2}{\sqrt{4n}} = \frac{1}{\sqrt{1000}} \approx 0.032.$$

Or, in words, at least 75% of the probability distribution of $\overline{p}$ is within 0.032 of its mean, p.

The example and demonstration illustrate the following theorems about binomial experiments. Both theorems use the following notation: X is the number of successes, p is the probability of success on a single trial, n is the number of trials, and $\overline{p} = X/n$ is the estimate of p.

7–1 Theorem. *Mean and variance of $\overline{p}$.* In a binomial experiment the mean of $\overline{p}$, $\mu_{\overline{p}}$, and the standard deviation of $\overline{p}$, $\sigma_{\overline{p}}$, are given by

$$\boxed{\mu_{\overline{p}} = E(\overline{p}) = p,} \tag{6}$$

and

$$\boxed{\sigma_{\overline{p}} = \sqrt{pq/n}.} \tag{7}$$

7–2 Theorem. *Law of large numbers.* For any positive number d, as n tends to infinity the probability tends to 1 that the inequality

$$|\overline{p} - p| \leq d$$

is satisfied.

Alternatively, we may state the theorem thus: by making n sufficiently large, we can be as sure as we please that the estimate $\overline{p}$ is within a given nonzero distance d of p.

Proof of Theorem 7–2. For any positive number h, the following inequality is true:

$$1 \geq P\left(|\overline{p} - p| \leq \frac{h}{\sqrt{4n}}\right) \geq 1 - \frac{1}{h^2}. \tag{8}$$

The first inequality in (8) is true because every probability is less than or equal to one, and the last inequality follows from the Chebyshev relation (5), Section 5–6. By proper choice of h, the distance d in Theorem 7–2 can be equated to $h/\sqrt{4n}$:

$$d = \frac{h}{\sqrt{4n}}, \tag{9}$$

provided

$$h = d\sqrt{4n}. \tag{10}$$

Throughout the inequality (8), we substitute for h its value $d\sqrt{4n}$ from Eq. (10), and get

$$1 \geq P(|\bar{p} - p| \leq d) \geq 1 - \frac{1}{4nd^2}. \tag{11}$$

Holding d fixed and letting n increase, we see from the first and last inequalities in (11) that

$$P(|\bar{p} - p| \leq d)$$

tends to 1, as stated in Theorem 7–2. □

EXAMPLE 2. It is desired to use $\bar{p}$ to estimate p, with probability 0.97 or higher, that $\bar{p}$ is within 0.05 of p. How large should n be?

Solution. Using inequality (11), which is equivalent to using the conservative Chebyshev approach, we take

$$d = 0.05, \qquad 1 - \frac{1}{4nd^2} = 0.97.$$

Solving for n, we find

$$n = \frac{1}{(0.03)(4d^2)} \approx 3333.$$

REMARK. The Chebyshev approach is quite conservative. More advanced methods, not treated here, suggest that $n \approx 471$ would be adequate (see Mosteller, Rourke, and Thomas, *Probability with Statistical Applications*, p. 294).

EXERCISES FOR SECTION 7–2

Many of these problems require the use of Table IV–A or IV–B.

1. What additional considerations, besides lack of bias, influence the choice of a method of estimation?

2. Make a graph like that of Fig. 7–1 for the probability function of $\bar{p}$, $n = 5, p = 0.2$.

3. Use the three-place values from the binomial table IV–A for $n = 5$, $p = 0.2$, to obtain $E(\bar{p})$ by direct calculation.

4. For $n = 5$, $p = 0.2$, find $P(|\bar{p} - p| \leq 0.2)$.

5. For $n = 20$, $p = 0.01$, make a table of the probability function for $\bar{p}$.

6. By direct calculation from tabled values find $E(\bar{p})$ for $n = 20$, $p = 0.01$.

7. For $n = 20$, $p = 0.01$, find $P(|\bar{p} - p| \leq 0.1)$.

8. Check the value of the ordinate of Fig. 7–2 for $p = 0.7$.

9. Compute the value of the ordinate of Fig. 7–2 for $p = 0.75$ (interpolation needed).

10. For $n = 3$, make a graph like that of Fig. 7–2 for $P(|\bar{p} - p| \leq \frac{1}{6})$.

Fill in the missing cells in the following table:

	n	p	$\sigma_{\bar{p}}$
11.	4	$\frac{1}{2}$	
12.	9	0.2	
13.	100		0.05
14.		0.1	0.1
15.		p	p
16.	1000		0.01

17. Find the maximum value of $\sigma_{\bar{p}}$ when $n = 4$, 100, and 1000.

18. For $n = 5$, $p = 0.2$, compute $\sigma_{\bar{p}}$ directly from values in Table IV–A.

Find the conservative Chebyshev estimates for $P(|\bar{p} - p| \leq d)$ for

19. $d = 0.1$, $n = 1000$ 20. $d = 0.05$, $n = 100$

21. $d = 0.2$, $n = 10$ 22. $d = 0.01$, $n = 400$

23. The unknown size of a total population of animals is x. From this population, m are captured at random, marked, and released. On a second occasion, n are captured, of which r are found to be marked. Suggest an estimate for x.

7–3. CONSERVATIVE CONFIDENCE LIMITS FOR p WITH LARGE n

In addition to reporting a value of $\bar{p}$ as an estimate of p, it may be helpful to make a statement to summarize our knowledge and our uncertainty about an interval in which p lies. The method of confidence limits offers a way to do this. In this method, we make a statement based on the result of the experiment. For example, with $n = 100$, $x = 40$, and the value of $\bar{p} = 0.4$, we can report with about 95% confidence that the statement

$$0.3 \leq p \leq 0.5$$

is true. Each performance of an experiment gives rise to a statement that p is contained in a specific interval. Some statements will be true, some false, but 95% confidence means that in the long run 95% or more are to be true.

Before indicating a method that yields limits as sharp as those just described, we discuss the conservative Chebyshev approach. Using $h = 2$, we showed that the probability was at least 0.75 that

$$|\bar{p} - p| \leq \frac{2}{\sqrt{4n}}. \tag{1}$$

Stated in words, this inequality says that p is within a distance of $2/\sqrt{4n}$ of $\overline{p}$. We could rewrite the statement then as

$$\overline{p} - \frac{2}{\sqrt{4n}} \le p \le \overline{p} + \frac{2}{\sqrt{4n}}. \tag{2}$$

Both $\overline{p}$ and n are determined from an experiment, so we get upper and lower numerical limits for p. They are called upper and lower *confidence* limits. The probability 0.75 or, equivalently, 75% is the confidence coefficient. Thus if $\overline{p} = 0.4$, $n = 100$, our confidence is at least 75% that

$$0.3 \le p \le 0.5.$$

There is no disagreement between this result and that at the beginning of the section where we said that the confidence is about 95%, but we are disappointed that the Chebyshev result is so conservative.

There is no difficulty about generalizing the Chebyshev result to other values of h. Thus, with confidence at least $1 - 1/h^2$ we can say

$$\overline{p} - \frac{h}{\sqrt{4n}} \le p \le \overline{p} + \frac{h}{\sqrt{4n}}. \tag{3}$$

EXAMPLE 1. *Bowling.* In a league season, a good bowler bowled 400 frames and got 120 strikes. Set conservative 50% confidence limits on p, which measures his probability of a strike. (Assume independence between frames.)

Solution. Setting $h = \sqrt{2}$ in Eq. (3) gives a conservative 50% confidence. Thus the limits are

$$0.300 - \frac{\sqrt{2}}{\sqrt{4(400)}} \le p \le 0.300 + \frac{\sqrt{2}}{\sqrt{4(400)}},$$

or, approximately,

$$0.265 \le p \le 0.335.$$

COMMENT. By rather heavy algebraic methods it is possible to compute limits that are not as conservative as these, and by using extensive tables we can compute limits for small as well as large values of n. We shall not develop such methods here, but since there is a chart that is easy to use for 0.95 confidence limits, we present it as Chart I at the back of the book.

We enter the chart with the observed value $\overline{p}$ on the horizontal axis, and erect a perpendicular from that point. The perpendicular crosses the two curves for the given value of n in two points. Using the vertical scale, we read the upper and lower confidence limits for p as the heights of the points.

EXAMPLE 2. Use the curves in Chart I to get 95% confidence limits for the bowling example.

Solution. Entering with $\bar{p} = 0.3$ and interpolating roughly between the curves for $n = 250$ and $n = 1000$, we find 0.26 and 0.35 as the lower and upper confidence limits.

EXERCISES FOR SECTION 7-3

All the following problems deal with binomial distributions.

1. A random sample of 25 households from a large town shows that 10 buy newspaper A. (a) Use inequality (3) to set 50% confidence limits on the proportion p in the town who buy newspaper A. (b) Set 95% confidence limits, using Chart I.

2. In a sample of 20 students drawn from a large population, 16 recalled recently learned material better immediately after sleeping 8 hours than after 8 hours awake. Set 75% confidence limits on the population proportion p who would have performed better after sleeping 8 hours, had all been tested.

3. If a random sample of 50 families from Cambridge, Mass., showed 10 families with incomes over $5000 during 1951, set a 90% confidence interval on p, the percent of families with incomes over $5000.

4. On 100 different local telephone calls, a secretary fails to complete 25 at the first attempt. Use Chart I to set 95% confidence limits on p, the long-run proportion completed on the first attempt.

5. Some parents of the 5th grade pupils in a large school system complained that their children could not read clear handwriting. A lengthy test on hand-written material showed that 225 out of a random sample of 250 pupils did read the handwriting ($\bar{p} = 0.90$). Use Chart I to set 95% confidence limits on the population proportion p reading handwriting.

6. Use Chart I to set 95% confidence limits on p, the proportion of defective teacups produced, if a random sample of 25 had no defectives.

7. Use inequality (3) to decide on the sample size required to set a 95% confidence limit of total length less than or equal to 0.04.

8. Use Chart I to answer Exercise 7 (note that the broadest limits occur when the value of $\bar{p} = \frac{1}{2}$).

7-4. BAYESIAN APPROACH WHEN PRIOR INFORMATION IS AVAILABLE

In setting confidence limits, we give some notion of the unreliability of our estimate. Sometimes we may have prior information, and then we may try to combine it with experimental information to get an improved estimate of p. Bayes' Theorem, Theorem 4-9, offers some assistance. Since p can take every value from 0 to 1, it is a continuous variable, and we have not developed distributions for such variables. We have dealt mainly with distributions of random variables that take only a finite number of values—that is, *discrete* distributions. Consequently, we shall give an approximate treatment that assumes p has only a finite number of possible values.

EXAMPLE 1.   A manufacturing process has a machine that inspects every item for internal flaws. Over a long period, lots have had the following relative frequencies of percent of defective items.

TABLE 7–1.   DISTRIBUTION OF PERCENT DEFECTIVES.

Relative frequencies of lots	0.6	0.3	0.1
Percent defective	1	5	10

Thus 60% of the lots are classified as in the 1% defective class, 30% in the 5% defective class, and 10% in the 10% defective class.

The usual inspecting machine is broken, but the rest of the production process is working and a new lot is to be inspected by another more expensive operation. A sample of 20 items is drawn from a large lot and none have internal flaws. What can we say of p, the proportion of defectives, for this lot?

Solution.   We regard the discrete distribution of this example as approximately the prior probability distribution for the random variable $100p$, the percent of defectives in a random lot chosen from this process. The new lot (the population from which the sample of 20 items is drawn) has some unknown percent of defectives, say $100p_0$. On the basis of the past data, we want to use the sample information that 0 defectives were observed in 20 trials to find a posterior distribution for $100p_0$. As usual in applying Bayes' Theorem, we set up in Table 7–2 the probabilities of getting this sample from each of the 3 possible compositions of the lot. We get the probabilities of 0 defectives in 20 trials from our binomial Table IV–A.

For example, the prior probability that the new lot is in the 5% defective class is 0.3. Given the new lot is in this class, the probability of 0 defectives in 20 items is $(0.95)^{20} \approx 0.358$. Consequently the probability that the new lot is in the 5% class and produces 0 defectives in the sample is $0.3(0.358) = 0.1074$. The posterior probability for the 5% class is the conditional probability that the lot is in the 5% class, given the sample outcome, or $0.1074/0.6104 \approx 0.176$ (see Table 7–2).

The table of posterior probabilities suggests that the odds are 4 to 1 that $100p_0$ is in the class symbolized by 1%, about 1 to 5 that it is in the class symbolized by 5%, and that the chance is very small that it is in

TABLE 7-2.   CALCULATION OF POSTERIOR PROBABILITIES.

Lot composition (% defective)	Probabilities of 0 defectives in 20 trials	Posterior probabilities
1	$.6(.99)^{20} \approx .6(.818) = .4908$	.804
5	$.3(.95)^{20} \approx .3(.358) = .1074$	.176
10	$.1(.90)^{20} \approx .1(.122) = .0122$	.020
	.6104	1.000

the class symbolized by 10%. One estimate of $100p_0$ could be obtained by computing the mean of the posterior distribution (we round to two decimals):

$$\mu = 1(0.80) + 5(0.18) + 10(0.02) = 1.90.$$

One advantage of the Bayes approach is that the probabilities derived apply to this lot, whereas the confidence coefficient of a confidence limit statement applies to a long sequence of confidence statements. A difficulty is to supply a prior distribution for p, with the view that the p for the new lot is drawn from that distribution. Practical problems in the use of prior distributions are currently being studied by experts in probability and statistics.

EXERCISES FOR SECTION 7-4

1. In the textual example, replace the prior relative frequencies of lots 0.6, 0.3, 0.1, by 0.7, 0.3, 0, respectively. Find the posterior probabilities and the mean, μ, for the posterior distribution.

2. In the textual example, replace the prior relative frequencies 0.6, 0.3, 0.1, by 0.4, 0.4, 0.2, respectively. Find the posterior probabilities and the mean, μ, for the posterior distribution.

3. In the textual example, refer to Table 7-2. If the manufacturer uses the lot, he makes a profit of $100 if the lot is in the 1% class, loses $10 if the lot is in the 5% class, and loses $1000 if the lot is in the 10% class. Based on the posterior distribution, should he use the lot? That is, is his expected profit positive?

4. In the textual example, change the sample size to 25 and the number of defectives observed to 4. Find the posterior distribution and the mean, μ, for this distribution. (Strictly, $p^4 q^{21}$ is the probability of the sample, given p, but since $b(4; 25, p)$ is tabled and is proportional to $p^4 q^{21}$, we use the binomial probability in the calculation of the posterior probabilities.)

7–5. TESTING OF A BINOMIAL STATISTICAL HYPOTHESIS

Sometimes we want to know whether the performance of a binomial process is consistent with the assumption that the probability of success has a given value, p_0.

EXAMPLE 1. *Acceptance sampling or quality control.* A production process has been in control for some time with percent defectives $p_0 \approx 0.05$. Samples of 25 are inspected, and if 4 or more defectives are observed the process is regarded as "out of control"; otherwise the process is accepted as "in control." For various values of the *true* percent defective p, how likely is this criterion to accept the process as "in control"?

Solution. Let the random variable X be the number of defectives in the sample. From Table IV–B, the probability of accepting the process as "in control," $P(X \leq 3)$, can be readily computed for any given proportion of defectives, p. Figure 7–3 shows $P(X \leq 3)$, for different proportions of defectives p, $0 \leq p \leq 0.30$. The ordinate gives the probability of accepting the process as "in control" for the value of p shown by the

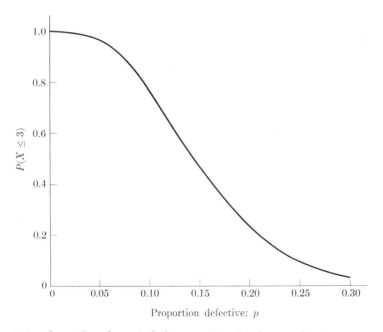

FIG. 7–3. Operating characteristic: $n = 25$, rejection number 4, acceptance number 3.

abscissa. The graph is called the *operating characteristic* of the test. When the process is operating at a level of 5% or fewer defectives the sample rarely gives the judgment "out of control." The graph shows the probability of accepting as greater than 0.95. On the other hand, if p is large compared with 0.05, say $p = 0.15$, 4 or more defectives occur more than half the time, and the sampling process is likely to detect the change soon, if not immediately. If p is very large, say 0.25, the sample is almost certain to detect this at once, and appropriate action will be taken.

For $p = 0.15$, Fig. 7–3 shows that about half the time the fact that the process is "out of control" will not be detected by the sample. The manufacturer may wish to steepen the curve so as to discriminate more immediately and sharply between a process producing 5% defectives and, say, 15%. By increasing the sample size n and changing the rejection number r ($r = 4$ in the example), the shape of the operating characteristic can be changed.

Figure 7–4 shows a set of operating characteristics for several acceptance sampling plans, all designed to have probability of about $\frac{1}{2}$ of rejecting the process when $p = 0.07$. As n increases, r increases, and the operating characteristic becomes steeper at $p = 0.07$. The curves were made with the aid of large binomial tables.

Such plans are used to help control a process or to help a buyer decide whether the lot of material he purchases has the quality the seller claims.

Variations on the theme of acceptance sampling are quite common in scientific work. The *sign test* is typical of these. On the basis of a sample from a population, one wants to decide whether some percentile of the population, for example the median, is equal to a known standard or not. The method proceeds by translating measurements in the sample into a $+$ or $-$ according as the measurement is above or below the standard. If the standard equals the population percentile, then binomial theory applies to the number of $+$'s and $-$'s, as we describe in the following examples.

EXAMPLE 2. National results on a standardized achievement test are scored so that half of all students score 100 or over, and half score less (100 is the population median). A teacher wonders whether his class differs from this standard. Of his class of 20, 16 scored higher than 100, 4 lower. He sees at once that the class has more than half above the standard. But he may also ask, "Considering sampling fluctuations, is it reasonable that my class is a sample from a large population of students half of whom score 100 or more, and half less?" Specifically, he visualizes the population from which his students are drawn as the students attending his school over a number of years, and he is willing to regard this class as a random sample from such a population.

P (accept)

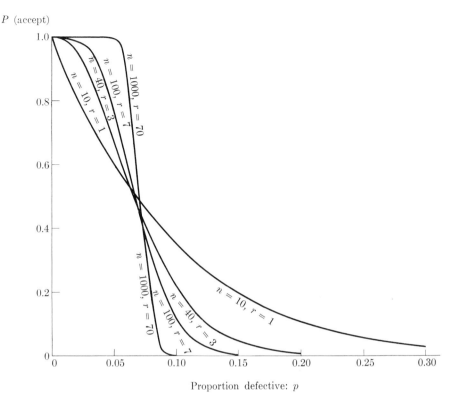

FIG. 7–4.   Operating characteristics of several plans.

Discussion.   In this question, the teacher visualizes a population in which the probability of scoring 100 or more is $p_0 = \frac{1}{2}$. We call p_0 his *null hypothesis*, or standard. The word "null," in this setting, means that there is nothing special about the population. As an *alternative hypothesis* he considers that the true p for the population of students from which his school draws has $p \neq \frac{1}{2}$. He thinks his school's population may be worse or better than the national average.

One way to test such questions is to use the sample to set confidence limits on the unknown p. If the confidence interval contains the value $p = \frac{1}{2}$, we accept the possibility that the null hypothesis is true, otherwise we reject the null hypothesis in favor of the alternative. In a testing problem, we speak of the *significance level* of the test. It measures the probability of rejecting the null hypothesis when it is true. It is the complement of the confidence level, if a confidence interval is used to make the test. Thus if the confidence level is chosen as 0.95, the significance level is 0.05.

In Example 2, the 95% confidence limits for p, when 16 successes are observed out of 20, can be read from Chart I. We get 0.56 and 0.95 as lower and upper confidence limits for p. Since $p = \frac{1}{2}$ is not in the interval, at the 5% level we reject the null hypothesis that $p = \frac{1}{2}$ for the population of students from which the class is drawn.

One-sided tests. In the test just described, the approach was two-sided, because the teacher thought both $p > \frac{1}{2}$ and $p < \frac{1}{2}$ were possibilities. He might have formulated the problem with the null hypothesis $p \leq \frac{1}{2}$ and the alternative $p > \frac{1}{2}$. Then he would reject the null hypothesis only for large values of X.

The worst value of the null hypothesis, from the point of view of being able to distinguish it from the alternative hypothesis, is $p = \frac{1}{2}$. Assume, temporarily, that $p = \frac{1}{2}$ and compute the probability of observing a result as extreme as, or more extreme than, the one observed in the direction of the alternative (16 or more above 100 in our example). The resulting probability is called a *descriptive level of significance*. If it is as small as or smaller than the level of significance the investigator would use in the problem, he rejects the null hypothesis in favor of the alternative. Our descriptive level of significance computed on the basis of the largest null hypothesis value of p (from Table IV–B) is $P(X \geq 16) = 0.006$, and we again would reject at the 0.05 level of significance.

Other null hypotheses. The sorts of tests just described are not limited to null hypotheses related to $p = \frac{1}{2}$.

EXAMPLE 3. A standard medication reduces reports of post-operative pain in 80% of patients treated. A new medication for the same purpose produces 90 patients relieved among the first 100 tested. What is an appropriate test of significance?

Solution. If the new medication is better than the old—few are—we want to detect it. We take as the null hypothesis $p \leq 0.8$ and as the alternative $p > 0.8$. We compute $P(X \geq 90)$ for $n = 100$, $p = 0.8$, because 0.8 is the standard the new medication ought to exceed if it is to replace the old medication. From large binomial tables we find

$$P(X \geq 90) \approx 0.0057,$$

which is approximately the descriptive level of significance. If the investigator is using the 5% or the 1% level of significance he rejects the null hypothesis in favor of the alternative. Operationally, he decides to use the new medication in preference to the old.

Accepting or rejecting the null hypothesis. Why do we reject the null hypothesis, or accept it? As you must have observed, we reject it when the probability of the occurrence of the observed event, or more extreme ones, is small. But that alone is not the reason. We reject it because the data do not support it, *and* because we think the alternative hypothesis is tenable and that the data do support the alternative. The quality control man rejects the hypothesis that the process is "in control" in favor of the hypothesis that the process is "out of control" because he knows there is a good chance it may be, since machine settings, inattention, and new raw materials are all common sources of trouble. Therefore, when he sees a high number of defectives, he would rather assume that something has gone wrong and look for it, than merely assume that a very unusual sample has occurred in a process that is in control. Similarly, the teacher knows that there is variation in teaching ability and in school systems. His students were not randomly drawn from the national population, but from a special neighborhood. And the doctor looking for a new medication knows that medications better than the standard ones are found from time to time (after all, the standard was once unknown) but not often, so he will be very cautious about replacing a standard. In all these examples the decisions are not final; new data can overthrow them.

What does it mean to accept the null hypothesis? Suppose the teacher had observed 12 students with scores of 100 or over and 8 with lower scores and had tested the null hypothesis $p = \frac{1}{2}$ against the alternative $p \neq \frac{1}{2}$. At usual levels of significance he accepts the null hypothesis. However, he does not believe therefore that $p = \frac{1}{2}$ exactly. A sample of 20 carries practically no information for discriminating $p = 0.500$ from $p = 0.501$. All the teacher accepts is that p is near $\frac{1}{2}$. Furthermore, he reserves the right to change his mind if he gets more data that conflict with the hypothesis that p is near $\frac{1}{2}$.

EXERCISES FOR SECTION 7–5

1. From Fig. 7–3, what is the probability that the process is judged "in control" if $p = 0.10$? If $p = 0.30$? What is the probability it is judged "out of control" if $p = 0.20$?

2. From Fig. 7–3, what proportions of defectives lead to judgments of "in control" 80% of the time? 10% of the time?

3. Check the answers to Exercise 2, using binomial tables.

4. Make an operating characteristic like Fig. 7–3 for the plan: samples of size 2, reject if 1 or more defectives are found. Compare with Fig. 7–3.

5. (Continuation.) Suppose 2 items are randomly drawn without replacement from 10 items, and the lot of 10 is rejected if the sample has one or more defectives. Show on the same graph as that of Exercise 4 the probabilities of accepting the lot of 10 for each fraction defective in the lot. (Thus you are in a position to compare the exact probabilities of this exercise with the binomial probabilities of Exercise 4 as an approximation. Binomial calculations are often made *as if*

sampling were done with replacement, as an approximation for calculations for sampling without replacement.)

6. From Fig. 7–4, find for the four plans the values of p for which lots are accepted 95% of the time.

7. Use your binomial tables to find a plan (sample size n and rejection number r) that accepts about 85% of lots or processes with $p = 0.05$, and rejects about 90% of lots with $p = 0.20$.

For Exercises 8 and 9, consider the plan of Fig. 7–3 ($n = 25$, $r = 4$), and suppose that 100 large lots have 1% defectives, 100 have 5% defectives, and 100 have 20% defectives.

8. Find the expected number of lots accepted by the plan.

9. Find the expected number of defective items accepted if each of the 300 lots has 1000 items. Compute the percent of defective items accepted, and compare it with the percent in the original 300 lots.

10. Suppose a buyer uses one of the sampling plans described in this chapter. Suppose the seller always persuades the buyer to give any rejected lot a "second chance," using the same plan. What is the relationship between the actual operating characteristic for the new procedure and the operating characteristic of the original plan?

11. An accepted lot is worth about $500 to a manufacturer. A rejected one costs $200 for reworking, and so has a net worth of about $300. He can produce at $p = 0.10$ at no additional cost, and he can reduce p by an additional $0.01x$ for $5x$ dollars. If the plan of Fig. 7–3 is used, the probabilities of rejection for various values of p are as follows:

p	.10	.09	.08	.07	.06	.05	.04	.03	.02	.01
P (rejection$\mid p$)	.236	.183	.135	.094	.060	.034	.017	.006	.0015	.0001

At what p should he operate to maximize expected profit (or to minimize expected losses compared with the $500 value for an accepted lot)?

12. Madame X says that she can tell by taste whether tea has been made with tea bags or with bulk tea. She sips from 10 pairs of cups, one with each kind of tea, and correctly identifies 9 of the pairs. What descriptive level of significance would you attach to this experiment?

13. For the data of Exercise 12, use Chart I to set 95% confidence limits on p, the probability of correctly identifying a pair of cups. Then, at the 5% significance level, reject the null hypothesis, $p = \frac{1}{2}$, in favor of the alternative, $p \neq \frac{1}{2}$, if $p = \frac{1}{2}$ is outside the confidence interval.

14. Fred has a die he believes may be loaded in favor of the side marked "six." He tosses it 4 times and gets three "sixes." Using the 5% level of significance, do these results cause you to reject the null hypothesis $p = \frac{1}{6}$?

15. Mr. Williams played 5 hands of bridge one evening and got no aces 4 times. He complains of poor shuffling. Assuming good shuffling, the probability p of getting at least one ace, on any one deal, is 0.7 (approximately).

Are 4 no-ace hands out of 5 hands enough to reject the null hypothesis $p = 0.7$ at the 5% level of significance? (Use the binomial formula.)

16. A manufacturer of light bulbs says that only 10% of the frosted bulbs he manufactures have defective frosting, and that these defective bulbs occur at random during manufacture. A carton of 4 of his bulbs was purchased and 2 of these had defective frosting. Would you reject his claim at the 1% level of significance?

17. A patient suffering from chronic headaches has had 60% of a large number of headaches relieved by standard medication. A new component is added to his medication, and 17 of his next 20 headaches are relieved. Would you reject, at 5% level, the null hypothesis of $p = 0.6$? Criticize the application of the binomial distribution to this experiment.

18. Find a 95% confidence interval for p in Exercise 17.

19. Five items are drawn from a large lot. If two or fewer are defective, the lot is accepted. Compute roughly the operating characteristic of this test, graph it, and tell for what percent defective half the lots will be accepted and half rejected.

20. To decide whether a coin is unbiased, one man flips the coin 4 times. If it comes up heads on all 4 flips, he rejects the hypothesis that it is unbiased. A second man thoroughly mixes an urn containing 15 white balls and 1 red one, all alike except for color, and draws out 1 ball. If it is red, he rejects the hypothesis that the coin is unbiased, otherwise he assumes it is unbiased. (a) What is the null hypothesis for each man? (b) What is the significance level for each test? (c) What are the circumstances under which the first man's test is preferable to the second man's?

21. Fertilizers A and B are used on 5 pairs of adjacent (randomly selected) plots of cabbage. The differences in yield in hundreds of pounds $(A - B)$ are 6, 4, 2, 2, 1. Use the sign test to decide at the 10% level whether the fertilizers are equally likely to provide high yields.

22. In a psycho-physical experiment, a subject has a 30% detection rate for a signal, established by thousands of trials. After a vacation he returns to the laboratory and detects the signal on only one of the first 20 trials. The experimenter wonders whether the equipment and/or the subject have changed, or whether this large a deviation from the 30% rate is a frequent occurrence under sampling variation. Advise him and state your assumptions.

23. In a coffee-tasting experiment a subject tastes each of 10 pairs of cups of coffee and decides for each pair which cup contains the instant rather than the percolated coffee. The experimenter decides to call a person a "taster" if he decides correctly in at least 8 out of 10 pairs, otherwise he is called a "non-taster." Regarding this operation as a test of significance: (a) What is the null hypothesis? (b) What are the alternative hypotheses? (c) What is the level of significance? (d) If a subject has probability 0.8 of correctly calling a pair, what is the chance he will be called a "taster"?

Data for Exercises 24, 25, 26. Of two brands of "fireproof" glass ovenware, a wholesaler wants to choose the one that withstands a greater sudden change of temperature. In testing the brands, he uses an oven and a tub of icewater. He tests a Brand A piece and a Brand B piece simultaneously as follows. He transfers the two pieces from the tub to the oven, which is set at 300° F. If neither breaks, both are returned to the tub. If neither breaks now, both are returned to the oven, in which the temperature has been advanced to 350° F. This process continues with 50° increases in oven temperature until one piece breaks. (Forget about both breaking at the same time.) The piece that breaks first is regarded as poorer, and its brand is regarded as poorer on that trial.

24. In 10 trials, Brand A broke first 9 times. Is this often enough to reject at the 5% level the hypothesis that the two brands are of equal quality?

25. Another wholesaler ran a series of trials. He reported that Brand A always broke first in his trials and that he rejected the hypothesis of the equality of the brands at the 5% level. What is the smallest number of trials he could have run?

26. A third wholesaler said he had run a lot of trials, and Brand A had always broken first in his, too. He had concluded that Brand A would always break first. In answer to a question, he said he supposed the probability of A's breaking first was 1.00. How many times in 1000 trials would Brand B have to break first to reject this supposition?

27. Cartons of 8 60-watt lamps are called lots. Each carton is inspected by testing 2 of the lamps, selected at random. The acceptance rule is that if both the tested lamps light, the carton is accepted; if either fails, the carton is rejected. A customer who has adopted this acceptance plan picks up a carton which happens to contain 2 defective lamps and 6 nondefective ones. What is the probability that he will accept the carton?

7–6. BAYESIAN INFERENCE WITH PERSONAL PROBABILITIES

Hypotheses are rejected because we believe their alternatives have a good chance of being true in the light of the total evidence. If we can quantify our prior beliefs, then Bayes' Theorem can aid us in problems like those treated in Section 7–5. Many people are unwilling to make such personalistic quantifications, but the following example illustrates how the personalistic approach through probability as degree of belief would work. The example is one about which you may have views.

Extrasensory perception. Art claims that he has extrasensory perception (ESP). He says that if Bob conceals a red card in one hand and a black card in the other, he can tell which hand holds the red card. Bob doesn't believe it. Art admits he can't do this all the time, just "pretty often."

First, we give an approach like that of Section 7–5. In this form the problem is appropriate for a significance test with null hypothesis $p = \frac{1}{2}$ (Art has no ESP, and performs by guessing), alternative hypothesis $p > \frac{1}{2}$ (Art has some ESP). Bob can give Art a test consisting of a number of trials and a criterion for passing such that Art has a good chance of passing the test if he has a noticeable amount of ESP, say $p = 0.7$, and not much chance of passing if he doesn't ($p = \frac{1}{2}$). Let X be the number of successes in n trials. Then we read from our binomial tables that, with 25 trials, if $p = \frac{1}{2}$, $P(X \geq 16) \approx 0.115$, and if $p = 0.7$, $P(X \geq 16) \approx 0.811$. One test is to try 25 times and be right 16 or more times. Thus if Art has no ESP he will fail in about 89% of such tests, and if he has ESP amounting to $p = 0.7$ he will pass in about 81%. Tests with more trials can reduce the risk of passing or failing Art erroneously, and improve his chance of passing if he has some ESP but less than $p = 0.7$. This approach is like that of the previous section. Let us turn now to the personalistic approach.

To give a numerical value of Bob's disbelief in Art's ability, we would have to ask Bob what he thinks the chances are that Art has no ability ($p = 0.5$), or that he has probability $p = 0.6$, $p = 0.7$, or so on, of passing. (Properly, the probability distribution would treat p as a continuous variable, but we shall treat the prior distribution with a discrete approximation, as we did in Section 7–4.) For simplicity, suppose Bob's degrees of belief in Art's ability are as follows:

Hypothesis	Art's ability	Bob's prior degree of belief
H_1:	$p = 0.5$	0.98
H_2:	$p = 0.7$	0.02
		1.00

If n trials are performed and Art has x successes, then the following table helps in calculating the posterior degrees of belief from Bayes' Theorem.

Probability of outcome

$p = 0.5$ $0.98(0.5)^x(0.5)^{n-x}$

$$= P \text{ (Bob has } p = 0.5)P \text{ (sample|Bob has } p = 0.5)$$

$p = 0.7$ $0.02(0.7)^x(0.3)^{n-x}$

$$= P \text{ (Bob has } p = 0.7)P \text{ (sample|Bob has } p = 0.7)$$

There are no binomial coefficients because we compute the probability of the particular sample in the order of occurrence of the calls. Had we introduced binomial coefficients they would have dropped out of the later calculations. Therefore we may use them if there is any advantage in calculation.

In advance, Bob's odds (ratio of degrees of belief) were 0.98 to 0.02 or 49 to 1 against Art having ESP. After the experiment, Bob's odds against Art having ability are given by the ratio

$$\frac{0.98(0.5)^x(0.5)^{n-x}}{0.02(0.7)^x(0.3)^{n-x}} = \frac{49(0.5)^x(0.5)^{n-x}}{(0.7)^x(0.3)^{n-x}} .$$

EXAMPLE 1. Suppose $n = 25$, $x = 17$. Find the posterior odds.

Solution. From our Table IV–A, we get

$$\frac{49b(17; 25, 0.5)}{b(17; 25, 0.7)} \approx \frac{49(0.032)}{0.165} \approx 9.5.$$

Thus if Art correctly identifies exactly 17 cards out of 25, Bob's odds have gone down from 49 to 1 to 9.5 to 1 against Art having the ability. He still doesn't believe much in Art's ability, but he has weakened by a factor of 5.

Additional data can readily be added.

EXERCISES FOR SECTION 7–6

The first three of the following exercises assume that Bob's odds against Art are 9.5 to 1, and are concerned with the effects of further data on the odds. Start each problem at the 9.5 to 1 odds.

1. If Art's next 3 trials are successes, what are the new odds?

2. If Art's next 3 trials are failures, what are the new odds?

3. If Art has 3 successes and 3 failures, what are the new odds?

4. If Art gets exactly half right and half wrong in a test of size n, what value of n yields odds of about 1000 to 1 against him, starting with 49 to 1 against?

5. Bob holds prior odds of 1 to 1 that Madame X of Exercise 12 in Section 7–5 has $p = 0.5$ or $p = 0.7$ of being able to distinguish the pairs of teacups. After she gets 9 out of 10 right, what are his posterior odds?

APPENDICES

APPENDICES

I

COLLECTIONS OF
OBJECTS: SETS

I-1. THE NOTION OF A SET

The idea of a *set* is common in everyday life, where it implies a recognition of some common property possessed by a group of objects. We speak of a set of dishes, a set of stamps, a set of books, and so on. The implication is that one can tell whether or not a given dish or stamp or book belongs to the group under discussion.

The idea of a set is basic in mathematics. Indeed, it has been said that the whole of contemporary mathematics can be derived from the concept of a set and the rules of logic. In mathematics, we use the word *set* to denote any well-defined collection of objects, things, or symbols. By "well-defined" we mean that it must be possible to tell beyond doubt whether or not a given object belongs to the collection that we are considering. Thus the connotation of the word *set* is the same as when it is used in its nontechnical, everyday sense.

Anything that is a member of a set is called an *element* of the set. If some positive number or zero is the number of elements in a set, we say that the set is *finite;* otherwise, the set is *infinite.* Our present purpose is to introduce some of the vocabulary and ideas of the theory of sets, because these notions will contribute to the ease and clarity with which probability and statistics can be treated. Here are some examples.

EXAMPLE 1. The following collections satisfy the requirements of a set:

(a) the people in your immediate family (father, mother, you, your sisters and brothers);

(b) your class in school;

(c) the students who take mathematics in your school;

(d) the eighty-second Congress of the United States;

(e) the fifty states in the U.S.A.;

(f) the positive integers with two digits;

(g) the prime numbers less than 50.

EXAMPLE 2. What is the set of points (x, y) whose coordinates satisfy the inequality $y \geq 4 - 2x$?

Solution. All points whose coordinates satisfy $y = 4 - 2x$ lie on the straight line passing through the points $(2, 0)$ and $(0, 4)$. The points whose coordinates satisfy $y > 4 - 2x$ lie *above* this line. Therefore the required set of points consists of the half-plane *above and including* the line whose equation is $y = 4 - 2x$. (See Fig. I–1.)

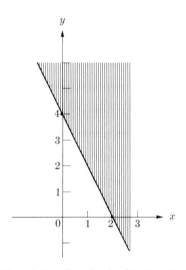

FIG. I–1.   Graph of $y \geq 4 - 2x$.

EXERCISES FOR SECTION I–1

1. Give two examples of sets whose elements are: (a) people, (b) books, (c) letters of the alphabet, (d) numbers, (e) geometrical objects.

2. Each of the numbers 0, 1, 2, 3, 4, 5 is written on a ping-pong ball, and the balls are put in a hat and thoroughly mixed. A blindfolded person reaches into the hat and draws out two balls in succession. The number x on the first ball and the number y on the second ball are recorded, in order.

(a) Plot the points (x, y) that correspond to the set of all possible outcomes of this experiment. [*Note.* Order counts in these pairs; for example, $(1, 2)$ is different from $(2, 1)$.]

(b) How many points are there in the set of part (a)?

(c) Complete the following chart to show the set of all possible sums $x + y$ that can be formed by adding the numbers on the two ping-pong balls, and the set of all pairs (x, y) that give each sum.

(d) Indicate the sums of part (c) by drawing the set of lines $x + y = k$ for $k = 1, 2, 3, \ldots, 9$ on your diagram of part (a).

$x + y$	(x, y) having given sum $x + y$
1	$(0,\ 1),\ \ (1,\ 0)$
2	$(0,\ 2),\qquad\quad (2,\ 0)$
3	$(0,\ 3),\ \ (1,\ 2),\ \ (2,\ 1),\ \ (3,\ 0)$
$\vdots$	$\vdots$

3. In the experiment of Exercise 2, suppose that the first ball is put back into the hat before the second ball is drawn. Repeat the four parts of Exercise 2 for this new experiment.

4. Describe and sketch the sets of points whose x and y coordinates satisfy each of the following conditions:

$$\text{(a)}\ \ y = x, \qquad \text{(b)}\ \ y > x, \qquad \text{(c)}\ \ y < x,$$

$$\text{(d)}\ \ y > x + 1, \qquad \text{(e)}\ \ x + y \le 4.$$

I–2. TWO WAYS OF SPECIFYING SETS

In common practice, there are two ways of specifying a set:

(1) *List the names of all members of the set* (the "roster" method). This method is clear-cut and convenient when the number of elements of the set is not too great. It is customary to use a capital letter (for example, $A, B, S, \ldots$) for the name of the whole set, and to enclose the names of the members of the set in braces. Thus, the set S consisting of the numbers of dots on the faces of a die is

$$S = \{1,\ 2,\ 3,\ 4,\ 5,\ 6\}.$$

(2) *State the requirements that any object must meet in order to be a member of the set* (the "rule" method). In stating a rule for membership, we can express it in words:

"S is the set of all elements x *such that* x is an integer and x is between 1 and 6, inclusive."

However, it is much more compact to express the rule thus:

$$S = \{x : x \text{ is an integer and } 1 \le x \le 6\}.$$

The notation

$$\text{"}\{\ :\ \}\text{"}$$

is called the "set-builder." The colon "$:$" is read "such that." On the left of the colon is a symbol for an arbitrary element of the set; on the right is the rule that defines membership in the set.

EXAMPLE 1. Specify the set of vowels S in two ways.

Solution. We can write

$$S = \{a,\ e,\ i,\ o,\ u\} \qquad \text{(roster method)},$$

or

$$S = \{* : * \text{ is a vowel}\} \qquad \text{(rule method)}.$$

NOTE. The asterisk and the "x" are used in the foregoing as symbols that hold places for arbitrary elements of a set. Thus "x" is not used in this connection as a letter of the alphabet.

EXAMPLE 2. If $S = \{1, 2, 3, 4, 5, 6\}$ and T is the set of numbers that are squares of the elements of S, specify the set T in two ways.

Solutions. We have

$$T = \{1,\ 4,\ 9,\ 16,\ 25,\ 36\} \qquad \text{(roster method)},$$

$$T = \{x^2 : x \text{ is an element of } S\} \qquad \text{(rule method)}.$$

EXAMPLE 3. Specify the set of all points inside the circle $x^2 + y^2 = 4$.

Solution. $S = \{(x, y) : x \text{ and } y \text{ are real numbers and } x^2 + y^2 < 4\}$.

EXAMPLE 4. A cent and a dime are tossed into the air. Let x represent the face of the cent that lands on top, and y that of the dime. Specify in two ways the set S of possible pairs (x, y) that the coins may show.

Solution. We can write

$$S = \{(H, H),\ \ (H, T),\ \ (T, H),\ \ (T, T)\},$$

or

$$S = \{(x, y) : x \text{ is } H \text{ or } T \text{ and } y \text{ is } H \text{ or } T\},$$

where we have used H for "head" and T for "tail."

REMARK. Note that in Example 4 we use x to represent something other than a number: x is used as a symbol to represent an element of the set $\{H, T\}$.

EXERCISES FOR SECTION I–2

1. Use both the roster method and the rule method to specify the following sets: (a) the consonants in the first half of the alphabet; (b) the prime numbers less than 25.

2. Specify the following sets by the rule method and discuss why the roster method is difficult or impossible: (a) the set of people who live in your community; (b) the set of all even numbers; (c) the set consisting of squares of integers.

Inequalities and absolute values: useful symbols in specifying sets. Many of the sets that we shall study are sets of numbers whose elements can be concisely specified by the use of equations, inequalities, and other mathematical symbols. The rules for dealing with inequalities are summarized as follows:

(1) If the same number is added to, or subtracted from, both sides of an inequality, the new inequality holds with the *same* inequality sign.

(2) If both sides of an inequality are multiplied or divided by the same *positive* number, the new inequality holds with the *same* inequality sign.

(3) If both sides of an inequality are multiplied or divided by the same *negative* number, the new inequality holds with the *reversed* inequality sign.

Note that the operations with inequalities are similar to those with equations, *except for rule (3)*. Thus,

if $x > y$,

then $kx > ky$,   if k is positive,

and $kx < ky$,   if k is negative.

What becomes of the inequality if $k = 0$?

A useful mathematical symbol is that of absolute value, which we shall now discuss. Suppose the number a is represented by the point A on a number scale (Fig. I–2). Then *the absolute value of a*, denoted by $|a|$, is

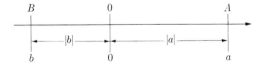

Fig. I–2.   Absolute value.

the number of units in the distance OA. Thus, if $a = +3$, $|a| = 3$; and if $b = -2$, $|b| = 2$. Similarly, we have

$$|-\tfrac{7}{2}| = \tfrac{7}{2}, \qquad |\pi| = \pi, \qquad |-\sqrt{2}| = \sqrt{2}, \qquad \text{and so on.}$$

The foregoing geometrical interpretation of $|a|$ leads to the following algebraic definition.

I-1. Definition.   *Absolute value.*

> If $a \geq 0$, then $|a| = a$; if a < 0, then $|a| = -a$.

EXAMPLE 1. Represent graphically $\{x : |x| \leq 2\}$, where x is real.

Solution. The inequality $|x| \leq 2$ states that the measure of the distance from point x to point 0 on the number scale is less than or equal to 2. Hence the domain of x extends from -2 to $+2$, inclusive, as shown in Fig. I–3.

$$\xrightarrow{\hspace{2cm}\bullet\hspace{2cm}\mid\hspace{2cm}\bullet\hspace{2cm}} x$$

$$\qquad -2 \qquad\qquad 0 \qquad\qquad 2$$

FIG. I–3.   Graph of $\{x : |x| \leq 2\}$.

NOTE. We use the filled-in dot, "•," at 2 and -2 to indicate that these numbers are *included* in the set. An open dot, "∘," may be used to indicate that a number is *excluded*.

What geometrical interpretation can be given to $|x - 5|$? The definition of absolute value suggests two cases:

(1) If $x - 5 \geq 0$, then $|x - 5| = x - 5$. For this case, Fig. I–4 shows that $|x - 5|$, or $x - 5$, represents the measure of the distance from x to 5 on the number scale. (If $x - 5 = 0$, $x = 5$ and $|x - 5| = 0$.)

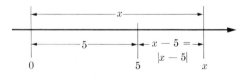

FIG. I–4. $|x - 5|$ for $x - 5 \geq 0$.

(2) If $x - 5 < 0$, then $|x - 5| = 5 - x$. Referring to Fig. I–5, we see that once again $|x - 5|$, or $5 - x$, measures the distance from x to 5. Thus, in all possible cases, $|x - 5|$ *measures the distance between x and 5 on the number scale.* In general, $|x - a|$ is the distance between x and a on the number scale.

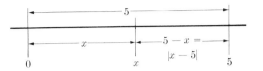

Fig. I-5. $|x - 5|$ for $x - 5 < 0$.

EXAMPLE 2. Represent graphically $\{x : |x - 4| \leq 2\}$, where x is a real number.

Solution. The inequality $|x - 4| \leq 2$ states that the distance from x to 4 is less than or equal to 2. This means that x may have values from 2 to 6, inclusive:

$$2 \leq x \leq 6.$$

Figure I-6 is a graph of the domain of x.

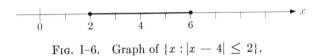

Fig. I-6. Graph of $\{x : |x - 4| \leq 2\}$.

The following table exhibits some sets of real numbers, defined with and without the absolute value symbol. Graphs are included.

TABLE I-1

SPECIFICATION OF SETS OF REAL NUMBERS.

Using absolute values	Without absolute values	Graph
$\{x : |x| \geq 3\}$	$\{x : x^2 \geq 9\}$ or $\{x : x \geq 3$ or $x \leq -3\}$	
$\{x : |x - 1| < 2\}$	$\{x : -1 < x < 3\}$	
$\{x : |x + 5| > 1\}$	$\{x : x < -6$ or $x > -4\}$	
$\{x : |x - a| < 2\}$	$\{x : a - 2 < x < a + 2\}$	

FURTHER EXERCISES FOR SECTION I–2

1. Evaluate each of the following: $|-5|$, $|-\sqrt{3}|$, $|+4| + |-4|$, $|5 - 8|$, $|8 - 5|$, $|c - 7|$, $|7 - c|$, $|m|$.

2. Verify by trial, using both positive and negative values of c, that $\sqrt{c^2} = |c|$.

3. Verify by trial, using both positive and negative values of x, that $x \leq |x|$ and $-x \leq |x|$.

4. Given that x is a real number, describe each of the following sets by using the set-builder notation and the absolute value symbol. Represent each of the sets on a graph.

   (a) x is between -4 and 4, inclusive;
   (b) x is greater than 6 or less than -6;
   (c) x is numerically greater than 2;
   (d) x is numerically equal to, or less than, 1;
   (e) x differs from 5 by 2 or less;
   (f) the distance from x to 7 is less than 3 units on the number scale.

5. Describe each of the following intervals with a statement involving the word "distance." Represent each interval on a graph. (a) $|x| < 3$, (b) $|x| \geq 2$, (c) $|x| \leq 4$, (d) $|x| \geq 0$, (e) $|x - 5| \leq 1$, (f) $|x + 3| \leq 1$, (g) $|x - 3| \geq 2$, (h) $|x - k| \leq 5$.

6. Below are shown the graphs of a number of sets of real numbers. For each graph, specify the set, using the set-builder and any other mathematical symbols that you wish.

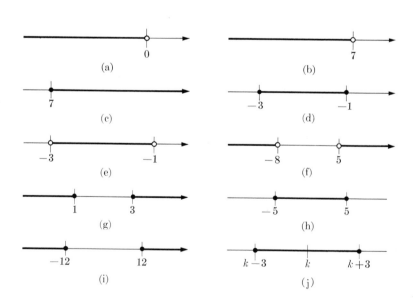

I-3. UNIVERSAL SET AND SUBSETS

In some contexts, we may wish to restrict our attention to objects that belong to some fixed, large set. In plane geometry, for example, this large set might be the set of all points in a plane. We could call this totality of all points under consideration our "universal set," U. From U, we might then select special subsets: for example, the points on a given line L, or the points inside a given circle, or the points of intersection of a line and a circle, and so on.

As another example, consider

$U =$ the set of all automobiles registered in the U.S.A. in 1960,

$A =$ the set of all automobiles registered in New Jersey in 1960,

$B =$ the set of all registered automobiles in the U.S.A., and not involved in an accident in 1960.

Sets A and B are subsets of the universal set U.

Venn diagrams. It is often helpful to have a schematic representation of the universal set and its subsets. One such scheme is known as a *Venn diagram* (Fig. I–7). The rectangle U in the diagram represents the universal set U, and the *elements* of U are represented by the points in the rectangle. *Sets of elements* of U (such as A and B) are represented by the points in circles within the rectangle. See Fig. I–7.

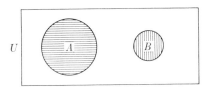

Fig. I–7. Venn Diagram.

I–2 Definition. *Subset.* If every element of set A is also an element of set B, then we say that A is a *subset* of B. (See Fig. I–8.)

Thus if U is the set of all students, B the set of students in your school, and A the set of all students of mathematics in your school, then A is a subset of B.

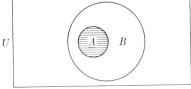

Fig. I–8. A is a subset of B.

Subsets of a given set. Consider a finite, universal set U. If we know the number of elements in U, can we tell how many different subsets U has? The answer is "yes," and we shall show a method for finding the number of subsets. Let us first illustrate the method for the case where U has four elements, and then extend it to the case where U has any finite number n of elements.

EXAMPLE 1. Let $U = \{a, b, c, d\}$. How many different subsets has U?

Solution. The multiplication principle of Section 2–1 provides the method we seek. For the number of possible subsets of U is simply the number of ways of making a selection from the four elements a, b, c, and d. The procedure is as follows.

We can deal with a in 2 ways (take it into the set or leave it out). Then, after dealing with a in either of these ways, we can deal with b in 2 ways (take it or leave it). Similarly, we can deal with c in 2 ways, and then with d in 2 ways. Therefore, by the multiplication principle, there are exactly

$$2 \times 2 \times 2 \times 2 = 2^4 = 16$$

ways of making a selection from the four elements of U.

All of these 16 selections except two give rise to readily acceptable subsets of U. These two deserve special mention:

(1) The selection in which we *take* a and b and c and d gives rise to the set

$$\{a, b, c, d\},$$

which is identical with U. Shall we call U a subset of itself? Since every element of U is an element of U, the definition of subset is satisfied, so we agree that U is a subset of itself.

(2) The selection in which we *leave* a and b and c and d gives rise to a set with no elements. We call such a set the *empty* set or the *null* set, and denote it by ϕ. (This symbol for the empty set is the Greek letter phi, pronounced "fie" or "fee.") By special agreement, *we accept the empty set as a subset of any set whatever.* Why do we adopt such a convention? Here are two reasons:

(1) The empty set plays a role similar to that of zero in the number system: if the empty set is adjoined to any set A, the result is A. We are saved from making exceptions in stating theorems.

(2) The convention does not violate the definition, which requires that every element of ϕ must belong to any given set B. There are no members of ϕ to violate this condition.

I-3 Theorem. If U is a finite set having n elements, then there are 2^n different subsets of U, including U and ϕ.

The proof is left as an exercise for the reader.

EXERCISES FOR SECTION I-3

1. Make up some examples of universal sets and subsets, using sets of people, or objects, or ideas.

2. Let U be the set of fingers (including thumb) on your right hand. How many different "sets of fingers" can you make from U (a) if at least one finger must be included, (b) if the empty set (fingers closed in a fist) is permitted?

3. Suppose that a code is devised so that one symbol of the form

$$(x_1, x_2, \ldots, x_{20}), \qquad \text{where } x_i = 0 \text{ or } 1, \quad i = 1, 2, \ldots 20,$$

is assigned to a complete message. Can a million different messages be so encoded? What is the exact number of messages possible?

4. How many nonempty subsets can be formed from a set of n elements?

5. A *proper* subset of U is defined to be a subset that does not include the entire set U. How many proper subsets can be formed from a set of n elements?

6. Prove Theorem I-3.

I-4. OPERATIONS WITH SETS

Let U denote the universal set, and let $A, B, C, \ldots$ denote subsets of U. We can perform on these subsets certain operations that produce other (or perhaps the same) subsets. Three particularly important operations are *intersection*, *union*, and *complementation*. We shall define these terms, and illustrate their meanings with Venn diagrams.

I-4 Definition. *Intersection.* The intersection of A and B is the set of all elements of U that belong to both A and B.

We denote the intersection of A and B by "$A \cap B$" (read: "A intersect B," or "A cap B"). In symbols,

$$A \cap B = \{x : x \text{ belongs to } A \text{ and } x \text{ belongs to } B\}.$$

The intersection of A and B is indicated by the shaded area in Fig. I-9.

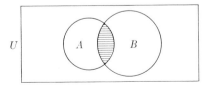

FIG. I-9. Intersection of A and B.

I–5 Definition. *Disjoint; mutually exclusive.* Two sets A and B are said to be disjoint, or mutually exclusive, if they have no elements in common.

In other words, A and B are disjoint if their intersection is the empty set. (See Fig. I–10.)

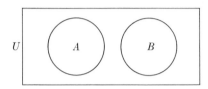

FIG. I–10.   Disjoint sets.

I–6 Definition. *Union.* The union of A and B is the set of all elements of U that belong either to A or to B or to both.

We denote the union of A and B by $A \cup B$ (read: "A union B," or "A cup B"). In symbols,

$$A \cup B = \{x : x \text{ belongs to } A \text{ or to } B \text{ or to both}\}.$$

The union of A and B is indicated by the shaded area in Fig. I–11.

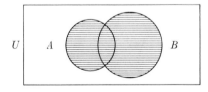   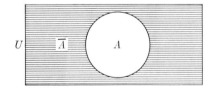

FIG. I–11.   Union of A and B.   FIG. I–12.   Complement of A.

I–7 Definition. *Complement.* The complement of A is the set of all elements in U that are not in A.

We denote the complement of A by $\overline{A}$ (read: "A bar"). In symbols,

$$\overline{A} = \{x : x \text{ belongs to } U \text{ but not to } A\}.$$

The complement of A is indicated by the shaded region in Fig. I–12.

EXAMPLE 1. Let U consist of the numbers 1, 2, 3, $\ldots$, 9 and the 26 letters of the alphabet, a, b, c, $\ldots$, z. If

$$A = \{1, 3, 5, a, e, h\}$$

and

$$B = \{1, 2, 3, 4, 5, a, b, c, d, e\},$$

find (a) $\overline{B}$, (b) $A \cap B$, (c) $A \cup B$, (d) $A \cap \overline{B}$.

Solution. From the foregoing definitions, we have

$$\overline{B} = \{6, 7, 8, 9, f, g, h, \ldots, z\},$$
$$A \cap B = \{1, 3, 5, a, e\},$$
$$A \cup B = \{1, 2, 3, 4, 5, a, b, c, d, e, h\},$$
$$A \cap \overline{B} = \{h\}.$$

EXAMPLE 2. Given that $U = \{0, 1, 2, 3, 4, 5, \ldots\}$,

$$A = \{3x : x \text{ is in } U\},$$
$$B = \{5x : x \text{ is in } U\}.$$

Find $A \cap B$.

Solution. In words, "A is the set of all integral multiples of 3," and "B is the set of all integral multiples of 5." In order that an element belong to both A and B, it must be a multiple of 3 and also a multiple of 5, and hence a multiple of 15. Therefore,

$$A \cap B = \{15x : x \text{ is in } U\}.$$

EXERCISES FOR SECTION 1-4

1. Let U be the set of all points in the (x, y)-plane:

$$U = \{(x, y) : x \text{ and } y \text{ are real numbers}\}.$$

Given that

$$A = \{(x, y) : y = |x|\}, \qquad B = \{(x, y) : y > |x|\},$$
$$L = \{(x, y) : x + y = 2\}, \qquad M = \{(x, y) : x + y < 2\}.$$

Indicate, by graphs, the following sets: (a) A, (b) B, (c) $A \cup B$, (d) $\overline{B}$, (e) L, (f) $A \cap L$, (g) $B \cap M$, (h) $\overline{M}$, (i) $\overline{L}$.

2. If A is any subset of the universal set U, prove that (a) $A \cup A = A$, (b) $A \cap A = A$, (c) $A \cup \overline{A} = U$, (d) $A \cap \overline{A} = \phi$.

3. Given that A and B are subsets of a finite universal set U, and that the numbers of elements in various sets are as recorded in the first four rows of the following table. Make a Venn diagram to illustrate the given data, indicating members of sets by dots in your diagram. Then complete the table by filling in the number of elements for each of the last five sets.

Set	U	A	B	$A \cap B$	$\bar{A} \cap B$	$A \cap \bar{B}$	$A \cup B$	$\bar{A}$	$\bar{A} \cup B$
No. of elements	20	7	8	3					

For those who may wish to undertake further study of sets, the following reference list is appended:

Aiken and Beseman, *Modern Mathematics: Topics and Problems*, pp. 1–127. New York: McGraw-Hill Book Co.

Breuer, J. (translated by H. F. Fehr), *Introduction to the Theory of Sets*. Englewood Cliffs, N.J.: Prentice-Hall, Inc.

Christian, R., *Introduction to Logic and Sets*. Boston: Ginn & Co.

Committee on the Undergraduate Program, Mathematical Association of America, *Elementary Mathematics of Sets with Applications*. New Orleans: Tulane University Book Store.

Halmos, P. R., *Naive Set Theory*. Princeton, N.J.: D. Van Nostrand Co.

Kemeny, J. G., J. L. Snell, and G. L. Thompson, *Introduction to Finite Mathematics*, Ch. 2. Englewood Cliffs, N.J.: Prentice-Hall, Inc.

May, K. O., *Elements of Modern Mathematics*, Ch. 3. Reading, Mass.: Addison-Wesley Publishing Co., Inc.

McShane, E. J., *Insights into Modern Mathematics*, Ch. 3 ("Operating with Sets"). National Council of Teachers of Mathematics, 1201 Sixteenth St., N. W., Washington 6, D.C.

Woodward, E. J., and R. C. McLennan, *Elementary Concepts of Sets*. New York: Henry Holt and Co.

II

SUMMATIONS
AND SUBSCRIPTS

II–1. SUBSCRIPTS AND THE SUMMATION SYMBOL, Σ

We often wish to indicate the sum of several measurements or observations. For example, if 30 students take a test, we may wish to know their average score, which is $\frac{1}{30}$ the sum of their scores. Or we may wish to talk about the sum of the points on the top face of a die thrown many times. It is convenient to be able to express such sums in compact form. The Greek letter Σ (capital *sigma*) is used for this purpose, to denote "summation of."

Suppose, for example, we arrange the names of the 30 students in alphabetical order, and then let x_1 represent the test score of the first student, x_2 the score of the second student, and so on, with x_{30} representing the score of the 30th student. The subscripts $1, 2, \ldots, 30$ correspond to the positions of the students' names on the alphabetical list. If the first 3 students received scores of 85, 79, and 94, in that order, then

$$x_1 = 85, \qquad x_2 = 79, \qquad x_3 = 94.$$

The sum of the 30 scores could be represented by

$$x_1 + x_2 + \cdots + x_{30}, \tag{1}$$

where the three dots are used to indicate "and so on." Another way of representing the same sum, using the summation symbol Σ, is

$$\sum_{i=1}^{30} x_i. \tag{2}$$

We read expression (2): "summation of x-sub-i from $i = 1$ through 30." It has exactly the same meaning as expression (1); both indicate the sum of the thirty scores x_1, x_2, and so on through x_{30}. In other words, the symbol

$$\sum_{i=1}^{30}$$

means that we are to replace i by integers in ascending order, beginning at 1 and ending at 30, and add the results.

The subscript may be any convenient letter, although i, j, k, and n are most frequently used.

EXAMPLE 1. If $x_1 = -3$, $x_2 = 5$, $x_3 = 7$, and $x_4 = 6$, find

(a) $\sum_{i=1}^{4} x_i$, (b) $\sum_{i=2}^{4} x_i$, (c) $\sum_{j=1}^{3} x_j$,

(d) $\sum_{k=1}^{4} 5x_k$, (e) $\sum_{n=1}^{3} (x_n + x_{n+1})$, (f) $\sum_{i=1}^{4} x_i^2$.

Solutions.

(a) $\sum_{i=1}^{4} x_i = x_1 + x_2 + x_3 + x_4 = -3 + 5 + 7 + 6 = 15.$

(b) $\sum_{i=2}^{4} x_i = x_2 + x_3 + x_4 = 5 + 7 + 6 = 18.$

(c) $\sum_{j=1}^{3} x_j = x_1 + x_2 + x_3 = -3 + 5 + 7 = 9.$

(d) $\sum_{k=1}^{4} 5x_k = 5x_1 + 5x_2 + 5x_3 + 5x_4$

$= 5(x_1 + x_2 + x_3 + x_4)$

$= 5(15) = 75.$

(e) $\sum_{n=1}^{3} (x_n + x_{n+1}) = (x_1 + x_2) + (x_2 + x_3) + (x_3 + x_4)$

$= (x_1 + x_2 + x_3) + (x_2 + x_3 + x_4)$

$= 9 + 18 = 27.$

(f) $\displaystyle\sum_{i=1}^{4} x_i^2 = x_1^2 + x_2^2 + x_3^2 + x_4^2 = (-3)^2 + 5^2 + 7^2 + 6^2 = 119.$

REMARK 1.   Part (b) of this example illustrates a sum from $i = 2$ through $i = 4$. The equation "$i = 2$" written beneath the summation sign tells us where the sum starts. The subscript i on x_i is first to be replaced by 2. We then proceed through *the integers* from the starting place (in this case, 2) until we reach the integer corresponding to the symbol written above the summation sign (here, 4). Thus, in x_i, we replace i by 2, 3, and 4, and add the results:

$$x_2 + x_3 + x_4.$$

REMARK 2.   In part (c) we used the letter j, instead of i, for the subscript on x, and for the corresponding *index of summation*. The notation "$j = 1$" beneath the sigma tells us the first value to substitute for j, and this substitution converts x_j into x_1. We then proceed one-by-one through the integers until we reach the *upper limit of summation*, in this case 3. Then we add the results, and get

$$x_1 + x_2 + x_3.$$

REMARK 3.   In Example 1(d), we replace the subscript k by 1, 2, 3, and 4, in that order, but we have the common factor 5 in each term. In fact, we see that

$$\sum_{k=1}^{4} 5x_k = 5 \sum_{k=1}^{4} x_k,$$

and this result can easily be generalized. We shall do so in the next section.

REMARK 4.   In part (e), the index of summation n takes the values 1, 2, and 3. The subscript on x_n takes these same values, but the subscript on x_{n+1} takes the values $n + 1 = 2$, 3, and 4, in that order. By rearranging terms, we also see that

$$\sum_{n=1}^{3} (x_n + x_{n+1}) = \sum_{n=1}^{3} x_n + \sum_{n=1}^{3} x_{n+1}$$

$$= \sum_{i=1}^{3} x_i + \sum_{j=2}^{4} x_j. \tag{3}$$

REMARK 5. Equation (3) and Examples 1(c, d, e) illustrate that the letter used for the index of summation is immaterial. This also explains why that index is often called a "dummy index." The only requirement is that when the index is everywhere replaced by the consecutive integers, beginning with the *lower limit of summation* (written beneath the sigma) and extending through the *upper limit of summation* (written above the sigma), we get the desired result by adding these expressions. Thus

$$x_2 + x_3 + x_4 = \sum_{j=2}^{4} x_j = \sum_{k=-1}^{1} x_{k+3} = \sum_{k=-1}^{1} x_{3-k}.$$

II-1 Definitions. *Summation.* With each integer i from m through n, let there be associated a number denoted by x_i. The sum of the numbers

$$x_m, \; x_{m+1}, \; \ldots, \; x_n$$

is represented in summation notation by $\sum_{i=m}^{n} x_i$:

$$\sum_{i=m}^{n} x_i = x_m + x_{m+1} + \cdots + x_n. \tag{4}$$

Limits of summation. In Eq. (4) the *lower limit* of summation is m, the *upper limit* is n.

The omission of limits of summation. We sometimes omit the limits and write simply $\sum x_i$. This notation means that the *summation is to extend over all values of x_i under discussion*, unless something is said to the contrary. For instance, if the only values in a particular discussion are x_1, x_2, x_3, x_4, then $\sum x_i$ means $x_1 + x_2 + x_3 + x_4$.

EXAMPLE 2. If $x_i = i(i - 1)$, evaluate $\sum_{i=1}^{5} x_i$.

Solution.
$$\sum_{i=1}^{5} x_i = x_1 + x_2 + x_3 + x_4 + x_5$$
$$= 1(1 - 1) + 2(2 - 1) + 3(3 - 1) + 4(4 - 1)$$
$$+ 5(5 - 1)$$
$$= 0 + 2 + 6 + 12 + 20 = 40.$$

EXAMPLE 3. Evaluate $\sum_{j=0}^{2} \dfrac{j+1}{j+3}$.

Solution. $\sum_{j=0}^{2} \dfrac{j+1}{j+3} = \dfrac{0+1}{0+3} + \dfrac{1+1}{1+3} + \dfrac{2+1}{2+3} = \dfrac{1}{3} + \dfrac{2}{4} + \dfrac{3}{5} = \dfrac{43}{30}$.

EXAMPLE 4. Express the following sum as a simple function of n:

$$\sum_{k=0}^{n} [(k+1)^2 - k^2]. \tag{5}$$

Solution. Replacing k by $0, 1, 2, \ldots, n$ and adding, we get

$$\sum_{k=0}^{n} [(k+1)^2 - k^2] = [1^2 - 0^2] + [2^2 - 1^2] + [3^2 - 2^2]$$
$$+ \cdots + [(n+1)^2 - n^2]. \tag{6}$$

The positive terms on the right side of Eq. (6) have a sum expressed by

$$1^2 + 2^2 + 3^2 + \cdots + (n+1)^2, \tag{7}$$

and from this we must subtract

$$0^2 + 1^2 + 2^2 + \cdots + n^2. \tag{8}$$

Therefore

$$\sum_{k=0}^{n} [(k+1)^2 - k^2] = [1^2 + 2^2 + \cdots + n^2 + (n+1)^2]$$
$$- [0^2 + 1^2 + \cdots + n^2]$$
$$= (n+1)^2. \tag{9}$$

EXERCISES FOR SECTION II–1

Evaluate the following sums:

1. $\sum_{n=1}^{3} n^2$

2. $\sum_{n=1}^{3} 2^n$

3. $\sum_{n=1}^{3} x^n$

4. $\sum_{k=0}^{2} (2k+1)$

5. $\sum_{k=0}^{3} (2k+1)$

6. $\sum_{k=0}^{4} (2k+1)$

7. $\displaystyle\sum_{i=1}^{3} (i^2 + i)$ 8. $\displaystyle\sum_{n=-2}^{2} (n^2 - 4)$ 9. $\displaystyle\sum_{n=100}^{102} n$

10. $\displaystyle\sum_{n=0}^{2} (n + 100)$

11. Use the result of Eq. (9) and the fact that

$$(k + 1)^2 - k^2 = 2k + 1$$

is an odd integer to prove that the sum of the first $n + 1$ positive odd integers is a perfect square. What square?

12. By expanding the left side of the following equation and rearranging terms, show that

$$\sum_{k=0}^{3} (a_k + b_k) = \sum_{k=0}^{3} a_k + \sum_{k=0}^{3} b_k.$$

Can you generalize this result in two ways?

13. By expanding the left side of the following equation and using the distributive law, show that

$$\sum_{i=1}^{3} 7x_i = 7 \sum_{i=1}^{3} x_i.$$

Generalize the result in as many ways as you can.

14. If all the x_i's are equal to the same constant c, what is the value of $\displaystyle\sum_{i=1}^{n} x_i$?

II-2. THEOREMS ABOUT SUMMATIONS

In Exercise 12 above you probably discovered the result stated in the following theorem.

II-2. Theorem The summation of the sum of two or more variables is the sum of their summations. Thus,

$$\sum_{i=m}^{n} (a_i + b_i) = \sum_{i=m}^{n} a_i + \sum_{i=m}^{n} b_i. \tag{1}$$

Proof. To prove Eq. (1), we need only expand the left side and rearrange terms, as follows:

$$\sum_{i=m}^{n} (a_i + b_i) = (a_m + b_m) + (a_{m+1} + b_{m+1}) + \cdots + (a_n + b_n)$$

$$= (a_m + a_{m+1} + \cdots + a_n) + (b_m + b_{m+1} + \cdots + b_n)$$

$$= \sum_{i=m}^{n} a_i + \sum_{i=m}^{n} b_i.$$

The result can be extended to the summation of three or more variables by repeated applications of Eq. (1). For example,

$$\sum (a_i + b_i + c_i) = \sum a_i + \sum (b_i + c_i) = \sum a_i + \sum b_i + \sum c_i,$$

where i goes from m to n in all summations. □

II–3 Theorem. A constant factor can be moved across the summation sign. Thus, if c is a constant,

$$\sum_{i=m}^{n} cx_i = c \sum_{i=m}^{n} x_i. \tag{2}$$

Proof. We expand the left side of Eq. (2) and get

$$cx_m + cx_{m+1} + \cdots + cx_n,$$

which can also be written in the form of the right side of Eq. (2). □

EXAMPLE 1.
$$\sum_{i=1}^{3} 2i^2 = 2 \sum_{i=1}^{3} i^2 = 2(1 + 4 + 9) = 28,$$

$$\sum_{i=1}^{3} (2i)^2 = 4 \sum_{i=1}^{3} i^2 = 4(1 + 4 + 9) = 56.$$

II–4 Theorem. The summation of a constant is equal to the product of that constant and the number of integers from the lower limit of summation through the upper limit. Thus

$$\sum_{i=1}^{n} c = cn. \tag{3}$$

Proof. If each x_i is equal to c, for $i = 1, 2, \ldots, n$, then

$$\sum_{i=1}^{n} x_i = x_1 + x_2 + \cdots + x_n = c + c + \cdots + c = cn. \quad \square$$

EXAMPLE 2. Use Eq. (9) of Section II–1 and Theorems II–2, II–3, II–4, to evaluate $\sum_{k=0}^{n} k$ as a function of n.

Solution. From Eq. (9), we have

$$\sum_{k=0}^{n} [(k + 1)^2 - k^2] = (n + 1)^2. \tag{4}$$

But also,

$$(k + 1)^2 - k^2 = k^2 + 2k + 1 - k^2 = 2k + 1.$$

Reversing the order in Eq. (4) and substituting $2k + 1$ for the difference of squares, we get

$$(n + 1)^2 = \sum_{k=0}^{n} (2k + 1) = \sum_{k=0}^{n} 2k + \sum_{k=0}^{n} 1 = 2 \sum_{k=0}^{n} k + (n + 1). \tag{5}$$

To find the value of $\sum k$, we subtract $(n + 1)$ and get, after reversing the order of the first and last terms,

$$2 \sum_{k=0}^{n} k = (n + 1)^2 - (n + 1) = (n + 1)[(n + 1) - 1] = (n + 1)n.$$

Therefore

$$\boxed{\sum_{k=0}^{n} k = \frac{(n + 1)n}{2}.} \tag{6}$$

EXERCISES FOR SECTION II–2

Write the following summations in expanded form and simplify the results as much as possible.

1. $\displaystyle\sum_{k=0}^{3} k a_k$ 2. $\displaystyle\sum_{k=1}^{3} k^2 (\tfrac{1}{2})^k$ 3. $\displaystyle\sum_{j=-1}^{2} 10^j$

4. $\displaystyle\sum_{i=2}^{5} (2i - 5)$ 　　　　 5. $\displaystyle\sum_{n=1}^{3} (a_n + b_{n-1})$ 　　 6. $\displaystyle\sum_{n=0}^{2} (2x_n - 3y_n)$

7. $\displaystyle\sum_{k=0}^{2} \binom{2}{k} x^k$ 　　　　　　　　　 8. $\displaystyle\sum_{k=0}^{2} \binom{2}{k} x^{2-k} y^k$

9. $\displaystyle\sum_{x=0}^{3} \binom{3}{x} p^x q^{3-x}$ 　　　　　　 10. $\displaystyle\sum_{x=0}^{2} \frac{x^2}{x!}$

11. Show that

$$\sum_{k=0}^{n} [(k + 1)^3 - k^3]$$

is equal to $(n + 1)^3$.

12. (Continuation.) Use the result of Exercise 11 above and the relation $(k + 1)^3 - k^3 = 3k^2 + 3k + 1$ to show that

$$3 \sum_{k=0}^{n} k^2 = (n + 1)^3 - 3 \sum_{k=0}^{n} k - \sum_{k=0}^{n} 1.$$

13. (Continuation.) Use the results of Exercise 12 and Eqs. (3) and (6) in the text to show that

$$\sum_{k=0}^{n} k^2 = \frac{n(n + 1)(2n + 1)}{6}. \tag{7}$$

14. How would the results in Eq. (6) and in Exercise 13 be affected if the lower limits of summation were changed to $k = 1$? Explain.

15. Write each of the following sums in summation form:

(a) 　　　　　　　　　 $z_1 + z_2 + \cdots + z_{23}.$

(b) 　　　　　　　　　 $x_1 y_1 + x_2 y_2 + \cdots + x_8 y_8.$

(c) 　　　　 $(x_1 - y_1) + (x_2 - y_2) + \cdots + (x_m - y_m).$

(d) 　　　　　　　　　 $x_1^3 f_1 + x_2^3 f_2 + \cdots + x_9^3 f_9.$

16. Prove that $\displaystyle\sum_{i=1}^{n} (x_i - m)^2 = \sum_{i=1}^{n} x_i^2 - 2m \sum_{i=1}^{n} x_i + nm^2.$

17. In Exercise 16, suppose that $m = \bar{x}$, the arithmetic mean of $x_1, x_2, \ldots, x_n$. Prove that

$$\sum_{i=1}^{n} (x_i - \bar{x})^2 = \sum_{i=1}^{n} x_i^2 - n\bar{x}^2.$$

18. Express

$$\sum_{i=1}^{n} (ax_i + by_i)^2$$

as a sum of three summations.

REMARK. We sometimes have to deal with sums of the form $\sum x_i y_j$, where the sum is to be extended over certain pairs of values of i and j. Suppose, for example, that i goes from 1 through 3, and j takes the values 1 and 2. Then there are 3×2, or 6, pairs of i, j values, and the corresponding summation is

$$\sum x_i y_j = x_1 y_1 + x_1 y_2 + x_2 y_1 + x_2 y_2 + x_3 y_1 + x_3 y_2.$$

TABLES

Table I

2500 random digits

00	49487 52802	28667 62058	87822 14704	18519 17889	45869 14454
01	29480 91539	46317 84803	86056 62812	33584 70391	77749 64906
02	25252 97738	23901 11106	86864 55808	22557 23214	15021 54268
03	02431 42193	96960 19620	29188 05863	92900 06836	13433 21709
04	69414 89353	70724 67893	23218 72452	03095 68333	13751 37260
05	77285 35179	92042 67581	67673 68374	71115 98166	43352 06414
06	52852 11444	71868 34534	69124 02760	06406 95234	87995 78560
07	98740 98054	30195 09891	18453 79464	01156 95522	06884 55073
08	85022 58736	12138 35146	62085 36170	25433 80787	96496 40579
09	17778 03840	21636 56269	08149 19001	67367 13138	02400 89515
10	81833 93449	57781 94621	90998 37561	59688 93299	27726 82167
11	63789 54958	33167 10909	40343 81023	61590 44474	39810 10305
12	61840 81740	60986 12498	71546 42249	13812 59902	27864 21809
13	42243 10153	20891 90883	15782 98167	86837 99166	92143 82441
14	45236 09129	53031 12260	01278 14404	40969 33419	14188 69557
15	40338 42477	78804 36272	72053 07958	67158 60979	79891 92409
16	54040 71253	88789 98203	54999 96564	00789 68879	47134 83941
17	49158 20908	44859 29089	76130 51442	34453 98590	37353 61137
18	80958 03808	83655 18415	96563 43582	82207 53322	30419 64435
19	07636 04876	61063 57571	69434 14965	20911 73162	33576 52839
20	37227 80750	08261 97048	60438 75053	05939 34414	16685 32103
21	99460 45915	45637 41353	35335 69087	57536 68418	10247 93253
22	60248 75845	37296 33783	42393 28185	31880 00241	31642 37526
23	95076 79089	87380 28982	97750 82221	35584 27444	85793 69755
24	20944 97852	26586 32796	51513 47475	48621 20067	88975 39506
25	30458 49207	62358 41532	30057 53017	10375 97204	98675 77634
26	38905 91282	79309 49022	17405 18830	09186 07629	01785 78317
27	96545 15638	90114 93730	13741 70177	49175 42113	21600 69625
28	21944 28328	00692 89164	96025 01383	50252 67044	70596 58266
29	36910 71928	63327 00980	32154 46006	62289 28079	03076 15619
30	48745 47626	28856 28382	60639 51370	70091 58261	70135 88259
31	32519 91993	59374 83994	59873 51217	62806 20028	26545 16820
32	75757 12965	29285 11481	31744 41754	24428 81819	02354 37895
33	07911 97756	89561 27464	25133 50026	16436 75846	83718 08533
34	89887 03328	76911 93168	56236 39056	67905 94933	05456 52347
35	30543 99488	75363 94187	32885 23887	10872 22793	26232 87356
36	68442 55201	33946 42495	28384 89889	50278 91985	58185 19124
37	22403 56698	88524 13692	55012 25343	76391 48029	72278 58586
38	70701 36907	51242 52083	43126 90379	60380 98513	85596 16528
39	69804 96122	42342 28467	79037 13218	63510 09071	52438 25840
40	65806 22398	19470 63653	27055 02606	43347 65384	02613 81668
41	43902 53070	54319 19347	59506 75440	90826 53652	92382 67623
42	49145 71587	14273 62440	15770 03281	58124 09533	43722 03856
43	47363 36295	62126 42358	20322 82000	52830 93540	13284 96496
44	26244 87033	90247 79131	38773 67687	45541 54976	17508 18367
45	72875 39496	06385 48458	30545 74383	22814 36752	10707 48774
46	09065 16283	61398 08288	00708 21816	39615 03102	02834 04116
47	68256 51225	92645 77747	33104 81206	00112 53445	04212 58476
48	38744 81018	41909 70458	72459 66136	97266 26490	10877 45022
49	44375 19619	35750 59924	82429 90288	61064 26489	87001 84273

Table II

Values of $n!$ and $\log n!$

The values of $n!$ are given to five significant figures, and for $n \geq 9$ these values must be multiplied by a power of ten. This power is the raised number to the right of the five significant figures. For example, $15! \approx 13{,}077 \times 10^8$.

n	$n!$	$\log n!$	n	$n!$	$\log n!$	n	$n!$	$\log n!$
1	1	.00000	26	$40{,}329^{22}$	26.60562	51	$15{,}511^{62}$	66.19065
2	2	.30103	27	$10{,}889^{24}$	28.03698	52	$80{,}658^{63}$	67.90665
3	6	.77815	28	$30{,}489^{25}$	29.48414	53	$42{,}749^{65}$	69.63092
4	24	1.38021	29	$88{,}418^{26}$	30.94654	54	$23{,}084^{67}$	71.36332
5	120	2.07918	30	$26{,}525^{28}$	32.42366	55	$12{,}696^{69}$	73.10368
6	720	2.85733	31	$82{,}228^{29}$	33.91502	56	$71{,}100^{70}$	74.85187
7	5,040	3.70243	32	$26{,}313^{31}$	35.42017	57	$40{,}527^{72}$	76.60774
8	40,320	4.60552	33	$86{,}833^{32}$	36.93869	58	$23{,}506^{74}$	78.37117
9	$36{,}288^{1}$	5.55976	34	$29{,}523^{34}$	38.47016	59	$13{,}868^{76}$	80.14202
10	$36{,}288^{2}$	6.55976	35	$10{,}333^{36}$	40.01423	60	$83{,}210^{77}$	81.92017
11	$39{,}917^{3}$	7.60116	36	$37{,}199^{37}$	41.57054	61	$50{,}758^{79}$	83.70550
12	$47{,}900^{4}$	8.68034	37	$13{,}764^{39}$	43.13874	62	$31{,}470^{81}$	85.49790
13	$62{,}270^{5}$	9.79428	38	$52{,}302^{40}$	44.71852	63	$19{,}826^{83}$	87.29724
14	$87{,}178^{6}$	10.94041	39	$20{,}398^{42}$	46.30959	64	$12{,}689^{85}$	89.10342
15	$13{,}077^{8}$	12.11650	40	$81{,}592^{43}$	47.91165	65	$82{,}477^{86}$	90.91633
16	$20{,}923^{9}$	13.32062	41	$33{,}453^{45}$	49.52443	66	$54{,}434^{88}$	92.73587
17	$35{,}569^{10}$	14.55107	42	$14{,}050^{47}$	51.14768	67	$36{,}471^{90}$	94.56195
18	$64{,}024^{11}$	15.80634	43	$60{,}415^{48}$	52.78115	68	$24{,}800^{92}$	96.39446
19	$12{,}165^{13}$	17.08509	44	$26{,}583^{50}$	54.42460	69	$17{,}112^{94}$	98.23331
20	$24{,}329^{14}$	18.38612	45	$11{,}962^{52}$	56.07781	70	$11{,}979^{96}$	100.07841
21	$51{,}091^{15}$	19.70834	46	$55{,}026^{53}$	57.74057	71	$85{,}048^{97}$	101.92966
22	$11{,}240^{17}$	21.05077	47	$25{,}862^{55}$	59.41267	72	$61{,}234^{99}$	103.78700
23	$25{,}852^{18}$	22.41249	48	$12{,}414^{57}$	61.09391	73	$44{,}701^{101}$	105.65032
24	$62{,}045^{19}$	23.79271	49	$60{,}828^{58}$	62.78410	74	$33{,}079^{103}$	107.51955
25	$15{,}511^{21}$	25.19065	50	$30{,}414^{60}$	64.48307	75	$24{,}809^{105}$	109.39461

TABLE III. SQUARES AND SQUARE ROOTS

n	n^2	$\sqrt{n}$	$\sqrt{10n}$	n	n^2	$\sqrt{n}$	$\sqrt{10n}$
1.0	1.00	1.000	3.162	5.5	30.25	2.345	7.416
1.1	1.21	1.049	3.317	5.6	31.36	2.366	7.483
1.2	1.44	1.095	3.464	5.7	32.49	2.387	7.550
1.3	1.69	1.140	3.606	5.8	33.64	2.408	7.616
1.4	1.96	1.183	3.742	5.9	34.81	2.429	7.681
1.5	2.25	1.225	3.873	6.0	36.00	2.449	7.746
1.6	2.56	1.265	4.000	6.1	37.21	2.470	7.810
1.7	2.89	1.304	4.123	6.2	38.44	2.490	7.874
1.8	3.24	1.342	4.243	6.3	39.69	2.510	7.937
1.9	3.61	1.378	4.359	6.4	40.96	2.530	8.000
2.0	4.00	1.414	4.472	6.5	42.25	2.550	8.062
2.1	4.41	1.449	4.583	6.6	43.56	2.569	8.124
2.2	4.84	1.483	4.690	6.7	44.89	2.588	8.185
2.3	5.29	1.517	4.796	6.8	46.24	2.608	8.246
2.4	5.76	1.549	4.899	6.9	47.61	2.627	8.307
2.5	6.25	1.581	5.000	7.0	49.00	2.646	8.367
2.6	6.76	1.612	5.099	7.1	50.41	2.665	8.426
2.7	7.29	1.643	5.196	7.2	51.84	2.683	8.485
2.8	7.84	1.673	5.292	7.3	53.29	2.702	8.544
2.9	8.41	1.703	5.385	7.4	54.76	2.720	8.602
3.0	9.00	1.732	5.477	7.5	56.25	2.739	8.660
3.1	9.61	1.761	5.568	7.6	57.76	2.757	8.718
3.2	10.24	1.789	5.657	7.7	59.29	2.775	8.775
3.3	10.89	1.817	5.745	7.8	60.84	2.793	8.832
3.4	11.56	1.844	5.831	7.9	62.41	2.811	8.888
3.5	12.25	1.871	5.916	8.0	64.00	2.828	8.944
3.6	12.96	1.897	6.000	8.1	65.61	2.846	9.000
3.7	13.69	1.924	6.083	8.2	67.24	2.864	9.055
3.8	14.44	1.949	6.164	8.3	68.89	2.881	9.110
3.9	15.21	1.975	6.245	8.4	70.56	2.898	9.165
4.0	16.00	2.000	6.325	8.5	72.25	2.915	9.220
4.1	16.81	2.025	6.403	8.6	73.96	2.933	9.274
4.2	17.64	2.049	6.481	8.7	75.69	2.950	9.327
4.3	18.49	2.074	6.557	8.8	77.44	2.966	9.381
4.4	19.36	2.098	6.633	8.9	79.21	2.983	9.434
4.5	20.25	2.121	6.708	9.0	81.00	3.000	9.487
4.6	21.16	2.145	6.782	9.1	82.81	3.017	9.539
4.7	22.09	2.168	6.856	9.2	84.64	3.033	9.592
4.8	23.04	2.191	6.928	9.3	86.49	3.050	9.644
4.9	24.01	2.214	7.000	9.4	88.36	3.066	9.695
5.0	25.00	2.236	7.071	9.5	90.25	3.082	9.747
5.1	26.01	2.258	7.141	9.6	92.16	3.098	9.798
5.2	27.04	2.280	7.211	9.7	94.09	3.114	9.849
5.3	28.09	2.302	7.280	9.8	96.04	3.130	9.899
5.4	29.16	2.324	7.348	9.9	98.01	3.146	9.950

TABLE IV

THREE-PLACE TABLES OF THE BINOMIAL DISTRIBUTION

Part A of this table gives the values of the function

$$b(x; n, p) = \binom{n}{x} p^x (1 - p)^{n-x}$$
$$= \frac{n!}{x!(n - x)!} p^x(1 - p)^{n-x}.$$

This is the probability of exactly x successes in n independent binomial trials with probability of success on a single trial equal to p.

Part B gives the values of the cumulative binomial

$$P(X \geq r) = \sum_{x=r}^{n} b(x; n, p)$$
$$= \sum_{x=r}^{n} \binom{n}{x} p^x(1 - p)^{n-x}.$$

$P(X \geq r)$ is the probability of r or more successes in n independent binomial trials with probability p of success on a single trial.

In both parts of the table values of the functions are given for x (or r) = 0, 1, ..., n; n = 2, 3, ..., 25, and p = .01, .05, .10, .20, .30, .40, .50, .60, .70, .80, .90, .95, and .99.

In these tables, each three-digit entry should be read with a decimal preceding it. For entries 1—, the probability is larger than 0.9995 but less than 1. For entries 0+, the probability is less than 0.0005 but greater than 0.

TABLE IV   293

PART A: INDIVIDUAL TERMS, $b(x; n, p)$

n	x	.01	.05	.10	.20	.30	.40	p .50	.60	.70	.80	.90	.95	.99	x
2	0	980	902	810	640	490	360	250	160	090	040	010	002	0+	0
	1	020	095	180	320	420	480	500	480	420	320	180	095	020	1
	2	0+	002	010	040	090	160	250	360	490	640	810	902	980	2
3	0	970	857	729	512	343	216	125	064	027	008	001	0+	0+	0
	1	029	135	243	384	441	432	375	288	189	096	027	007	0+	1
	2	0+	007	027	096	189	288	375	432	441	384	243	135	029	2
	3	0+	0+	001	008	027	064	125	216	343	512	729	857	970	3
4	0	961	815	656	410	240	130	062	026	008	002	0+	0+	0+	0
	1	039	171	292	410	412	346	250	154	076	026	004	0+	0+	1
	2	001	014	049	154	265	346	375	346	265	154	049	014	001	2
	3	0+	0+	004	026	076	154	250	346	412	410	292	171	039	3
	4	0+	0+	0+	002	008	026	062	130	240	410	656	815	961	4
5	0	951	774	590	328	168	078	031	010	002	0+	0+	0+	0+	0
	1	048	204	328	410	360	259	156	077	028	006	0+	0+	0+	1
	2	001	021	073	205	309	346	312	230	132	051	008	001	0+	2
	3	0+	001	008	051	132	230	312	346	309	205	073	021	001	3
	4	0+	0+	0+	006	028	077	156	259	360	410	328	204	048	4
	5	0+	0+	0+	0+	002	010	031	078	168	328	590	774	951	5
6	0	941	735	531	262	118	047	016	004	001	0+	0+	0+	0+	0
	1	057	232	354	393	303	187	094	037	010	002	0+	0+	0+	1
	2	001	031	098	246	324	311	234	138	060	015	001	0+	0+	2
	3	0+	002	015	082	185	276	312	276	185	082	015	002	0+	3
	4	0+	0+	001	015	060	138	234	311	324	246	098	031	001	4
	5	0+	0+	0+	002	010	037	094	187	303	393	354	232	057	5
	6	0+	0+	0+	0+	001	004	016	047	118	262	531	735	941	6
7	0	932	698	478	210	082	028	008	002	0+	0+	0+	0+	0+	0
	1	066	257	372	367	247	131	055	017	004	0+	0+	0+	0+	1
	2	002	041	124	275	318	261	164	077	025	004	0+	0+	0+	2
	3	0+	004	023	115	227	290	273	194	097	029	003	0+	0+	3
	4	0+	0+	003	029	097	194	273	290	227	115	023	004	0+	4
	5	0+	0+	0+	004	025	077	164	261	318	275	124	041	002	5
	6	0+	0+	0+	0+	004	017	055	131	247	367	372	257	066	6
	7	0+	0+	0+	0+	0+	002	008	028	082	210	478	698	932	7
8	0	923	663	430	168	058	017	004	001	0+	0+	0+	0+	0+	0
	1	075	279	383	336	198	090	031	008	001	0+	0+	0+	0+	1
	2	003	051	149	294	296	209	109	041	010	001	0+	0+	0+	2
	3	0+	005	033	147	254	279	219	124	047	009	0+	0+	0+	3
	4	0+	0+	005	046	136	232	273	232	136	046	005	0+	0+	4
	5	0+	0+	0+	009	047	124	219	279	254	147	033	005	0+	5
	6	0+	0+	0+	001	010	041	109	209	296	294	149	051	003	6
	7	0+	0+	0+	0+	001	008	031	090	198	336	383	279	075	7
	8	0+	0+	0+	0+	0+	001	004	017	058	168	430	663	923	8

TABLE IV

Part A: Individual terms, $b(x; n, p)$

								p							
n	x	.01	.05	.10	.20	.30	.40	.50	.60	.70	.80	.90	.95	.99	x
9	0	914	630	387	134	040	010	002	0+	0+	0+	0+	0+	0+	0
	1	083	299	387	302	156	060	018	004	0+	0+	0+	0+	0+	1
	2	003	063	172	302	267	161	070	021	004	0+	0+	0+	0+	2
	3	0+	008	045	176	267	251	164	074	021	003	0+	0+	0+	3
	4	0+	001	007	066	172	251	246	167	074	017	001	0+	0+	4
	5	0+	0+	001	017	074	167	246	251	172	066	007	001	0+	5
	6	0+	0+	0+	003	021	074	164	251	267	176	045	008	0+	6
	7	0+	0+	0+	0+	004	021	070	161	267	302	172	063	003	7
	8	0+	0+	0+	0+	0+	004	018	060	156	302	387	299	083	8
	9	0+	0+	0+	0+	0+	0+	002	010	040	134	387	630	914	9
10	0	904	599	349	107	028	006	001	0+	0+	0+	0+	0+	0+	0
	1	091	315	387	268	121	040	010	002	0+	0+	0+	0+	0+	1
	2	004	075	194	302	233	121	044	011	001	0+	0+	0+	0+	2
	3	0+	010	057	201	267	215	117	042	009	001	0+	0+	0+	3
	4	0+	001	011	088	200	251	205	111	037	006	0+	0+	0+	4
	5	0+	0+	001	026	103	201	246	201	103	026	001	0+	0+	5
	6	0+	0+	0+	006	037	111	205	251	200	088	011	001	0+	6
	7	0+	0+	0+	001	009	042	117	215	267	201	057	010	0+	7
	8	0+	0+	0+	0+	001	011	044	121	233	302	194	075	004	8
	9	0+	0+	0+	0+	0+	002	010	040	121	268	387	315	091	9
	10	0+	0+	0+	0+	0+	0+	001	006	028	107	349	599	904	10
11	0	895	569	314	086	020	004	0+	0+	0+	0+	0+	0+	0+	0
	1	099	329	384	236	093	027	005	001	0+	0+	0+	0+	0+	1
	2	005	087	213	295	200	089	027	005	001	0+	0+	0+	0+	2
	3	0+	014	071	221	257	177	081	023	004	0+	0+	0+	0+	3
	4	0+	001	016	111	220	236	161	070	017	002	0+	0+	0+	4
	5	0+	0+	002	039	132	221	226	147	057	010	0+	0+	0+	5
	6	0+	0+	0+	010	057	147	226	221	132	039	002	0+	0+	6
	7	0+	0+	0+	002	017	070	161	236	220	111	016	001	0+	7
	8	0+	0+	0+	0+	004	023	081	177	257	221	071	014	0+	8
	9	0+	0+	0+	0+	001	005	027	089	200	295	213	087	005	9
	10	0+	0+	0+	0+	0+	001	005	027	093	236	384	329	099	10
	11	0+	0+	0+	0+	0+	0+	0+	004	020	086	314	569	895	11
12	0	886	540	282	069	014	002	0+	0+	0+	0+	0+	0+	0+	0
	1	107	341	377	206	071	017	003	0+	0+	0+	0+	0+	0+	1
	2	006	099	230	283	168	064	016	002	0+	0+	0+	0+	0+	2
	3	0+	017	085	236	240	142	054	012	001	0+	0+	0+	0+	3
	4	0+	002	021	133	231	213	121	042	008	001	0+	0+	0+	4
	5	0+	0+	004	053	158	227	193	101	029	003	0+	0+	0+	5
	6	0+	0+	0+	016	079	177	226	177	079	016	0+	0+	0+	6
	7	0+	0+	0+	003	029	101	193	227	158	053	004	0+	0+	7
	8	0+	0+	0+	001	008	042	121	213	231	133	021	002	0+	8
	9	0+	0+	0+	0+	001	012	054	142	240	236	085	017	0+	9

TABLE IV   295

PART A: INDIVIDUAL TERMS, $b(x; n, p)$

n	x	.01	.05	.10	.20	.30	.40	p .50	.60	.70	.80	.90	.95	.99	x
12	10	0+	0+	0+	0+	0+	002	016	064	168	283	230	099	006	10
	11	0+	0+	0+	0+	0+	0+	003	017	071	206	377	341	107	11
	12	0+	0+	0+	0+	0+	0+	0+	002	014	069	282	540	886	12
13	0	878	513	254	055	010	001	0+	0+	0+	0+	0+	0+	0+	0
	1	115	351	367	179	054	011	002	0+	0+	0+	0+	0+	0+	1
	2	007	111	245	268	139	045	010	001	0+	0+	0+	0+	0+	2
	3	0+	021	100	246	218	111	035	006	001	0+	0+	0+	0+	3
	4	0+	003	028	154	234	184	087	024	003	0+	0+	0+	0+	4
	5	0+	0+	006	069	180	221	157	066	014	001	0+	0+	0+	5
	6	0+	0+	001	023	103	197	209	131	044	006	0+	0+	0+	6
	7	0+	0+	0+	006	044	131	209	197	103	023	001	0+	0+	7
	8	0+	0+	0+	001	014	066	157	221	180	069	006	0+	0+	8
	9	0+	0+	0+	0+	003	024	087	184	234	154	028	003	0+	9
	10	0+	0+	0+	0+	001	006	035	111	218	246	100	021	0+	10
	11	0+	0+	0+	0+	0+	001	010	045	139	268	245	111	007	11
	12	0+	0+	0+	0+	0+	0+	002	011	054	179	367	351	115	12
	13	0+	0+	0+	0+	0+	0+	0+	001	010	055	254	513	878	13
14	0	869	488	229	044	007	001	0+	0+	0+	0+	0+	0+	0+	0
	1	123	359	356	154	041	007	001	0+	0+	0+	0+	0+	0+	1
	2	008	123	257	250	113	032	006	001	0+	0+	0+	0+	0+	2
	3	0+	026	114	250	194	085	022	003	0+	0+	0+	0+	0+	3
	4	0+	004	035	172	229	155	061	014	001	0+	0+	0+	0+	4
	5	0+	0+	008	086	196	207	122	041	007	0+	0+	0+	0+	5
	6	0+	0+	001	032	126	207	183	092	023	002	0+	0+	0+	6
	7	0+	0+	0+	009	062	157	209	157	062	009	0+	0+	0+	7
	8	0+	0+	0+	002	023	092	183	207	126	032	001	0+	0+	8
	9	0+	0+	0+	0+	007	041	122	207	196	086	008	0+	0+	9
	10	0+	0+	0+	0+	001	014	061	155	229	172	035	004	0+	10
	11	0+	0+	0+	0+	0+	003	022	085	194	250	114	026	0+	11
	12	0+	0+	0+	0+	0+	001	006	032	113	250	257	123	008	12
	13	0+	0+	0+	0+	0+	0+	001	007	041	154	356	359	123	13
	14	0+	0+	0+	0+	0+	0+	0+	001	007	044	229	488	869	14
15	0	860	463	206	035	005	0+	0+	0+	0+	0+	0+	0+	0+	0
	1	130	366	343	132	031	005	0+	0+	0+	0+	0+	0+	0+	1
	2	009	135	267	231	092	022	003	0+	0+	0+	0+	0+	0+	2
	3	0+	031	129	250	170	063	014	002	0+	0+	0+	0+	0+	3
	4	0+	005	043	188	219	127	042	007	001	0+	0+	0+	0+	4
	5	0+	001	010	103	206	186	092	024	003	0+	0+	0+	0+	5
	6	0+	0+	002	043	147	207	153	061	012	001	0+	0+	0+	6
	7	0+	0+	0+	014	081	177	196	118	035	003	0+	0+	0+	7
	8	0+	0+	0+	003	035	118	196	177	081	014	0+	0+	0+	8
	9	0+	0+	0+	001	012	061	153	207	147	043	002	0+	0+	9

TABLE IV

Part A: Individual terms, $b(x; n, p)$

n	x	.01	.05	.10	.20	.30	.40	p .50	.60	.70	.80	.90	.95	.99	x
15	10	0+	0+	0+	0+	003	024	092	186	206	103	010	001	0+	10
	11	0+	0+	0+	0+	001	007	042	127	219	188	043	005	0+	11
	12	0+	0+	0+	0+	0+	002	014	063	170	250	129	031	0+	12
	13	0+	0+	0+	0+	0+	0+	003	022	092	231	267	135	009	13
	14	0+	0+	0+	0+	0+	0+	0+	005	031	132	343	366	130	14
	15	0+	0+	0+	0+	0+	0+	0+	0+	005	035	206	463	860	15
16	0	851	440	185	028	003	0+	0+	0+	0+	0+	0+	0+	0+	0
	1	138	371	329	113	023	003	0+	0+	0+	0+	0+	0+	0+	1
	2	010	146	275	211	073	015	002	0+	0+	0+	0+	0+	0+	2
	3	0+	036	142	246	146	047	009	001	0+	0+	0+	0+	0+	3
	4	0+	006	051	200	204	101	028	004	0+	0+	0+	0+	0+	4
	5	0+	001	014	120	210	162	067	014	001	0+	0+	0+	0+	5
	6	0+	0+	003	055	165	198	122	039	006	0+	0+	0+	0+	6
	7	0+	0+	0+	020	101	189	175	084	019	001	0+	0+	0+	7
	8	0+	0+	0+	006	049	142	196	142	049	006	0+	0+	0+	8
	9	0+	0+	0+	001	019	084	175	189	101	020	0+	0+	0+	9
	10	0+	0+	0+	0+	006	039	122	198	165	055	003	0+	0+	10
	11	0+	0+	0+	0+	001	014	067	162	210	120	014	001	0+	11
	12	0+	0+	0+	0+	0+	004	028	101	204	200	051	006	0+	12
	13	0+	0+	0+	0+	0+	001	009	047	146	246	142	036	0+	13
	14	0+	0+	0+	0+	0+	0+	002	015	073	211	275	146	010	14
	15	0+	0+	0+	0+	0+	0+	0+	003	023	113	329	371	138	15
	16	0+	0+	0+	0+	0+	0+	0+	0+	003	028	185	440	851	16
17	0	843	418	167	023	002	0+	0+	0+	0+	0+	0+	0+	0+	0
	1	145	374	315	096	017	002	0+	0+	0+	0+	0+	0+	0+	1
	2	012	158	280	191	058	010	001	0+	0+	0+	0+	0+	0+	2
	3	001	041	156	239	125	034	005	0+	0+	0+	0+	0+	0+	3
	4	0+	008	060	209	187	080	018	002	0+	0+	0+	0+	0+	4
	5	0+	001	017	136	208	138	047	008	001	0+	0+	0+	0+	5
	6	0+	0+	004	068	178	184	094	024	003	0+	0+	0+	0+	6
	7	0+	0+	001	027	120	193	148	057	009	0+	0+	0+	0+	7
	8	0+	0+	0+	008	064	161	185	107	028	002	0+	0+	0+	8
	9	0+	0+	0+	002	028	107	185	161	064	008	0+	0+	0+	9
	10	0+	0+	0+	0+	009	057	148	193	120	027	001	0+	0+	10
	11	0+	0+	0+	0+	003	024	094	184	178	068	004	0+	0+	11
	12	0+	0+	0+	0+	001	008	047	138	208	136	017	001	0+	12
	13	0+	0+	0+	0+	0+	002	018	080	187	209	060	008	0+	13
	14	0+	0+	0+	0+	0+	0+	005	034	125	239	156	041	001	14
	15	0+	0+	0+	0+	0+	0+	001	010	058	191	280	158	012	15
	16	0+	0+	0+	0+	0+	0+	0+	002	017	096	315	374	145	16
	17	0+	0+	0+	0+	0+	0+	0+	0+	002	023	167	418	843	17

TABLE IV   297

PART A: INDIVIDUAL TERMS, $b(x; n, p)$

n	x	.01	.05	.10	.20	.30	.40	p .50	.60	.70	.80	.90	.95	.99	x
18	0	835	397	150	018	002	0+	0+	0+	0+	0+	0+	0+	0+	0
	1	152	376	300	081	013	001	0+	0+	0+	0+	0+	0+	0+	1
	2	013	168	284	172	046	007	001	0+	0+	0+	0+	0+	0+	2
	3	001	047	168	230	105	025	003	0+	0+	0+	0+	0+	0+	3.
	4	0+	009	070	215	168	061	012	001	0+	0+	0+	0+	0+	4
	5	0+	001	022	151	202	115	033	004	0+	0+	0+	0+	0+	5
	6	0+	0+	005	082	187	166	071	015	001	0+	0+	0+	0+	6
	7	0+	0+	001	035	138	189	121	037	005	0+	0+	0+	0+	7
	8	0+	0+	0+	012	081	173	167	077	015	001	0+	0+	0+	8
	9	0+	0+	0+	003	039	128	185	128	039	003	0+	0+	0+	9
	10	0+	0+	0+	001	015	077	167	173	081	012	0+	0+	0+	10
	11	0+	0+	0+	0+	005	037	121	189	138	035	001	0+	0+	11
	12	0+	0+	0+	0+	001	015	071	166	187	082	005	0+	0+	12
	13	0+	0+	0+	0+	0+	004	033	115	202	151	022	001	0+	13
	14	0+	0+	0+	0+	0+	001	012	061	168	215	070	009	0+	14
	15	0+	0+	0+	0+	0+	0+	003	025	105	230	168	047	001	15
	16	0+	0+	0+	0+	0+	0+	001	007	046	172	284	168	013	16
	17	0+	0+	0+	0+	0+	0+	0+	001	013	081	300	376	152	17
	18	0+	0+	0+	0+	0+	0+	0+	0+	002	018	150	397	835	18
19	0	826	377	135	014	001	0+	0+	0+	0+	0+	0+	0+	0+	0
	1	159	377	285	068	009	001	0+	0+	0+	0+	0+	0+	0+	1
	2	014	179	285	154	036	005	0+	0+	0+	0+	0+	0+	0+	2
	3	001	053	180	218	087	017	002	0+	0+	0+	0+	0+	0+	3
	4	0+	011	080	218	149	047	007	001	0+	0+	0+	0+	0+	4
	5	0+	002	027	164	192	093	022	002	0+	0+	0+	0+	0+	5
	6	0+	0+	007	095	192	145	052	008	001	0+	0+	0+	0+	6
	7	0+	0+	001	044	153	180	096	024	002	0+	0+	0+	0+	7
	8	0+	0+	0+	017	098	180	144	053	008	0+	0+	0+	0+	8
	9	0+	0+	0+	005	051	146	176	098	022	001	0+	0+	0+	9
	10	0+	0+	0+	001	022	098	176	146	051	005	0+	0+	0+	10
	11	0+	0+	0+	0+	008	053	144	180	098	017	0+	0+	0+	11
	12	0+	0+	0+	0+	002	024	096	180	153	044	001	0+	0+	12
	13	0+	0+	0+	0+	001	008	052	145	192	095	007	0+	0+	13
	14	0+	0+	0+	0+	0+	002	022	093	192	164	027	002	0+	14
	15	0+	0+	0+	0+	0+	001	007	047	149	218	080	011	0+	15
	16	0+	0+	0+	0+	0+	0+	002	017	087	218	180	053	001	16
	17	0+	0+	0+	0+	0+	0+	0+	005	036	154	285	179	014	17
	18	0+	0+	0+	0+	0+	0+	0+	001	009	068	285	377	159	18
	19	0+	0+	0+	0+	0+	0+	0+	0+	001	014	135	377	826	19
20	0	818	358	122	012	001	0+	0+	0+	0+	0+	0+	0+	0+	0
	1	165	377	270	058	007	0+	0+	0+	0+	0+	0+	0+	0+	1
	2	016	189	285	137	028	003	0+	0+	0+	0+	0+	0+	0+	2
	3	001	060	190	205	072	012	001	0+	0+	0+	0+	0+	0+	3
	4	0+	013	090	218	130	035	005	0+	0+	0+	0+	0+	0+	4

Part A: Individual terms, $b(x; n, p)$

n	x	.01	.05	.10	.20	.30	.40	p .50	.60	.70	.80	.90	.95	.99	x
20	5	0+	002	032	175	179	075	015	001	0+	0+	0+	0+	0+	5
	6	0+	0+	009	109	192	124	037	005	0+	0+	0+	0+	0+	6
	7	0+	0+	002	055	164	166	074	015	001	0+	0+	0+	0+	7
	8	0+	0+	0+	022	114	180	120	035	004	0+	0+	0+	0+	8
	9	0+	0+	0+	007	065	160	160	071	012	0+	0+	0+	0+	9
	10	0+	0+	0+	002	031	117	176	117	031	002	0+	0+	0+	10
	11	0+	0+	0+	0+	012	071	160	160	065	007	0+	0+	0+	11
	12	0+	0+	0+	0+	004	035	120	180	114	022	0+	0+	0+	12
	13	0+	0+	0+	0+	001	015	074	166	164	055	002	0+	0+	13
	14	0+	0+	0+	0+	0+	005	037	124	192	109	009	0+	0+	14
	15	0+	0+	0+	0+	0+	001	015	075	179	175	032	002	0+	15
	16	0+	0+	0+	0+	0+	0+	005	035	130	218	090	013	0+	16
	17	0+	0+	0+	0+	0+	0+	001	012	072	205	190	060	001	17
	18	0+	0+	0+	0+	0+	0+	0+	003	028	137	285	189	016	18
	19	0+	0+	0+	0+	0+	0+	0+	0+	007	058	270	377	165	19
	20	0+	0+	0+	0+	0+	0+	0+	0+	001	012	122	358	818	20
21	0	810	341	109	009	001	0+	0+	0+	0+	0+	0+	0+	0+	0
	1	172	376	255	048	005	0+	0+	0+	0+	0+	0+	0+	0+	1
	2	017	198	284	121	022	002	0+	0+	0+	0+	0+	0+	0+	2
	3	001	066	200	192	058	009	001	0+	0+	0+	0+	0+	0+	3
	4	0+	016	100	216	113	026	003	0+	0+	0+	0+	0+	0+	4
	5	0+	003	038	183	164	059	010	001	0+	0+	0+	0+	0+	5
	6	0+	0+	011	122	188	105	026	003	0+	0+	0+	0+	0+	6
	7	0+	0+	003	065	172	149	055	009	0+	0+	0+	0+	0+	7
	8	0+	0+	001	029	129	174	097	023	002	0+	0+	0+	0+	8
	9	0+	0+	0+	010	080	168	140	050	006	0+	0+	0+	0+	9
	10	0+	0+	0+	003	041	134	168	089	018	001	0+	0+	0+	10
	11	0+	0+	0+	001	018	089	168	134	041	003	0+	0+	0+	11
	12	0+	0+	0+	0+	006	050	140	168	080	010	0+	0+	0+	12
	13	0+	0+	0+	0+	002	023	097	174	129	029	001	0+	0+	13
	14	0+	0+	0+	0+	0+	009	055	149	172	065	003	0+	0+	14
	15	0+	0+	0+	0+	0+	003	026	105	188	122	011	0+	0+	15
	16	0+	0+	0+	0+	0+	001	010	059	164	183	038	003	0+	16
	17	0+	0+	0+	0+	0+	0+	003	026	113	216	100	016	0+	17
	18	0+	0+	0+	0+	0+	0+	001	009	058	192	200	066	001	18
	19	0+	0+	0+	0+	0+	0+	0+	002	022	121	284	198	017	19
	20	0+	0+	0+	0+	0+	0+	0+	0+	005	048	255	376	172	20
	21	0+	0+	0+	0+	0+	0+	0+	0+	001	009	109	341	810	21
22	0	802	324	098	007	0+	0+	0+	0+	0+	0+	0+	0+	0+	0
	1	178	375	241	041	004	0+	0+	0+	0+	0+	0+	0+	0+	1
	2	019	207	281	107	017	001	0+	0+	0+	0+	0+	0+	0+	2
	3	001	073	208	178	047	006	0+	0+	0+	0+	0+	0+	0+	3
	4	0+	018	110	211	096	019	002	0+	0+	0+	0+	0+	0+	4

TABLE IV   299

PART A: INDIVIDUAL TERMS, $b(x; n, p)$

n	x	.01	.05	.10	.20	.30	.40	p .50	.60	.70	.80	.90	.95	.99	x
22	5	0+	003	044	190	149	046	006	0+	0+	0+	0+	0+	0+	5
	6	0+	001	014	134	181	086	018	001	0+	0+	0+	0+	0+	6
	7	0+	0+	004	077	177	131	041	005	0+	0+	0+	0+	0+	7
	8	0+	0+	001	036	142	164	076	014	001	0+	0+	0+	0+	8
	9	0+	0+	0+	014	095	170	119	034	003	0+	0+	0+	0+	9
	10	0+	0+	0+	005	053	148	154	066	010	0+	0+	0+	0+	10
	11	0+	0+	0+	001	025	107	168	107	025	001	0+	0+	0+	11
	12	0+	0+	0+	0+	010	066	154	148	053	005	0+	0+	0+	12
	13	0+	0+	0+	0+	003	034	119	170	095	014	0+	0+	0+	13
	14	0+	0+	0+	0+	001	014	076	164	142	036	001	0+	0+	14
	15	0+	0+	0+	0+	0+	005	041	131	177	077	004	0+	0+	15
	16	0+	0+	0+	0+	0+	001	018	086	181	134	014	001	0+	16
	17	0+	0+	0+	0+	0+	0+	006	046	149	190	044	003	0+	17
	18	0+	0+	0+	0+	0+	0+	002	019	096	211	110	018	0+	18
	19	0+	0+	0+	0+	0+	0+	0+	006	047	178	208	073	001	19
	20	0+	0+	0+	0+	0+	0+	0+	001	017	107	281	207	019	20
	21	0+	0+	0+	0+	0+	0+	0+	0+	004	041	241	375	178	21
	22	0+	0+	0+	0+	0+	0+	0+	0+	0+	007	098	324	802	22
23	0	794	307	089	006	0+	0+	0+	0+	0+	0+	0+	0+	0+	0
	1	184	372	226	034	003	0+	0+	0+	0+	0+	0+	0+	0+	1
	2	020	215	277	093	013	001	0+	0+	0+	0+	0+	0+	0+	2
	3	001	079	215	163	038	004	0+	0+	0+	0+	0+	0+	0+	3
	4	0+	021	120	204	082	014	001	0+	0+	0+	0+	0+	0+	4
	5	0+	004	051	194	133	035	004	0+	0+	0+	0+	0+	0+	5
	6	0+	001	017	145	171	070	012	001	0+	0+	0+	0+	0+	6
	7	0+	0+	005	088	178	113	029	003	0+	0+	0+	0+	0+	7
	8	0+	0+	001	044	153	151	058	009	0+	0+	0+	0+	0+	8
	9	0+	0+	0+	018	109	168	097	022	002	0+	0+	0+	0+	9
	10	0+	0+	0+	006	065	157	136	046	005	0+	0+	0+	0+	10
	11	0+	0+	0+	002	033	123	161	082	014	0+	0+	0+	0+	11
	12	0+	0+	0+	0+	014	082	161	123	033	002	0+	0+	0+	12
	13	0+	0+	0+	0+	005	046	136	157	065	006	0+	0+	0+	13
	14	0+	0+	0+	0+	002	022	097	168	109	018	0+	0+	0+	14
	15	0+	0+	0+	0+	0+	009	058	151	153	044	001	0+	0+	15
	16	0+	0+	0+	0+	0+	003	029	113	178	088	005	0+	0+	16
	17	0+	0+	0+	0+	0+	001	012	070	171	145	017	001	0+	17
	18	0+	0+	0+	0+	0+	0+	004	035	133	194	051	004	0+	18
	19	0+	0+	0+	0+	0+	0+	001	014	082	204	120	021	0+	19
	20	0+	0+	0+	0+	0+	0+	0+	004	038	163	215	079	001	20
	21	0+	0+	0+	0+	0+	0+	0+	001	013	093	277	215	020	21
	22	0+	0+	0+	0+	0+	0+	0+	0+	003	034	226	372	184	22
	23	0+	0+	0+	0+	0+	0+	0+	0+	0+	006	089	307	794	23

Part A: Individual terms, $b(x; n, p)$

n	x	.01	.05	.10	.20	.30	.40	.50	.60	.70	.80	.90	.95	.99	x
24	0	786	292	080	005	0+	0+	0+	0+	0+	0+	0+	0+	0+	0
	1	190	369	213	028	002	0+	0+	0+	0+	0+	0+	0+	0+	1
	2	022	223	272	081	010	001	0+	0+	0+	0+	0+	0+	0+	2
	3	002	086	221	149	031	003	0+	0+	0+	0+	0+	0+	0+	3
	4	0+	024	129	196	069	010	001	0+	0+	0+	0+	0+	0+	4
	5	0+	005	057	196	118	027	003	0+	0+	0+	0+	0+	0+	5
	6	0+	001	020	155	160	056	008	0+	0+	0+	0+	0+	0+	6
	7	0+	0+	006	100	176	096	021	002	0+	0+	0+	0+	0+	7
	8	0+	0+	001	053	160	136	044	005	0+	0+	0+	0+	0+	8
	9	0+	0+	0+	024	122	161	078	014	001	0+	0+	0+	0+	9
	10	0+	0+	0+	009	079	161	117	032	003	0+	0+	0+	0+	10
	11	0+	0+	0+	003	043	137	149	061	008	0+	0+	0+	0+	11
	12	0+	0+	0+	001	020	099	161	099	020	001	0+	0+	0+	12
	13	0+	0+	0+	0+	008	061	149	137	043	003	0+	0+	0+	13
	14	0+	0+	0+	0+	003	032	117	161	079	009	0+	0+	0+	14
	15	0+	0+	0+	0+	001	014	078	161	122	024	0+	0+	0+	15
	16	0+	0+	0+	0+	0+	005	044	136	160	053	001	0+	0+	16
	17	0+	0+	0+	0+	0+	002	021	096	176	100	006	0+	0+	17
	18	0+	0+	0+	0+	0+	0+	008	056	160	155	020	001	0+	18
	19	0+	0+	0+	0+	0+	0+	003	027	118	196	057	005	0+	19
	20	0+	0+	0+	0+	0+	0+	001	010	069	196	129	024	0+	20
	21	0+	0+	0+	0+	0+	0+	0+	003	031	149	221	086	002	21
	22	0+	0+	0+	0+	0+	0+	0+	001	010	081	272	223	022	22
	23	0+	0+	0+	0+	0+	0+	0+	0+	002	028	213	369	190	23
	24	0+	0+	0+	0+	0+	0+	0+	0+	0+	005	080	292	786	24
25	0	778	277	072	004	0+	0+	0+	0+	0+	0+	0+	0+	0+	0
	1	196	365	199	024	001	0+	0+	0+	0+	0+	0+	0+	0+	1
	2	024	231	266	071	007	0+	0+	0+	0+	0+	0+	0+	0+	2
	3	002	093	226	136	024	002	0+	0+	0+	0+	0+	0+	0+	3
	4	0+	027	138	187	057	007	0+	0+	0+	0+	0+	0+	0+	4
	5	0+	006	065	196	103	020	002	0+	0+	0+	0+	0+	0+	5
	6	0+	001	024	163	147	044	005	0+	0+	0+	0+	0+	0+	6
	7	0+	0+	007	111	171	080	014	001	0+	0+	0+	0+	0+	7
	8	0+	0+	002	062	165	120	032	003	0+	0+	0+	0+	0+	8
	9	0+	0+	0+	029	134	151	061	009	0+	0+	0+	0+	0+	9
	10	0+	0+	0+	012	092	161	097	021	001	0+	0+	0+	0+	10
	11	0+	0+	0+	004	054	147	133	043	004	0+	0+	0+	0+	11
	12	0+	0+	0+	001	027	114	155	076	011	0+	0+	0+	0+	12
	13	0+	0+	0+	0+	011	076	155	114	027	001	0+	0+	0+	13
	14	0+	0+	0+	0+	004	043	133	147	054	004	0+	0+	0+	14
	15	0+	0+	0+	0+	001	021	097	161	092	012	0+	0+	0+	15
	16	0+	0+	0+	0+	0+	009	061	151	134	029	0+	0+	0+	16
	17	0+	0+	0+	0+	0+	003	032	120	165	062	002	0+	0+	17
	18	0+	0+	0+	0+	0+	001	014	080	171	111	007	0+	0+	18
	19	0+	0+	0+	0+	0+	0+	005	044	147	163	024	001	0+	19

TABLE IV   301

PART A: INDIVIDUAL TERMS, $b(x; n, p)$

n	x	.01	.05	.10	.20	.30	.40	p .50	.60	.70	.80	.90	.95	.99	x
25	20	0+	0+	0+	0+	0+	0+	002	020	103	196	065	006	0+	20
	21	0+	0+	0+	0+	0+	0+	0+	007	057	187	138	027	0+	21
	22	0+	0+	0+	0+	0+	0+	0+	002	024	136	226	093	002	22
	23	0+	0+	0+	0+	0+	0+	0+	0+	007	071	266	231	024	23
	24	0+	0+	0+	0+	0+	0+	0+	0+	001	024	199	365	196	24
	25	0+	0+	0+	0+	0+	0+	0+	0+	0+	004	072	277	778	25

TABLE IV

Part B: Cumulative terms, $\sum_{x=r}^{n} b(x; n, p)$

n	r	.01	.05	.10	.20	.30	.40	.50	.60	.70	.80	.90	.95	.99	r
2	0	1	1	1	1	1	1	1	1	1	1	1	1	1	0
	1	020	098	190	360	510	640	750	840	910	960	990	998	1−	1
	2	0+	002	010	040	090	160	250	360	490	640	810	902	980	2
3	0	1	1	1	1	1	1	1	1	1	1	1	1	1	0
	1	030	143	271	488	657	784	875	936	973	992	999	1−	1−	1
	2	0+	007	028	104	216	352	500	648	784	896	972	993	1−	2
	3	0+	0+	001	008	027	064	125	216	343	512	729	857	970	3
4	0	1	1	1	1	1	1	1	1	1	1	1	1	1	0
	1	039	185	344	590	760	870	938	974	992	998	1−	1−	1−	1
	2	001	014	052	181	348	525	688	821	916	973	996	1−	1−	2
	3	0+	0+	004	027	084	179	312	475	652	819	948	986	999	3
	4	0+	0+	0+	002	008	026	062	130	240	410	656	815	961	4
5	0	1	1	1	1	1	1	1	1	1	1	1	1	1	0
	1	049	226	410	672	832	922	969	990	998	1−	1−	1−	1−	1
	2	001	023	081	263	472	663	812	913	969	993	1−	1−	1−	2
	3	0+	001	009	058	163	317	500	683	837	942	991	999	1−	3
	4	0+	0+	0+	007	031	087	188	337	528	737	919	977	999	4
	5	0+	0+	0+	0+	002	010	031	078	168	328	590	774	951	5
6	0	1	1	1	1	1	1	1	1	1	1	1	1	1	0
	1	059	265	469	738	882	953	984	996	999	1−	1−	1−	1−	1
	2	001	033	114	345	580	767	891	959	989	998	1−	1−	1−	2
	3	0+	002	016	099	256	456	656	821	930	983	999	1−	1−	3
	4	0+	0+	001	017	070	179	344	544	744	901	984	998	1−	4
	5	0+	0+	0+	002	011	041	109	233	420	655	886	967	999	5
	6	0+	0+	0+	0+	001	004	016	047	118	262	531	735	941	6
7	0	1	1	1	1	1	1	1	1	1	1	1	1	1	0
	1	068	302	522	790	918	972	992	998	1−	1−	1−	1−	1−	1
	2	002	044	150	423	671	841	938	981	996	1−	1−	1−	1−	2
	3	0+	004	026	148	353	580	773	904	971	995	1−	1−	1−	3
	4	0+	0+	003	033	126	290	500	710	874	967	997	1−	1−	4
	5	0+	0+	0+	005	029	096	227	420	647	852	974	996	1−	5
	6	0+	0+	0+	0+	004	019	062	159	329	577	850	956	998	6
	7	0+	0+	0+	0+	0+	002	008	028	082	210	478	698	932	7
8	0	1	1	1	1	1	1	1	1	1	1	1	1	1	0
	1	077	337	570	832	942	983	996	999	1−	1−	1−	1−	1−	1
	2	003	057	187	497	745	894	965	991	999	1−	1−	1−	1−	2
	3	0+	006	038	203	448	685	855	950	989	999	1−	1−	1−	3
	4	0+	0+	005	056	194	406	637	826	942	990	1−	1−	1−	4
	5	0+	0+	0+	010	058	174	363	594	806	944	995	1−	1−	5
	6	0+	0+	0+	001	011	050	145	315	552	797	962	994	1−	6
	7	0+	0+	0+	0+	001	009	035	106	255	503	813	943	997	7
	8	0+	0+	0+	0+	0+	001	004	017	058	168	430	663	923	8

TABLE IV   303

Part B: Cumulative terms, $\sum_{x=r}^{n} b(x; n, p)$

n	r	.01	.05	.10	.20	.30	.40	.50	.60	.70	.80	.90	.95	.99	r
9	0	1	1	1	1	1	1	1	1	1	1	1	1	1	0
	1	086	370	613	866	960	990	998	1−	1−	1−	1−	1−	1−	1
	2	003	071	225	564	804	929	980	996	1−	1−	1−	1−	1−	2
	3	0+	008	053	262	537	768	910	975	996	1−	1−	1−	1−	3
	4	0+	001	008	086	270	517	746	901	975	997	1−	1−	1−	4
	5	0+	0+	001	020	099	267	500	733	901	980	999	1−	1−	5
	6	0+	0+	0+	003	025	099	254	483	730	914	992	999	1−	6
	7	0+	0+	0+	0+	004	025	090	232	463	738	947	992	1−	7
	8	0+	0+	0+	0+	0+	004	020	071	196	436	775	929	997	8
	9	0+	0+	0+	0+	0+	0+	002	010	040	134	387	630	914	9
10	0	1	1	1	1	1	1	1	1	1	1	1	1	1	0
	1	096	401	651	893	972	994	999	1−	1−	1−	1−	1−	1−	1
	2	004	086	264	624	851	954	989	998	1−	1−	1−	1−	1−	2
	3	0+	012	070	322	617	833	945	988	998	1−	1−	1−	1−	3
	4	0+	001	013	121	350	618	828	945	989	999	1−	1−	1−	4
	5	0+	0+	002	033	150	367	623	834	953	994	1−	1−	1−	5
	6	0+	0+	0+	006	047	166	377	633	850	967	998	1−	1−	6
	7	0+	0+	0+	001	011	055	172	382	650	879	987	999	1−	7
	8	0+	0+	0+	0+	002	012	055	167	383	678	930	988	1−	8
	9	0+	0+	0+	0+	0+	002	011	046	149	376	736	914	996	9
	10	0+	0+	0+	0+	0+	0+	001	006	028	107	349	599	904	10
11	0	1	1	1	1	1	1	1	1	1	1	1	1	1	0
	1	105	431	686	914	980	996	1−	1−	1−	1−	1−	1−	1−	1
	2	005	102	303	678	887	970	994	999	1−	1−	1−	1−	1−	2
	3	0+	015	090	383	687	881	967	994	999	1−	1−	1−	1−	3
	4	0+	002	019	161	430	704	887	971	996	1−	1−	1−	1−	4
	5	0+	0+	003	050	210	467	726	901	978	998	1−	1−	1−	5
	6	0+	0+	0+	012	078	247	500	753	922	988	1−	1−	1−	6
	7	0+	0+	0+	002	022	099	274	533	790	950	997	1−	1−	7
	8	0+	0+	0+	0+	004	029	113	296	570	839	981	998	1−	8
	9	0+	0+	0+	0+	001	006	033	119	313	617	910	985	1−	9
	10	0+	0+	0+	0+	0+	001	006	030	113	322	697	898	995	10
	11	0+	0+	0+	0+	0+	0+	0+	004	020	086	314	569	895	11
12	0	1	1	1	1	1	1	1	1	1	1	1	1	1	0
	1	114	460	718	931	986	998	1−	1−	1−	1−	1−	1−	1−	1
	2	006	118	341	725	915	980	997	1−	1−	1−	1−	1−	1−	2
	3	0+	020	111	442	747	917	981	997	1−	1−	1−	1−	1−	3
	4	0+	002	026	205	507	775	927	985	998	1−	1−	1−	1−	4
	5	0+	0+	004	073	276	562	806	943	991	999	1−	1−	1−	5
	6	0+	0+	001	019	118	335	613	842	961	996	1−	1−	1−	6
	7	0+	0+	0+	004	039	158	387	665	882	981	999	1−	1−	7
	8	0+	0+	0+	001	009	057	194	438	724	927	996	1−	1−	8
	9	0+	0+	0+	0+	002	015	073	225	493	795	974	998	1−	9

TABLE IV

$$\text{PART B: CUMULATIVE TERMS, } \sum_{x=r}^{n} b(x; n, p)$$

n	r	.01	.05	.10	.20	.30	.40	.50	.60	.70	.80	.90	.95	.99	r
12	10	0+	0+	0+	0+	0+	003	019	083	253	558	889	980	1−	10
	11	0+	0+	0+	0+	0+	0+	003	020	085	275	659	882	994	11
	12	0+	0+	0+	0+	0+	0+	0+	002	014	069	282	540	886	12
13	0	1	1	1	1	1	1	1	1	1	1	1	1	1	0
	1	122	487	746	945	990	999	1−	1−	1−	1−	1−	1−	1−	1
	2	007	135	379	766	936	987	998	1−	1−	1−	1−	1−	1−	2
	3	0+	025	134	498	798	942	989	999	1−	1−	1−	1−	1−	3
	4	0+	003	034	253	579	831	954	992	999	1−	1−	1−	1−	4
	5	0+	0+	006	099	346	647	867	968	996	1−	1−	1−	1−	5
	6	0+	0+	001	030	165	426	709	902	982	999	1−	1−	1−	6
	7	0+	0+	0+	007	062	229	500	771	938	993	1−	1−	1−	7
	8	0+	0+	0+	001	018	098	291	574	835	970	999	1−	1−	8
	9	0+	0+	0+	0+	004	032	133	353	654	901	994	1−	1−	9
	10	0+	0+	0+	0+	001	008	046	169	421	747	966	997	1−	10
	11	0+	0+	0+	0+	0+	001	011	058	202	502	866	975	1−	11
	12	0+	0+	0+	0+	0+	0+	002	013	064	234	621	865	993	12
	13	0+	0+	0+	0+	0+	0+	0+	001	010	055	254	513	878	13
14	0	1	1	1	1	1	1	1	1	1	1	1	1	1	0
	1	131	512	771	956	993	999	1−	1−	1−	1−	1−	1−	1−	1
	2	008	153	415	802	953	992	999	1−	1−	1−	1−	1−	1−	2
	3	0+	030	158	552	839	960	994	999	1−	1−	1−	1−	1−	3
	4	0+	004	044	302	645	876	971	996	1−	1−	1−	1−	1−	4
	5	0+	0+	009	130	416	721	910	982	998	1−	1−	1−	1−	5
	6	0+	0+	001	044	219	514	788	942	992	1−	1−	1−	1−	6
	7	0+	0+	0+	012	093	308	605	850	969	998	1−	1−	1−	7
	8	0+	0+	0+	002	031	150	395	692	907	988	1−	1−	1−	8
	9	0+	0+	0+	0+	008	058	212	486	781	956	999	1−	1−	9
	10	0+	0+	0+	0+	002	018	090	279	584	870	991	1−	1−	10
	11	0+	0+	0+	0+	0+	004	029	124	355	698	956	996	1−	11
	12	0+	0+	0+	0+	0+	001	006	040	161	448	842	970	1−	12
	13	0+	0+	0+	0+	0+	0+	001	008	047	198	585	847	992	13
	14	0+	0+	0+	0+	0+	0+	0+	001	007	044	229	488	869	14
15	0	1	1	1	1	1	1	1	1	1	1	1	1	1	0
	1	140	537	794	965	995	1−	1−	1−	1−	1−	1−	1−	1−	1
	2	010	171	451	833	965	995	1−	1−	1−	1−	1−	1−	1−	2
	3	0+	036	184	602	873	973	996	1−	1−	1−	1−	1−	1−	3
	4	0+	005	056	352	703	909	982	998	1−	1−	1−	1−	1−	4
	5	0+	001	013	164	485	783	941	991	999	1−	1−	1−	1−	5
	6	0+	0+	002	061	278	597	849	966	996	1−	1−	1−	1−	6
	7	0+	0+	0+	018	131	390	696	905	985	999	1−	1−	1−	7
	8	0+	0+	0+	004	050	213	500	787	950	996	1−	1−	1−	8
	9	0+	0+	0+	001	015	095	304	610	869	982	1−	1−	1−	9

TABLE IV   305

PART B: CUMULATIVE TERMS, $\sum_{x=r}^{n} b(x; n, p)$

n	r	.01	.05	.10	.20	.30	.40	p .50	.60	.70	.80	.90	.95	.99	r
15	10	0+	0+	0+	0+	004	034	151	403	722	939	998	1−	1−	10
	11	0+	0+	0+	0+	001	009	059	217	515	836	987	999	1−	11
	12	0+	0+	0+	0+	0+	002	018	091	297	648	944	995	1−	12
	13	0+	0+	0+	0+	0+	0+	004	027	127	398	816	964	1−	13
	14	0+	0+	0+	0+	0+	0+	0+	005	035	167	549	829	990	14
	15	0+	0+	0+	0+	0+	0+	0+	0+	005	035	206	463	860	15
16	0	1	1	1	1	1	1	1	1	1	1	1	1	1	0
	1	149	560	815	972	997	1−	1−	1−	1−	1−	1−	1−	1−	1
	2	011	189	485	859	974	997	1−	1−	1−	1−	1−	1−	1−	2
	3	001	043	211	648	901	982	998	1−	1−	1−	1−	1−	1−	3
	4	0+	007	068	402	754	935	989	999	1−	1−	1−	1−	1−	4
	5	0+	001	017	202	550	833	962	995	1−	1−	1−	1−	1−	5
	6	0+	0+	003	082	340	671	895	981	998	1−	1−	1−	1−	6
	7	0+	0+	001	027	175	473	773	942	993	1−	1−	1−	1−	7
	8	0+	0+	0+	007	074	284	598	858	974	999	1−	1−	1−	8
	9	0+	0+	0+	001	026	142	402	716	926	993	1−	1−	1−	9
	10	0+	0+	0+	0+	007	058	227	527	825	973	999	1−	1−	10
	11	0+	0+	0+	0+	002	019	105	329	660	918	997	1−	1−	11
	12	0+	0+	0+	0+	0+	005	038	167	450	798	983	999	1−	12
	13	0+	0+	0+	0+	0+	001	011	065	246	598	932	993	1−	13
	14	0+	0+	0+	0+	0+	0+	002	018	099	352	789	957	999	14
	15	0+	0+	0+	0+	0+	0+	0+	003	026	141	515	811	989	15
	16	0+	0+	0+	0+	0+	0+	0+	0+	003	028	185	440	851	16
17	0	1	1	1	1	1	1	1	1	1	1	1	1	1	0
	1	157	582	833	977	998	1−	1−	1−	1−	1−	1−	1−	1−	1
	2	012	208	518	882	981	998	1−	1−	1−	1−	1−	1−	1−	2
	3	001	050	238	690	923	988	999	1−	1−	1−	1−	1−	1−	3
	4	0+	009	083	451	798	954	994	1−	1−	1−	1−	1−	1−	4
	5	0+	001	022	242	611	874	975	997	1−	1−	1−	1−	1−	5
	6	0+	0+	005	106	403	736	928	989	999	1−	1−	1−	1−	6
	7	0+	0+	001	038	225	552	834	965	997	1−	1−	1−	1−	7
	8	0+	0+	0+	011	105	359	685	908	987	1−	1−	1−	1−	8
	9	0+	0+	0+	003	040	199	500	801	960	997	1−	1−	1−	9
	10	0+	0+	0+	0+	013	092	315	641	895	989	1−	1−	1−	10
	11	0+	0+	0+	0+	003	035	166	448	775	962	999	1−	1−	11
	12	0+	0+	0+	0+	001	011	072	264	597	894	995	1−	1−	12
	13	0+	0+	0+	0+	0+	003	025	126	389	758	978	999	1−	13
	14	0+	0+	0+	0+	0+	0+	006	046	202	549	917	991	1−	14
	15	0+	0+	0+	0+	0+	0+	001	012	077	310	762	950	999	15
	16	0+	0+	0+	0+	0+	0+	0+	002	019	118	482	792	988	16
	17	0+	0+	0+	0+	0+	0+	0+	0+	002	023	167	418	843	17

TABLE IV

PART B: CUMULATIVE TERMS, $\sum_{x=r}^{n} b(x; n, p)$

n	r	.01	.05	.10	.20	.30	.40	p .50	.60	.70	.80	.90	.95	.99	r
18	0	1	1	1	1	1	1	1	1	1	1	1	1	1	0
	1	165	603	850	982	998	1—	1—	1—	1—	1—	1—	1—	1—	1
	2	014	226	550	901	986	999	1—	1—	1—	1—	1—	1—	1—	2
	3	001	058	266	729	940	992	999	1—	1—	1—	1—	1—	1—	3
	4	0+	011	098	499	835	967	996	1—	1—	1—	1—	1—	1—	4
	5	0+	002	028	284	667	906	985	999	1—	1—	1—	1—	1—	5
	6	0+	0+	006	133	466	791	952	994	1—	1—	1—	1—	1—	6
	7	0+	0+	001	051	278	626	881	980	999	1—	1—	1—	1—	7
	8	0+	0+	0+	016	141	437	760	942	994	1—	1—	1—	1—	8
	9	0+	0+	0+	004	060	263	593	865	979	999	1—	1—	1—	9
	10	0+	0+	0+	001	021	135	407	737	940	996	1—	1—	1—	10
	11	0+	0+	0+	0+	006	058	240	563	859	984	1—	1—	1—	11
	12	0+	0+	0+	0+	001	020	119	374	722	949	999	1—	1—	12
	13	0+	0+	0+	0+	0+	006	048	209	534	867	994	1—	1—	13
	14	0+	0+	0+	0+	0+	001	015	094	333	716	972	998	1—	14
	15	0+	0+	0+	0+	0+	0+	004	033	165	501	902	989	1—	15
	16	0+	0+	0+	0+	0+	0+	001	008	060	271	734	942	999	16
	17	0+	0+	0+	0+	0+	0+	0+	001	014	099	450	774	986	17
	18	0+	0+	0+	0+	0+	0+	0+	0+	002	018	150	397	835	18
19	0	1	1	1	1	1	1	1	1	1	1	1	1	1	0
	1	174	623	865	986	999	1—	1—	1—	1—	1—	1—	1—	1—	1
	2	015	245	580	917	990	999	1—	1—	1—	1—	1—	1—	1—	2
	3	001	067	295	763	954	995	1—	1—	1—	1—	1—	1—	1—	3
	4	0+	013	115	545	867	977	998	1—	1—	1—	1—	1—	1—	4
	5	0+	002	035	327	718	930	990	999	1—	1—	1—	1—	1—	5
	6	0+	0+	009	163	526	837	968	997	1—	1—	1—	1—	1—	6
	7	0+	0+	002	068	334	692	916	988	999	1—	1—	1—	1—	7
	8	0+	0+	0+	023	182	512	820	965	997	1—	1—	1—	1—	8
	9	0+	0+	0+	007	084	333	676	912	989	1—	1—	1—	1—	9
	10	0+	0+	0+	002	033	186	500	814	967	998	1—	1—	1—	10
	11	0+	0+	0+	0+	011	088	324	667	916	993	1—	1—	1—	11
	12	0+	0+	0+	0+	003	035	180	488	818	977	1—	1—	1—	12
	13	0+	0+	0+	0+	001	012	084	308	666	932	998	1—	1—	13
	14	0+	0+	0+	0+	0+	003	032	163	474	837	991	1—	1—	14
	15	0+	0+	0+	0+	0+	001	010	070	282	673	965	998	1—	15
	16	0+	0+	0+	0+	0+	0+	002	023	133	455	885	987	1—	16
	17	0+	0+	0+	0+	0+	0+	0+	005	046	237	705	933	999	17
	18	0+	0+	0+	0+	0+	0+	0+	001	010	083	420	755	985	18
	19	0+	0+	0+	0+	0+	0+	0+	0+	001	014	135	377	826	19
20	0	1	1	1	1	1	1	1	1	1	1	1	1	1	0
	1	182	642	878	988	999	1—	1—	1—	1—	1—	1—	1—	1—	1
	2	017	264	608	931	992	999	1—	1—	1—	1—	1—	1—	1—	2
	3	001	075	323	794	965	996	1—	1—	1—	1—	1—	1—	1—	3
	4	0+	016	133	589	893	984	999	1—	1—	1—	1—	1—	1—	4

TABLE IV   307

Part B: Cumulative terms, $\sum_{x=r}^{n} b(x; n, p)$

n	r	.01	.05	.10	.20	.30	.40	p .50	.60	.70	.80	.90	.95	.99	r
20	5	0+	003	043	370	762	949	994	1—	1—	1—	1—	1—	1—	5
	6	0+	0+	011	196	584	874	979	998	1—	1—	1—	1—	1—	6
	7	0+	0+	002	087	392	750	942	994	1—	1—	1—	1—	1—	7
	8	0+	0+	0+	032	228	584	868	979	999	1—	1—	1—	1—	8
	9	0+	0+	0+	010	113	404	748	943	995	1—	1—	1—	1—	9
	10	0+	0+	0+	003	048	245	588	872	983	999	1—	1—	1—	10
	11	0+	0+	0+	001	017	128	412	755	952	997	1—	1—	1—	11
	12	0+	0+	0+	0+	005	057	252	596	887	990	1—	1—	1—	12
	13	0+	0+	0+	0+	001	021	132	416	772	968	1—	1—	1—	13
	14	0+	0+	0+	0+	0+	006	058	250	608	913	998	1—	1—	14
	15	0+	0+	0+	0+	0+	002	021	126	416	804	989	1—	1—	15
	16	0+	0+	0+	0+	0+	0+	006	051	238	630	957	997	1—	16
	17	0+	0+	0+	0+	0+	0+	001	016	107	411	867	984	1—	17
	18	0+	0+	0+	0+	0+	0+	0+	004	035	206	677	925	999	18
	19	0+	0+	0+	0+	0+	0+	0+	001	008	069	392	736	983	19
	20	0+	0+	0+	0+	0+	0+	0+	0+	001	012	122	358	818	20
21	0	1	1	1	1	1	1	1	1	1	1	1	1	1	0
	1	190	659	891	991	999	1—	1—	1—	1—	1—	1—	1—	1—	1
	2	019	283	635	942	994	1—	1—	1—	1—	1—	1—	1—	1—	2
	3	001	085	352	821	973	998	1—	1—	1—	1—	1—	1—	1—	3
	4	0+	019	152	630	914	989	999	1—	1—	1—	1—	1—	1—	4
	5	0+	003	052	414	802	963	996	1—	1—	1—	1—	1—	1—	5
	6	0+	0+	014	231	637	904	987	999	1—	1—	1—	1—	1—	6
	7	0+	0+	003	109	449	800	961	996	1—	1—	1—	1—	1—	7
	8	0+	0+	001	043	277	650	905	988	999	1—	1—	1—	1—	8
	9	0+	0+	0+	014	148	476	808	965	998	1—	1—	1—	1—	9
	10	0+	0+	0+	004	068	309	668	915	991	1—	1—	1—	1—	10
	11	0+	0+	0+	001	026	174	500	826	974	999	1—	1—	1—	11
	12	0+	0+	0+	0+	009	085	332	691	932	996	1—	1—	1—	12
	13	0+	0+	0+	0+	002	035	192	524	852	986	1—	1—	1—	13
	14	0+	0+	0+	0+	001	012	095	350	723	957	999	1—	1—	14
	15	0+	0+	0+	0+	0+	004	039	200	551	891	997	1—	1—	15
	16	0+	0+	0+	0+	0+	001	013	096	363	769	986	1—	1—	16
	17	0+	0+	0+	0+	0+	0+	004	037	198	586	948	997	1—	17
	18	0+	0+	0+	0+	0+	0+	001	011	086	370	848	981	1—	18
	19	0+	0+	0+	0+	0+	0+	0+	002	027	179	648	915	999	19
	20	0+	0+	0+	0+	0+	0+	0+	0+	006	058	365	717	981	20
	21	0+	0+	0+	0+	0+	0+	0+	0+	001	009	109	341	810	21
22	0	1	1	1	1	1	1	1	1	1	1	1	1	1	0
	1	198	676	902	993	1—	1—	1—	1—	1—	1—	1—	1—	1—	1
	2	020	302	661	952	996	1—	1—	1—	1—	1—	1—	1—	1—	2
	3	001	095	380	846	979	998	1—	1—	1—	1—	1—	1—	1—	3
	4	0+	022	172	668	932	992	1—	1—	1—	1—	1—	1—	1—	4

TABLE IV

PART B: CUMULATIVE TERMS, $\displaystyle\sum_{x=r}^{n} b(x; n, p)$

n	r	.01	.05	.10	.20	.30	.40	p .50	.60	.70	.80	.90	.95	.99	r
22	5	0+	004	062	457	835	973	998	1−	1−	1−	1−	1−	1−	5
	6	0+	001	018	267	687	928	992	1−	1−	1−	1−	1−	1−	6
	7	0+	0+	004	133	506	842	974	998	1−	1−	1−	1−	1−	7
	8	0+	0+	001	056	329	710	933	993	1−	1−	1−	1−	1−	8
	9	0+	0+	0+	020	186	546	857	979	999	1−	1−	1−	1−	9
	10	0+	0+	0+	006	092	376	738	945	996	1−	1−	1−	1−	10
	11	0+	0+	0+	002	039	228	584	879	986	1−	1−	1−	1−	11
	12	0+	0+	0+	0+	014	121	416	772	961	998	1−	1−	1−	12
	13	0+	0+	0+	0+	004	055	262	624	908	994	1−	1−	1−	13
	14	0+	0+	0+	0+	001	021	143	454	814	980	1−	1−	1−	14
	15	0+	0+	0+	0+	0+	007	067	290	671	944	999	1−	1−	15
	16	0+	0+	0+	0+	0+	002	026	158	494	867	996	1−	1−	16
	17	0+	0+	0+	0+	0+	0+	008	072	313	733	982	999	1−	17
	18	0+	0+	0+	0+	0+	0+	002	027	165	543	938	996	1−	18
	19	0+	0+	0+	0+	0+	0+	0+	008	068	332	828	978	1−	19
	20	0+	0+	0+	0+	0+	0+	0+	002	021	154	620	905	999	20
	21	0+	0+	0+	0+	0+	0+	0+	0+	004	048	339	698	980	21
	22	0+	0+	0+	0+	0+	0+	0+	0+	0+	007	098	324	802	22
23	0	1	1	1	1	1	1	1	1	1	1	1	1	1	0
	1	206	693	911	994	1−	1−	1−	1−	1−	1−	1−	1−	1−	1
	2	022	321	685	960	997	1−	1−	1−	1−	1−	1−	1−	1−	2
	3	002	105	408	867	984	999	1−	1−	1−	1−	1−	1−	1−	3
	4	0+	026	193	703	946	995	1−	1−	1−	1−	1−	1−	1−	4
	5	0+	005	073	499	864	981	999	1−	1−	1−	1−	1−	1−	5
	6	0+	001	023	305	731	946	995	1−	1−	1−	1−	1−	1−	6
	7	0+	0+	006	160	560	876	983	999	1−	1−	1−	1−	1−	7
	8	0+	0+	001	072	382	763	953	996	1−	1−	1−	1−	1−	8
	9	0+	0+	0+	027	229	612	895	987	999	1−	1−	1−	1−	9
	10	0+	0+	0+	009	120	444	798	965	998	1−	1−	1−	1−	10
	11	0+	0+	0+	003	055	287	661	919	993	1−	1−	1−	1−	11
	12	0+	0+	0+	001	021	164	500	836	979	999	1−	1−	1−	12
	13	0+	0+	0+	0+	007	081	339	713	945	997	1−	1−	1−	13
	14	0+	0+	0+	0+	002	035	202	556	880	991	1−	1−	1−	14
	15	0+	0+	0+	0+	001	013	105	388	771	973	1−	1−	1−	15
	16	0+	0+	0+	0+	0+	004	047	237	618	928	999	1−	1−	16
	17	0+	0+	0+	0+	0+	001	017	124	440	840	994	1−	1−	17
	18	0+	0+	0+	0+	0+	0+	005	054	269	695	977	999	1−	18
	19	0+	0+	0+	0+	0+	0+	001	019	136	501	927	995	1−	19
	20	0+	0+	0+	0+	0+	0+	0+	005	054	297	807	974	1−	20
	21	0+	0+	0+	0+	0+	0+	0+	001	016	133	592	895	998	21
	22	0+	0+	0+	0+	0+	0+	0+	0+	003	040	315	679	978	22
	23	0+	0+	0+	0+	0+	0+	0+	0+	0+	006	089	307	794	23

TABLE IV   309

PART B: CUMULATIVE TERMS, $\sum_{x=r}^{n} b(x; n, p)$

n	r	.01	.05	.10	.20	.30	.40	.50	.60	.70	.80	.90	.95	.99	r
24	0	1	1	1	1	1	1	1	1	1	1	1	1	1	0
	1	214	708	920	995	1−	1−	1−	1−	1−	1−	1−	1−	1−	1
	2	024	339	708	967	998	1−	1−	1−	1−	1−	1−	1−	1−	2
	3	002	116	436	885	988	999	1−	1−	1−	1−	1−	1−	1−	3
	4	0+	030	214	736	958	996	1−	1−	1−	1−	1−	1−	1−	4
	5	0+	006	085	540	889	987	999	1−	1−	1−	1−	1−	1−	5
	6	0+	001	028	344	771	960	997	1−	1−	1−	1−	1−	1−	6
	7	0+	0+	007	189	611	904	989	999	1−	1−	1−	1−	1−	7
	8	0+	0+	002	089	435	808	968	998	1−	1−	1−	1−	1−	8
	9	0+	0+	0+	036	275	672	924	992	1−	1−	1−	1−	1−	9
	10	0+	0+	0+	013	153	511	846	978	999	1−	1−	1−	1−	10
	11	0+	0+	0+	004	074	350	729	947	996	1−	1−	1−	1−	11
	12	0+	0+	0+	001	031	213	581	886	988	1−	1−	1−	1−	12
	13	0+	0+	0+	0+	012	114	419	787	969	999	1−	1−	1−	13
	14	0+	0+	0+	0+	004	053	271	650	926	996	1−	1−	1−	14
	15	0+	0+	0+	0+	001	022	154	489	847	987	1−	1−	1−	15
	16	0+	0+	0+	0+	0+	008	076	328	725	964	1−	1−	1−	16
	17	0+	0+	0+	0+	0+	002	032	192	565	911	998	1−	1−	17
	18	0+	0+	0+	0+	0+	001	011	096	389	811	993	1−	1−	18
	19	0+	0+	0+	0+	0+	0+	003	040	229	656	972	999	1−	19
	20	0+	0+	0+	0+	0+	0+	001	013	111	460	915	994	1−	20
	21	0+	0+	0+	0+	0+	0+	0+	004	042	264	786	970	1−	21
	22	0+	0+	0+	0+	0+	0+	0+	001	012	115	564	884	998	22
	23	0+	0+	0+	0+	0+	0+	0+	0+	002	033	292	661	976	23
	24	0+	0+	0+	0+	0+	0+	0+	0+	0+	005	080	292	786	24
25	0	1	1	1	1	1	1	1	1	1	1	1	1	1	0
	1	222	723	928	996	1−	1−	1−	1−	1−	1−	1−	1−	1−	1
	2	026	358	729	973	998	1−	1−	1−	1−	1−	1−	1−	1−	2
	3	002	127	463	902	991	1−	1−	1−	1−	1−	1−	1−	1−	3
	4	0+	034	236	766	967	998	1−	1−	1−	1−	1−	1−	1−	4
	5	0+	007	098	579	910	991	1−	1−	1−	1−	1−	1−	1−	5
	6	0+	001	033	383	807	971	998	1−	1−	1−	1−	1−	1−	6
	7	0+	0+	009	220	659	926	993	1−	1−	1−	1−	1−	1−	7
	8	0+	0+	002	109	488	846	978	999	1−	1−	1−	1−	1−	8
	9	0+	0+	0+	047	323	726	946	996	1−	1−	1−	1−	1−	9
	10	0+	0+	0+	017	189	575	885	987	1−	1−	1−	1−	1−	10
	11	0+	0+	0+	006	098	414	788	966	998	1−	1−	1−	1−	11
	12	0+	0+	0+	002	044	268	655	922	994	1−	1−	1−	1−	12
	13	0+	0+	0+	0+	017	154	500	846	983	1−	1−	1−	1−	13
	14	0+	0+	0+	0+	006	078	345	732	956	998	1−	1−	1−	14
	15	0+	0+	0+	0+	002	034	212	586	902	994	1−	1−	1−	15
	16	0+	0+	0+	0+	0+	013	115	425	811	983	1−	1−	1−	16
	17	0+	0+	0+	0+	0+	004	054	274	677	953	1−	1−	1−	17
	18	0+	0+	0+	0+	0+	001	022	154	512	891	998	1−	1−	18
	19	0+	0+	0+	0+	0+	0+	007	074	341	780	991	1−	1−	19

TABLE IV

PART B: CUMULATIVE TERMS, $\displaystyle\sum_{x=r}^{n} b(x; n, p)$

								p								
n	r	.01	.05	.10	.20	.30	.40	.50	.60	.70	.80	.90	.95	.99	r
25	20	0+	0+	0+	0+	0+	0+	002	029	193	617	967	999	1—	20
	21	0+	0+	0+	0+	0+	0+	0+	009	090	421	902	993	1—	21
	22	0+	0+	0+	0+	0+	0+	0+	002	033	234	764	966	1—	22
	23	0+	0+	0+	0+	0+	0+	0+	0+	009	098	537	873	998	23
	24	0+	0+	0+	0+	0+	0+	0+	0+	002	027	271	642	974	24
	25	0+	0+	0+	0+	0+	0+	0+	0+	0+	004	072	277	778	25

CHART I

Chart for 95% confidence limits on p, the probability of success on a single binomial trial.

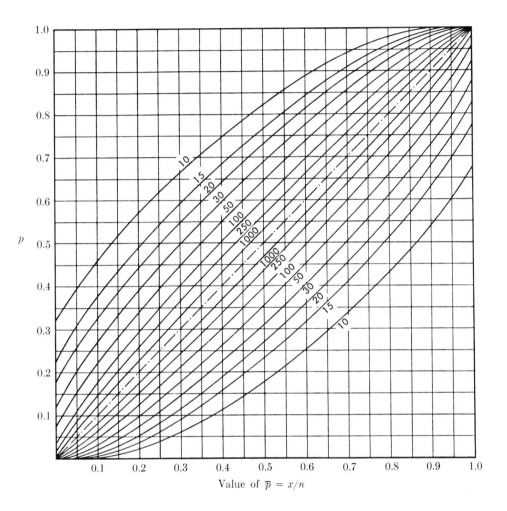

p

Value of $\overline{p} = x/n$

To obtain confidence limits for p enter the horizontal axis at the observed value of $\overline{p}$. Read the vertical axis at the two points where the two curves for n cross the vertical line erected from $\overline{p}$. *Example:* $\overline{p} = 0.3$, $n = 50$, lower confidence limit 0.18, upper confidence limit 0.45.

By permission of the Biometrika Trustees this chart has been reproduced from C. J. Clopper and E. S. Pearson, "The use of confidence or fiducial limits illustrated in the case of the binomial," *Biometrika*, Vol. 26 (1934), p. 410.

BIBLIOGRAPHY

Dixon, W. J., and F. J. Massey, Jr., *Introduction to Statistical Analysis.* New York: McGraw-Hill Book Company, Inc., 1957.

Goldberg, S., *Probability—An Introduction.* Englewood Cliffs, N. J.: Prentice-Hall, Inc., 1960.

Gray Book: *Introductory Probability and Statistical Inference.* 425 West 117th Street, New York: College Entrance Examination Board, 1959.

Hodges, J. L., Jr., and E. L. Lehmann, *Basic Concepts of Probability and Statistics,* San Francisco 11, Calif. (728 Montgomery St.): Holden-Day, Inc., 1960.

Mack, S. F., *Elementary Statistics.* New York: Henry Holt and Company, 1960.

Mosteller, F., R. E. K. Rourke, and G. B. Thomas, Jr., *Probability with Statistical Applications.* Reading, Mass.: Addison-Wesley Publishing Company, Inc., 1961.

Wallis, W. A., and H. V. Roberts, *Statistics—A New Approach.* Glencoe, Ill.: The Free Press, 1956.

Wilks, S. S., *Elementary Statistical Analysis.* Princeton: Princeton University Press, 1949.

The following books on probability are of a more advanced nature:

Feller, W., *An Introduction to Probability Theory and Its Applications.* New York: John Wiley & Sons, Inc., 1957.

Neyman, J., *First Course in Probability and Statistics.* New York: Henry Holt and Company, 1950.

Parzen, E., *Modern Probability Theory and Its Applications.* New York: John Wiley & Sons, Inc., 1960. This book requires calculus.

The following books, all requiring calculus, can serve as introductions to mathematical statistics:

Brunk, H. D., *An Introduction to Mathematical Statistics.* Boston: Ginn and Company, 1960.

Hoel, P. G., *Introduction to Mathematical Statistics.* New York: John Wiley & Sons, Inc., 1954.

Lindgren, B. W., and G. W. McElrath, *Introduction to Probability and Statistics,* Macmillan, 1959.

Mathematics refresher:

WALKER, H. M., *Mathematics Essential for Elementary Statistics*. New York: Henry Holt and Company, 1951.

Also, Chapter 1 of Mack, see above.

The following books offer a large variety of illustrations of uses of probability and statistics:

BROSS, I. D. J., *Design for Decision*. New York: Macmillan Company, Inc., 1953.

COX, D. R., *Planning of Experiments*. New York: John Wiley & Sons, Inc., 1958.

EDWARDS, A. L., *Experimental Design in Psychological Research*. New York: Rinehart & Company, Inc., 1950.

FISHER, R. A., *Statistical Methods for Research Workers*. New York: Hafner Publishing Company, Inc., 1958.

GRANT, E. L., *Statistical Quality Control*. New York: McGraw-Hill Book Company, Inc., 1952.

LEVINSON, H. C., *The Science of Chance*. New York: Rinehart & Company, 1950.

SCHLAIFER, R., *Probability and Statistics for Business Decisions*. New York: McGraw-Hill Book Company, Inc., 1959.

SNEDECOR, G. W., *Statistical Methods*. Ames, Iowa: The Iowa State College Press, 1956 (applications to experiments in agriculture and biology).

WILLIAMS, J. D., *The Compleat Strategyst*. New York: McGraw-Hill Book Company, Inc., 1954 (elementary game theory).

WILSON, E. B., JR., *An Introduction to Scientific Research*. New York: McGraw-Hill Book Company, Inc., 1952.

YOUDEN, W. J., *Statistical Methods for Chemists*. New York: John Wiley & Sons, Inc., 1951.

INDEX

Numbers in parentheses refer to exercises on the indicated pages.